Christoph[...] ist for over twenty years. He is currently Associate Pr[...] of Computing & Future Studies in Nott[...] Business [...] and the aut[...] Future.. [...] ciated [...] Tube ch[...] previou: books and numerou[...] studies and computing, and makes [...] and media appearances. You can follow [...] online at twitter.com/ChrisBarnatt.

By the same author:

A Brief Guide to Cloud Computing
Cyber Business: Mindsets for a Wired Age
Challenging Reality: In Search of the Future Organization
Valueware: Technology, Humanity and Organization
Management Strategy & Information Technology
The Computers in Business Blueprint

25 Things You Need to Know About the Future

Christopher Barnatt

Constable • London

Constable & Robinson Ltd
55–56 Russell Square
London WC1B 4HP
www.constablerobinson.com

First published in the UK by Constable,
an imprint of Constable & Robinson Ltd, 2012

A copy of the British Library Cataloguing in
Publication Data is available from the British Library

ISBN: 978-1-84901-697-1

Typeset by TW Typesetting, Plymouth, Devon

Printed and bound in the UK

Disclaimer
While every effort has been made to ensure that the content in this book is as
accurate as possible, no warranty or fitness is implied. The information is
provided on an 'as is' basis, and the author and the publisher take no
responsibility for any loss or damages arising from its use.
All trademarks included in this book are appropriately capitalized
and no attempt is made or implied to supersede the rights
of their respective owners.

1 3 5 7 9 10 8 6 4 2

To Mum & Dad. To Mark.
And to the Future.

CONTENTS

ACKNOWLEDGEMENTS

While writing this book I have been on quite a journey. I would therefore like to thank those people who have been along for the ride. For a start my thanks go to Leo Hollis at Constable & Robinson for asking me to write another book and coming up with the title, as well as Howard Watson for his copy-editing, and Nicola Jeanes for guiding these pages through the editorial and production processes. More broadly, I would also like to thank Sue Tempest, Ken Starkey, Steve Diacon, George Kuk, Sally Hopkinson, Teresa Bee, Andrea O'Mahony and many others in the University of Nottingham for their support over the past few months, years and even decades. None of us know where higher education is headed. However, thus far, our travels through the land of academia have largely been fruitful and fun.

Moving from the Ivory Tower to life's more brutal practicalities, I would like to thank Ian Beckingham for his surgical skill and Nicholas Browne for being an excellent GP. As detailed in Part V, there may be a medical revolution on the horizon. But today we are still very dependent on those who have mastered existing technologies and methods.

Finally, I would like to thank Mark Daintree for his friendship beyond the call of duty, as well as my parents for their support and guidance for over 40 years. To everybody I offer my best wishes as I unleash another tome on to an unsuspecting world. Little bits of you all have worked their way into some of these pages and most certainly in a positive manner.

Prologue
FUTURE GAZING
AS FUTURE SHAPING

How will we live in the future? And what will the human race become? These fundamental questions are important to us all. Some of the future possibilities now on the horizon may also startle, frighten and amaze.

By 2030 many parents may be able to choose the sex, hair colour and other characteristics of their children. Bioplastic bottles could also be growing on trees, while 200 million intelligent robots may be at our beck and call. 3D printers will probably also be widely used to manufacture all manner of products and even replacement human organs just as easily as we currently print out photos. Much of our food may also be farmed in skyscrapers, people could live to 150 or more, and our computers may be controlled by thought alone. As we shall see across the following 25 chapters, the potential scientific advancements on the horizon are nothing short of astonishing.

While technology may soon allow us to do many incredible things, there is also a distinct possibility that shortages of oil, fresh water and other natural resources will start to constrain our lifestyles. In little more than a decade we may therefore descend into a spiral of industrial decline. Like it or not, we are entering an age of unparalleled technological possibility just at the moment when the cupboard of Planet Earth is starting to run bare.

Perhaps more than at any other time in history, the

future of advanced human civilization now hangs in the balance. Without a crystal ball it is impossible to predict precisely what lies ahead. However, by studying known challenges, next-generation technologies and current trends, we can gain some insight into a range of possible futures. We can then act to make our most favoured vision of tomorrow a reality. Or in other words, we can use future gazing as a tool for future shaping.

This book is a toolkit for anybody wishing to future gaze and future shape. In some respects it is therefore a manifesto for understanding and changing the world! At one level, the intention is to examine in isolation 25 things that may determine what we can and cannot achieve in the next few decades. However, more fundamentally, this book also demonstrates how many future challenges and technologies will interrelate. From bioprinting to resource depletion, solar energy to space travel, climate change to vertical farming, and nuclear fusion to electric cars, 25 Things You Need to Know About the Future will provide you with a routemap to the possible world of tomorrow.

Seeing the Forest for the Trees

One of the greatest dangers for future gazers is getting so close to a particular interesting tree that we fail to notice the wider forest in which it is trying to grow. To try to help us avoid this, the 25 chapters of this book are grouped into five parts. Each of these parts then has a single overarching theme.

Part I concerns the Earth and its resources, and has as its theme 'The End of the Age of Plenty'. Like it or not, our civilization now faces the enormous challenge of continuing to expand in the face of diminishing natural resources. Some people see this as a cause for great concern. However, for future shapers, the end of the Age of Plenty is a call to arms that will drive radical innovation.

Part II turns to manufacturing and farming in order to identify 'The Next Industrial Wave'. From the bronze age to the iron age to the steam age and beyond, time and again our dominant means of making things have determined how we live. Part II therefore examines key manufacturing developments including nanotechnology, 3D printing and synthetic biology.

Future energy and transportation are the subjects of Part III, and are grouped together under the heading of 'Fuelling the Third Millennium'. Nobody knows precisely how long fossil fuels will last, let alone how long it will be considered appropriate to keep on burning them. However, we can be certain that fossil fuels will not be the bedrock of future civilization the way they have been for the last two centuries. Part III subsequently focuses on alternative forms of power. It also discusses how space travel may be developed to allow resources to be obtained from beyond our first planet.

Part IV focuses on 'Computing and Inorganic Life'. Topics covered include cloud computing, artificial intelligence and robots. We may still be scanning the heavens for other intelligent life out in space. However, within the next few decades we are far more likely to encounter new intelligent, digital species entirely of our own making.

Finally, under the banner of 'Humanity 2.0', Part V examines future healthcare and augmentation. Already our population is rapidly ageing, with extended periods of retirement becoming economically unsustainable. Add in the numerous new medical possibilities on the horizon, and it becomes clear that fairly soon many current social norms will need to be recast. As we start to take control of our own evolution, a great many ethical and even religious dilemmas will also need to be addressed.

Enhancing Our Future Consciousness

All of us have an awareness of time, and with it an appreciation of the past, the present and the future. What this implies is that we all have some level of 'future consciousness'. As defined by psychologist Tom Lombardo, future consciousness is the human capacity to have thoughts and feelings about the future. An individual's level of future consciousness is therefore a measure of their ability to envision future possibilities.

This book is intended to heighten your future consciousness. It will do this by allowing you to develop a deeper understanding of things that may be different in the future. Any suggestion that tomorrow will be different from today may seem rather obvious. However, it is worth remembering that constant, radical change is a fairly new phenomenon.

The vast majority of our ancestors spent their lives caught in the endless cycles of the natural world. The nights grew longer and shorter, and the climate colder and warmer, as the seasons and years marked the passage of time. Harvests and religious festivals arrived and were conducted in an identical, timeless fashion. Millions of individuals were also born, lived and died. However, for the most part, it was pretty much a case of 'same news, different names'.

For most of our forebears the passage of time was effectively a cyclical loop rather than a linear straight line. As illustrated in Prologue Figure 1, the general expectation was that life would repeat in a constant cycle. The past had been, the present was, and the future – usually associated with the end of the world – could only be influenced by the Gods.

Ancient (cyclical) perception of time

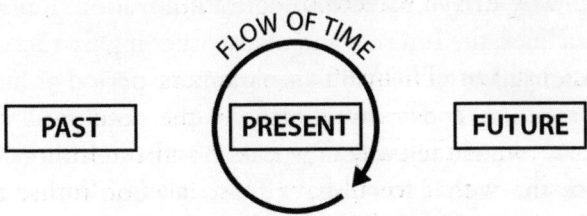

Life punctuated by the seasons
and other repeated events

Modern (linear) perception of time

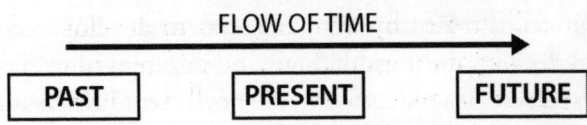

Life punctuated by transitions
between new states of the world

Prologue Figure 1: Changes in the perception of time

Perceivable differences between the past, the present and
the future only started to emerge when our more recent
ancestors began to change the world in which they lived.
For example, when the Ancient Egyptians constructed the
pyramids they altered the landscape for future generations.
A linear history could subsequently be traced from past
times before the pyramids, to a present when they were
being built, and to a future in which the mighty tombs
would dominate both skylines and minds.

As the actions of our ancestors started to separate the
past from the present and the future, so history began to be
perceived as a linear flow of events. More than anything,

radical distinctions between the past, the present and the future were driven by technological innovation. Railways, cars, airlines, the Internet and many other highly successful inventions have all helped to separate one period of history from another. Today, most of us in the developed world regularly watch television, speak on the telephone and browse the web. However, we also all know that these common, present-day activities would be incomprehensible to those who lived only a few generations ago.

Dispelling Mass Delusion

Given our awareness of the gulf between the recent past and the present, it is surprising how many people's perception of the future remains somewhat blinkered. For several decades most individuals and organizations seem to have focused almost entirely on short-term horizons. It is almost as if civilization has been trying to revert to a cyclical or even stationary perception of time.

Today a great many aspects of our lives are on the brink of a radical transformation. It is therefore alarming that we continue to act as if the future will be a facsimile of today. Granted, most people do expect to be wearing different fashions and talking on new models of mobile phone a few years from now. However, there is little common understanding that in only a few decades there are likely to be radical changes in our available raw materials, manufacturing methods, energy sources, diet, life expectancy and freedom to travel. Many people – and in particular a great many industrialists, politicians and others in authority – really do appear to possess a very limited level of future consciousness.

The popular delusion that the next few decades will be a point upgrade of the present is also starting to become dangerous. The recent calamity of the global financial crisis ought to have made us all question our rose-tinted perceptions of tomorrow. Yet unfortunately this has not been the case.

Never in history have property prices risen and economies expanded indefinitely. Permanent wealth has also never been created through the magic of financial mathematics. How the majority of those who run the world came to believe that these things had become the case is now the subject of many a book if not this one. This said, what I do want to signal here is that we are still jollying along in the grip of several even more dangerous mass delusions. Not least, we seem to have developed a belief that the Earth's natural resources are infinite; that current methods of agriculture will be able to feed nine billion; that most people in developed nations can be economically unproductive for a large proportion of their lives; and that human evolution has come to an end.

This book will set the record straight by explaining how the future cannot be a clone of today. Some of the following 25 chapters will explore future developments – such as electric cars, solar power and cloud computing – that are pretty certain to become commonplace within only a few years. Other chapters – such as those on space travel, artificial intelligence, quantum computing and transhumanism – will then really push at the limits of future possibility. As a consequence, it is inevitable that some of the 25 things I cover will turn out to be incorrect. However, what really matters is that this book helps us to engage with a wide range of future possibilities and the dynamics of radical change. Nobody knows exactly what the world will be like in a few decades' time. This said, given the number of challenges and opportunities on the horizon, I would place a pretty safe bet that by 2030 many aspects of our lives will be very different from today.

Next Week's Lottery Numbers?

Whenever I am introduced to an audience as a futurist I tend to get a wide range of reactions. Often there is at least one very enthusiastic person who thinks that it is all very exciting. However, there are usually also several more awkward audience members at the sceptical end of the spectrum. Some such individuals have even been known to preface my talk with long tirades to the effect that everything I say will be rubbish. More commonly, one or more subtle naysayers just asks if I can give them next week's lottery numbers.

As I have explained in this prologue, the goal of future studies is not to predict a single, definitive future. Rather, the intention is to put on the table as many credible options as possible. Each of the 25 things discussed in this book could have a major impact on many people's everyday lives. Yet which ones actually will has to depend on choices made by us all in the face of the challenges and opportunities that lie ahead.

More than anything I hope that this book will fire your imagination. As Winston Churchill once said, 'the empires of the future are the empires of the mind'. As this implies, we need to construct the future in our heads before we can craft it with our collective hands. Some people may choose to passively look ahead with no more than a mixture of fear, bewilderment or wonder. However, it is definitely far more satisfying and worthwhile to future gaze with intent.

Christopher Barnatt,
June 2011

Part I

THE END OF THE AGE OF PLENTY

I
PEAK OIL

When I started writing this book, a friend told me that it should only include one topic. As he only half-jokingly explained, in his opinion the only thing we need to know about the future is that 'we are all doomed'.

Future supplies of oil, fresh water, food and many other things we currently take for granted are at best uncertain. Climate change and a growing population will also make life more difficult over the next few decades. However, even in the face of these challenges, I reject the growing proposition that 'we are all doomed'. Time and again human civilization has thrived and risen to greatness in the face of monumental adversity. And there is no reason to believe that this will not happen again.

While tougher times ahead need not necessarily be feared, it is important to understand the challenges that will frame the next few decades. I therefore make no apology for starting this book with a set of chapters that outline the end of the Age of Plenty. However, I also want to make it clear that I have no intention of doom-mongering. Rather, my reason for including this material upfront is to establish the things that will make necessary the radical and often exciting innovations detailed in the rest of this book.

The Most Fundamental Challenge

If I had to highlight just one thing we need to know about the future then it would have to be Peak Oil. Today, oil has become the lifeblood of industrial civilization. Future changes in the supply of oil will therefore have a fundamental impact on our lives.

Peak Oil refers to the point in time when global oil production reaches its maximum, and after which there is less oil left in the ground than we have taken out. Whether we are very nearly at this point, or will reach it later this decade, next decade or the one after that is a matter of debate. This said, there is increasing evidence that Peak Oil can be no further away than about 2030. For example, in September 2009 the UK Energy Research Centre published its *Global Oil Depletion Report*. Based on a review of over 500 studies, an analysis of industry databases and a comparison of 14 global supply forecasts, this comprehensive work concluded that 'a peak in conventional oil production before 2030 appears likely and there is a significant risk of a peak before 2020'.

For more than 50 years it has been known that the rise and fall of oil production in a particular region follows a so-termed 'bell curve'. The first such curve was drawn in 1956 by geophysicist Marion King Hubbert to predict when oil production would peak in the United States. Hubbert estimated that this would be between 1966 and 1972. Most people at the time dismissed Hubbert's meticulous work as ridiculous. Nevertheless he was right, with the actual peak occurring in 1970.

Figure 1.1 illustrates a bell curve for global oil production. The historical data on the left-hand side of the curve has been approximated for clarity. As has been noted, the exact dates on the horizontal axis are also a matter of debate. This said, Figure 1.1 is indicative of most current predictions.

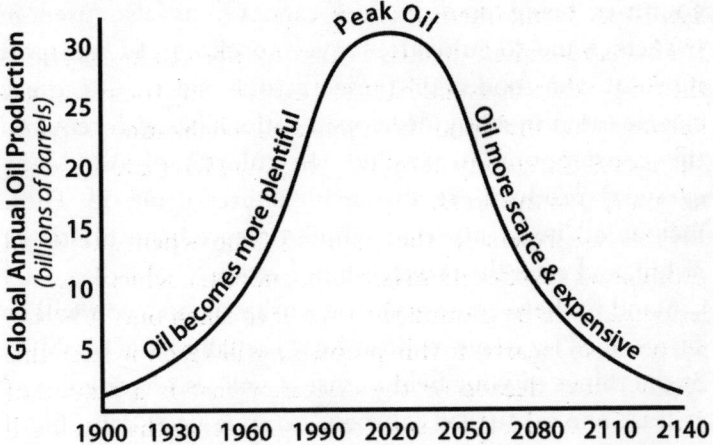

Figure 1.1: The Peak Oil curve

Peak Oil matters because, when the top of the global bell curve is reached, oil will start to become scarcer and more expensive. There are also many commentators who predict that Peak Oil price rises will trigger an oil crash on the financial markets. For example, LifeAfterTheOilCrash.net has suggested that a shortfall between the demand for oil and its supply of as little as 10 to 15 per cent could have serious implications for the global economy.

It is really important to understand that Peak Oil is not about the world running out of oil, even though this will happen in the longer term. Rather, Peak Oil concerns the very significant shorter-term implications of us hitting the top of the bell curve sometime in the next 20 years.

Our Reliance on Liquid Gold

All industrialized societies are based on oil. It is, in fact, quite difficult to stress just how dependent on oil human civilization has become. For a start, oil is the lifeblood of most personal travel, with almost 50 per cent of oil in some countries being used to fuel cars. Oil is also used in pesticides and to cultivate, harvest, package and transport most of our food. For these reasons, since 2002 every calorie eaten in many developed nations has also required the consumption of around ten calories of oil. Many everyday products are also manufactured using oil. These include all items made in whole or part from plastic or nylon, and even the tarmac on our roads.

Stand in the average home or workplace and you will be surrounded by items made at least partially from oil. Most of the things in your field of vision will also have enjoyed at least one oil-fuelled journey. Imagine your daily life if every item with a plastic casing were removed, not to mention all computers, mobile phones and other electronic devices. DVDs are made from oil. So are many carpets and furniture coverings. Most of our clothes are also made from at least some oil based materials, with even 100 per cent cotton garments usually having nylon buttons or fasteners. Detergents, most cosmetics and many medicines are also at least partly oil based, as is a great deal of packaging. A world with less and more expensive oil will therefore be a very different place indeed.

According to the International Energy Agency, the world currently consumes over 4 billion tonnes – or roughly 30 billion barrels – of oil a year. This level of demand is also expected to double by 2030, with China alone accounting for half of this anticipated increase. The magnitude of our global addiction to oil is simply staggering.

New sources of oil do continue to be discovered. However, on average we are discovering and exploiting new oil supplies far more slowly that we are burning up our existing reserves. As reported by Paul Roberts in his book *The End of Oil*, since 1995 new oil discoveries have only been running at about 40 per cent of the rate of global oil consumption. The gap between oil discovery and consumption is also increasing.

We clearly cannot go on indefinitely discovering fewer new oil reserves than we continue to deplete. Eventually the point will have to be reached when the level of global oil production starts to fall and continues to do so. That is, after all, what Peak Oil and the bell curve shown in Figure 1.1 are all about.

Using data gathered from the 2009 edition of the *BP Statistical Review of World Energy*, in 2009 TheOil-Drum.com carried a very clear article that made our situation absolutely explicit. As it noted, by 2009 only 14 out of 54 oil-producing countries and regions in the world were still increasing their oil production. A further 30 were then definitely past their production peak, with the remaining 10 appearing to have flat or declining production.

So How Much Oil is Left?

There are currently about 70,000 oil fields in the world. Of these, 25 giant fields account for about one-quarter of conventional oil production, and 100 for about half of it. Most giant oil fields are also well past their peak, with an average decline in their production of at least 6.5 per cent a year. To replace their lost output would require the equivalent of a new Saudi Arabia coming on stream roughly every three years. And few expect many new giant oil fields to be found.

While oil production is fairly easy to measure, there is a lot of controversy concerning just how much oil is actually left in the ground. It is also important to distinguish between oil reserves – or quantities of oil considered possible and economically viable to extract – and any estimate of total but not necessarily extractable oil resources.

Estimates of oil reserves are often split into those that are 'proven', 'probable' and 'possible'. However, even these terms are not used consistently. A widely reported estimate for the world's remaining proven oil reserves is about 1.2 trillion barrels. This figure is also about the same as total global oil production to this point in time. Estimates for total proven, probable and possible reserves – also known as the 'ultimate recoverable resource' (URR) – then range up to about 4 trillion barrels. This said, an upper estimate for the URR of around 2.3 trillion barrels is typical and appears most credible. An answer to the question 'how much oil is left?' is therefore 'probably somewhere between 1.2 and 2.3 trillion barrels'.

Reported oil reserves have been increasing for years. However, it needs to be understood that such 'reserve growth' has largely been due to a revision of initial estimates of the size of known fields and not as a result of the discovery of new ones. There are also a great many economic and political factors that influence oil reserve estimations.

For example, most of the world's major oil producers are members of the Organization of the Petroleum Exporting Countries (OPEC). In 1985 OPEC reserves were estimated at about 400 billion barrels. However, at that time OPEC decided that each country's permitted oil production and sales quota should be determined by its proven reserves. Every OPEC member subsequently re-evaluated its reserves, meaning that by 1986 OPEC had reserves of 700 billion barrels. At the end of 2009 OPEC was estimating proven member reserves to be just over 1 trillion barrels, with a claim that this represented 80 per cent of a proven global reserve of about 1.33 trillion barrels. The potential over-reporting of reserves by OPEC continues to be a matter of great controversy, with several reputable sources suggesting that OPEC has proven reserves of at most 900 billion barrels.

The growth in reported reserves in existing oil fields in part may be legitimate. Not least this is because rising oil prices will make it economically viable to extract some oil resources previously considered too costly to get at. Improved extraction techniques also continue to be developed, while the extent of some early giant fields really does appear to have been underestimated. This said, reserve growth is mainly associated with large, old and onshore fields, in turn meaning that we ought not to expect it to continue.

Unconventional Oil

Almost all current estimates of oil reserves focus only on petroleum, or what is sometimes now termed 'conventional oil'. However, those on the optimistic side of the Peak Oil debate suggest that the exploitation of so-termed 'unconventional oil' may fill the pending gap to be left by decreasing petroleum supplies.

Petroleum is a liquid that flows easily and can be pumped without treatment. In contrast, unconventional oil is far more viscous and requires processing or dilution before it can be extracted. Unconventional oil includes 'very heavy oil', as well as oil that may be extracted from oil sands, tar sands (bitumen) and oil shale. Extracting oil from tar sands is not only technically possible but proven. For example, Canada has achieved a production level of over one million barrels a day from tar sands since 2006.

While about 80 per cent of conventional oil reserves are in the Middle East, around the same percentage of unconventional oil reserves are in Venezuela, Canada and the United States. Some estimates suggest that these nations may have over three trillion barrels of unconventional oil resources. However, it is likely that only a relatively small percentage actually constitute a technically and economically recoverable reserve.

Even ignoring technical and economic limitations, many factors are likely to limit the exploitation of unconventional oil. For a start, environmental pressures may prevent unconventional oil being extracted in many regions. Unconventional oil can also be up to three times more energy intensive to extract than conventional oil, hence making it a less environmentally acceptable proposition and more expensive. There is also the concern that carbon emissions from burning unconventional oil are higher than those from conventional oil.

The UK Energy Research Centre's *Global Oil Depletion Report* did consider unconventional oil. However, even after taking it into account, it still explicitly concluded that a peak before 2030 is likely not just for conventional oil production, but for 'all oil production'.

Understanding the Implications

Based on our current global consumption level of roughly 30 billion barrels a year, and the likelihood of between 1.2 and 2.3 trillion barrels remaining, all conventional oil will be exhausted sometime in the next 40 to 75 years. However, as already noted, the global demand for oil is expected to double by 2030. Even if demand roughly plateaus by that time, this means that we actually have no more than maybe 25 to 40 years before conventional oil production drops to a very low level indeed.

Adding in some acceptable exploitation of unconventional oil may add ten or more years to the above estimates. However, even 50 years is not that much time for our civilization to wean itself off liquid gold. We also need to remember that it is when we hit the Peak Oil position of falling global oil production and demand starting to outstrip supply that we will start to feel the implications.

A great many commentators expect that we will hit Peak Oil before 2030, with a global oil supply crunch and significant price spike likely to occur well before that. For example, the International Energy Agency (IEA) warned in 2008 of a near-term oil supply crunch due to the cancellation or postponement of many projects following the global financial crisis. In 2010 Professor Sir David King, the UK government's former chief scientist, also predicted that global demand for oil would start outstripping supply as early as 2014. An estimated date for Peak Oil of 2014 was also determined by a team from Kuwait University in late 2009. Led by Ibrahim Sami Nashawi, this group of academics based their assertion on a revamping of Hubbert's bell curve model to account for technology changes and ecological, economic and political influences on production trends in all major oil-producing countries.

In 2010, a white paper published by Lloyds Insurance and Chatham House (the Royal Institute of International Affairs) predicted an oil-supply crunch 'in the medium term'. This heavyweight publication also highlighted that some expect this to be as early as 2013, with an accompanying price spike in excess of $200 per barrel being a credible possibility.

Increases in the price of oil beyond its supply peak will have major implications. For a start they will lead to an increase in the price of any product made in whole or part from oil. An increase in the price of oil will also raise prices more generally due to its direct impact on most transportation costs. However, it is the consequences of the widening gap between oil supply and demand that are likely to be the most serious.

Most estimates suggest that beyond its peak, the supply of oil will decrease by a few percentage points per year. This is also likely to be in the face of rising global demand. For economists, future supply/demand disparities may be 'fixed' by price rises that will deprive some consumers of some of the oil that they could previously afford. However, oil is currently so essential to our systems of transportation, agriculture and industrial production that the implications of all demand not being met are likely to be severe. For example, as will be discussed in Chapter 4, if levels of food production fall because some farmers have to produce less for a higher price there is likely to be widespread famine.

An Artificial Debate?

The only effective response to the future challenge of Peak Oil is a controlled transition to a post-petroleum economy. This will obviously take decades rather than years. Peak Oil therefore needs to start headlining a great many political and industrial agendas as soon as possible.

Despite the urgent need for widespread agreement and action, to date the debate surrounding future oil supply has become sidetracked into a showdown between two distinct factions. On the one hand we have the so-termed 'early toppers' who believe that we have around 1.2 trillion barrels of oil left and will hit Peak Oil sometime this decade. On the other hand there are the 'late toppers' who believe we have well over 2 trillion barrels of oil left. Late toppers also generally believe that increasingly advanced extraction technologies will allow previously unattainable conventional and unconventional oil resources to be viably exploited. Many late toppers therefore place Peak Oil out toward 2030 and sometimes beyond.

The above paragraph may suggest two entirely opposing positions. But sadly this is not the case. Basically we are witness to a hard-fought debate between those who believe we have between 10 and 20 years to migrate to a post-petroleum economy, and those who believe we have more like 20 to 30 years. For those seeking political election or planning medium-term investments or their individual careers, there may be a significant difference between these two time horizons. However, for wider civilization the message to be garnered from either perspective is that we need to start the transition from an oil-based economy right now. After all, even the most optimistic late toppers are banking on very significant near-term oil price rises in order to make viable many currently uneconomic reserves.

* * *

The Post-Petroleum Opportunity

At the start of this chapter I promised that I was not going to spread doom and gloom. Granted, Peak Oil is a serious issue that will have a significant impact on all of our lives over the next few decades. However, there are also many ways in which we may turn this largest of future problems into a whole host of future opportunities.

Most obviously, humanity may thrive in the face of Peak Oil by developing and exploiting new sources of energy and new means of transportation. As detailed in Part III, wind, wave, solar, nuclear and kinetic power are all set to play a role in fuelling the third millennium. As outlined in Part II, nanotechnology and synthetic biology also offer the hope of artificially synthesizing new fuels. An expanded use of genetically modified crops may also increase food yields while lowering the requirement for the use of oil-based pesticides.

More broadly, there are also already some signs that industrial civilization can and will evolve to become more energy and resource efficient. For example, as outlined in Chapter 16, cloud computing technologies are already enabling us to communicate and trade digitally, so requiring people and things to be moved around a lot less. As detailed in Chapter 10, we are also likely to start farming at least some of our food in urban areas, so reducing the distance that it needs to be transported.

Finally, almost all of the measures that we may employ to try to combat climate change are likely to assist with our transition to a post-petroleum economy. Indeed, at present it is our efforts to lessen the production of greenhouse gases that also constitute our best strategies for dealing with the implications of Peak Oil. Climate change, its implications and our future response also happen to be what the next chapter is all about.

2
CLIMATE CHANGE

Many of the subjects covered in this book may surprise and even amaze you. However, it can hardly be a surprise that there is a chapter here on climate change. Alongside Peak Oil, climate change has to be one of the two greatest challenges that we face. Climate change additionally has direct and serious implications for our future food and water supplies. Looking ahead, changes in the climate and measures to try to limit them will also drive many of the technological innovations covered elsewhere in this book.

This chapter reviews some of the most widely accepted climate change science, information and predictions. At present some of this material remains controversial and is disputed in some quarters. However, governments and other bodies are now starting to set policy as a result of their belief in climate change and its likely impact. Regardless of the legitimacy of the evidence, the new legislative regimes and business strategies that climate change is starting to generate will therefore affect us all. In this sense, a growing global belief in *potential* climate change is now becoming as significant as *actual* climate change itself.

The Science and Its Implications

According to the Intergovernmental Panel on Climate Change (IPCC), a wide range of evidence now suggests that a 'warming of the climate system is unequivocal'. Already it is on average 0.74°C hotter than it was a century ago. A continual rise in average global temperatures has now also been measured across several decades.

Climate change is occurring because the burning of fossil fuels and some other industrial activities are increasing the level of greenhouse gases in the atmosphere. This higher concentration of greenhouse gases is then leading to an increased retention of heat from the Sun. As a consequence, the IPCC predicts that by 2100 average global temperatures will rise by a minimum of 1.1°C and a maximum of 6.4°C.

A global temperature rise of a few degrees may not sound that much. However, in many parts of the world this is expected to result in higher levels of rainfall. In others there will be warmer, drier summers and an increased incidence of drought. The implications of climate change for agriculture will therefore be serious. For example, the International Rice Research Institute has suggested that yields of rice – the staple food for 60 per cent of humanity – could fall by 4 to 13 per cent in the coming decades. Cereal crop yields are also likely to fall. For example, crop yields in southern Europe are predicted to decline by 20 per cent following a 2°C rise in temperatures. Chapter 4 will look in more depth at the implications of climate change on future food production.

While climate change will result in a rise in average global temperatures, there is a possibility that some regions may actually become cooler. Already, melting icecaps are leading to an increase in the quantity of fresh water entering the Arctic Ocean. In turn there are fears that this may already be slowing down a Gulf Steam current called the

North Atlantic Drift. This flow of warm water carries heat to Europe. However, as a result of glacial melting, lower concentrations of salt in the ocean may be curtailing the process of thermohaline circulation on which the North Atlantic Drift depends. As a result, average temperatures in the United Kingdom and other northern European countries could fall by 5°C or more in as little as 20 years. Whether northern Europe will on average be hotter or cooler in the future is therefore very much open to debate.

What we do know for certain is that melting glaciers in the polar regions are causing a rise in sea levels. Over the past 100 years the oceans have already risen by about 17 cm. The IPCC predicts that climate change will cause global sea levels to rise further by a minimum of 18 cm and a maximum of 59 cm by 2100.

In most parts of the world, rising sea levels will increase flooding in the event of bad weather. In a significant number of locations they will also turn dry land into wetlands, convert wetlands to open water, erode beaches and increase the salinity of estuaries. In fact, estimates suggest that the melting or collapse of ice sheets due to global warming could eventually threaten land that is home to one person in twenty.

Approximately 100 million people live less than a metre above sea level. The higher end of the IPPC's predicted sea-level rises would therefore have very major implications. For example, around one fifth of Bangladesh would be flooded. The IPCC more broadly predicts that between 75 and 200 million people face flooding risks due to climate change. Many major cities are also built on or near great rivers or the sea. If or when global temperatures rise by 3 or 4°C, sea-level rises would therefore threaten many of our most important metropoli, including London, Shanghai, New York, Tokyo and Hong Kong.

Due to rising sea levels, some small island states will disappear entirely. Already the coral island of Tuvalu in the Pacific has had to accept that it will be inundated. It is therefore making plans to relocate its 11,000 inhabitants to New Zealand.

Climate change will also have an impact on the wider environment, with many ecosystems likely to be severely damaged or destroyed. Estimates suggest that between 15 to 40 per cent of all species face extinction in the face of a 2°C increase in average global temperatures. Some climate models even predict that the Amazon rainforest will be severely damaged by little more than this level of warming.

Greenhouse Gas Levels

The retention of heat in the atmosphere due to greenhouse gases is not only a natural process, but essential for life on Earth. Indeed, were it not for the greenhouse effect, the average temperature of the planet would be about −18°C, as opposed to the current average of about +15°C.

There are several gases whose presence in the atmosphere causes the Earth to retain heat. Not least, water vapour is a greenhouse gas. However, the ones that really matter – and whose increased concentration in our atmosphere is associated with rising industrialization – are carbon dioxide, methane and nitrous oxide. Most greenhouse gas emissions result from burning fossil fuels, making cement, clearing land and agricultural production. Specifically, carbon dioxide is released when we burn oil, natural gas, coal and wood. Carbon dioxide is also emitted from limestone when cement is mixed. The involved chemical process, coupled with the combustion of fuels in the kiln and other general energy requirements, means that the cement industry produces about 5 per cent of all carbon dioxide emissions.

Significant carbon dioxide emissions additionally result

from the felling of trees for logging, as well as the burning of peatland and forests to clear land for agriculture and human inhabitation. Trees, other vegetation and peatland absorb and store carbon dioxide. Their demise then releases it back into the atmosphere. In fact, according to scientists from the Global Canopy Programme, ongoing deforestation is currently responsible for around 25 per cent of all carbon dioxide emissions.

Methane is a rarer if more potent greenhouse gas than carbon dioxide, and is emitted during the production of coal, natural gas and oil. Methane is also emitted from landfill sites, water treatment plants, and the digestive systems of all livestock and other animals. Finally, nitrous oxide is released from the burning of fossil fuels, the use of fertilizers and a range of other industrial activities.

Greenhouse gas levels are measured in carbon dioxide parts per million (ppm), with an equivalent cited for other gases. Today, the total level of all greenhouse gases in the atmosphere is about 430 ppm. Of this about 380 ppm is carbon dioxide. This compares to about 280 ppm of carbon dioxide back in the mid-1700s before the Industrial Revolution. In 1958 – when famed climate scientist Charles David Keeling began to take detailed measurements – the carbon dioxide level was 317 ppm. Even if annual global emissions remain stable, we are likely to hit an equivalent of 550 ppm of carbon dioxide in the atmosphere by 2050. However, global emissions are actually rising rapidly, meaning that we could hit the 550 ppm figure by 2035. Most estimates suggest that this would result in a rise in global temperatures of more than 2°C. As already indicated, even this is likely to have major implications, with any temperature increase beyond 2°C being potentially very serious indeed.

If climate change is not to get out of control, then annual global greenhouse gas emissions need to fall to a level that balances the Earth's natural capacity to remove them from the atmosphere. In 2006 the Stern Review produced for the UK government provided a detailed analysis of our options. In particular, it suggested a realistic target of trying to limit greenhouse gas concentrations to between 450 and 550 ppm. At the upper end of this range, to stabilize at 550 ppm now requires global emissions to peak in the 2020s and to drop below 25 per cent of current levels by 2050. To stabilize at 450 ppm requires emissions to peak this decade and to fall by more than 5 per cent a year, reaching 70 per cent below current levels by 2050. All of these propositions clearly require deep global commitments to fairly rapid and radical change. For example, the Stern Review suggests that power generation will have to be decarbonized by between 60 and 75 per cent by 2050 to stabilize greenhouse gas levels at or below 550 ppm.

Dealing with the Consequences

Regardless of what we do now, climate change will continue to occur for several decades. Emergency situations created or heightened by climate change are also already becoming increasingly expensive. For example, in the United Kingdom, each day of snow and more extreme winter weather is now costing the economy between £230 million and £600 million. The number of such bad days is also going to increase – and very significantly so if northern Europe cools due to a cessation of the North Atlantic Drift. A level up, weather-related disasters on the scale of 2005's Hurricane Katrina and the Australian floods of 2011 are likely to become more frequent. At present Hurricane Katrina remains the most costly weather-related natural disaster in history. However, this sad record will continue to be broken.

Disaster recovery planning and preparation need to step up a gear in the face of climate change. In September 2010 the UK government acknowledged this when it shifted its focus away from pure climate change mitigation and toward climate change adaptation. The announcement included plans to protect power stations from flooding, as well as to safeguard hospitals from water shortages during dry summers. These and all other climate change adaptation measures will inevitably lead to higher taxes and higher prices for us all.

As discussed in the next two chapters, many countries need to take action to try to safeguard their future water and food supplies. We should also all expect continually rising food prices due to reduced crop yields, as well as agricultural produce being more regularly damaged by extreme weather.

Pressure is also likely to grow on people in industrialized nations to eat less meat. This would then help reduce greenhouse gas emissions on two fronts. Firstly, it would reduce methane emissions from farm animals reared for table. Secondly, it would lessen the requirement for deforestation. According to Greenpeace, in 2004–5 alone more than 2.9 million acres of Amazon rainforest were destroyed to clear land for growing animal feed, with up to 220 square feet sacrificed to produce each pound of hamburger.

In the face of climate change, some industries – such as insurance – will also need to fundamentally rethink their business models. For example, while today most property insurance is sold to cover all risks, in the future cover for fire and theft may be sold separately to that for flooding and weather damage. In fact, if this does not occur then many properties will become uninsurable.

Relatively soon most nations could be spending hundreds of millions of dollars, pounds, euros or yen on efforts to improve their flood defences and to limit coastal erosion. For example, in the United Kingdom the Environment

Agency suggests that the government will have to spend over £1 billion a year on these activities by 2035. However, it is quite possible that such costs will be deemed too high, with citizens having to relocate as climate change takes its toll. Deciding where this line is to be drawn is likely to become a major political issue. By the middle of the century politicians may even be campaigning on the basis of which areas of their country they pledge to protect, and which they consider unnecessary or uneconomic to maintain.

More immediately, planning applications need to start taking far greater heed of climate change. For example, in the United Kingdom house building on flood plains is continuing unabated. This has to stop or else we need to start building radically different types of dwellings that are capable of withstanding inevitable and regular inundation. Firms in the construction industry that rise to this design challenge could also do very well. So too will those who develop and deploy building methods less reliant on cement. Making existing buildings and infrastructure resilient to climate change is then another great construction challenge and opportunity. Indeed, according to the Stern Review, such building works could cost between $15 and $150 billion annually in OECD countries alone.

Preventing Future Climate Change

Measures to cope with the consequences of climate change will have to be substantial, yet they will probably have less impact on our lives than those likely to be taken to try to address the causes of climate change. Unless there is a major public backlash, most governments now look set to push forward with significant climate change mitigation measures. New industries and opportunities may well be created. However, as a result of government action, the majority of us will need to make some lifestyle changes.

The easiest sell for governments will be encouraging or cajoling people and businesses to increase their energy efficiency. Due to Peak Oil and broader resource depletion, energy prices are going to rise substantially over the coming decades. If, as is likely, schemes that directly or indirectly tax carbon emissions are put in place, then energy prices will increase further still. Switching to wind, wave, solar and nuclear power – as discussed in Part III of this book – will allow us to reduce greenhouse gas emissions. However, the energy produced by future alternative energy sources will almost certainly be more expensive than that currently obtained by burning fossil fuels. There can therefore be little doubt that most people's lifestyles will have to become less energy intensive.

Fortunately, technology will increasingly allow us to become more energy efficient. Already low-energy light bulbs use around 80 per cent less power than their traditional counterparts. Even more efficient LED light bulbs are also only a few years away.

It has been estimated that a switch to low-energy bulbs across the European Union has the potential to cut carbon emissions by 20 million tonnes a year. It is therefore not surprising that in 2009 the European Union banned the manufacture and import of 100 watt frosted incandescent bulbs. With many other kinds of electrical appliance capable of becoming far more energy efficient, similar future initiatives are inevitable. Today I am typing these words on a low-energy PC and monitor that together consume only 41 watts. In contrast, a year ago I would have been typing them on very typical desktop hardware that consumed around 220 watts. Very significant opportunities for all of us to reduce our energy usage really do exist. Given the cost savings that they in parallel deliver, many of us are therefore likely to be purchasing low-energy electrical devices before the end of the decade.

Getting people to reduce their energy demand via increased energy efficiency is one thing. But engendering broader behavioural change is quite another. Rising energy prices may in part trigger the mindset shift necessary to get more people to turn off electrical items that are not in use. They may even be enough to reduce some powered personal travel, not to mention the import of food that journeys for thousands of miles before reaching our plate. However, educating and persuading the majority of people to stop taking journeys and consuming things simply to protect the world of tomorrow is likely to be extremely difficult.

As discussed in the last chapter, within a few decades the supply of conventional oil is going to become more and more restricted. Yet supplies of coal and potentially unconventional oil will continue to be plentiful for a great many decades. Any future choice to burn to exhaustion either of these relatively abundant energy sources could push the level of greenhouse gases in the atmosphere far higher and so fuel further climate change. Potentially, carbon-capture technologies could be fitted to power stations to lessen this impact. However, once again, convincing those involved of the need to use such technology – and in so doing to make their supply of energy more expensive – may well be difficult. The growth of China is 80 per cent fuelled by coal, with 544 new coal power stations currently planned. The moral authority of the West to tell China, India and others not to industrialize and pollute as they themselves have done is also somewhat limited.

A similar dearth of moral authority is inevitably impeding efforts to lessen greenhouse gas emissions from deforestation. Currently we slash and burn around 50 million acres of rainforest a year – an area equivalent to the whole of England, Scotland and Wales. In turn this releases around two billion tonnes of carbon dioxide into the atmosphere. These emissions are far higher than those from the entire global transport industry, including aviation. As has been argued by Andrew Mitchell, the head of the Global Canopy Programme, 'tropical forests are the elephant in the living room of climate change'.

There is also considerable evidence to suggest that drastically curtailing deforestation is one of the world's cheapest options for limiting future climate change. The problem is making this happen. As already noted, a rising demand for meat is driving the clearing of land to grow animal feed. To some extent this is under everybody's control. However, international funding and support are desperately needed if those in Indonesia, Brazil and the Congo region are to be persuaded to pursue other activities. We simply cannot expect nations to destroy their economies unless the wider world offers them a tangible alternative to actions that are impacting all of our futures.

Geoengineering Solutions?

It is quite possible that our politicians will fail to agree and implement sufficient measures to reduce global carbon emissions. Over the coming decades the level of greenhouse gases in the atmosphere may therefore continue to significantly increase. As (and if) this happens, a far more radical solution for curtailing climate change will be needed way beyond anything already mentioned so far. In fact, many of those who argue against climate change measures today do so on the basis that we will in future be able to put in place grand, technological solutions on a planetary scale.

Future 'geoengineering' options already proposed for controlling climate change include liquefying industrial carbon dioxide emissions and burying them deep underground, or cultivating new forms of marine algae to absorb more carbon dioxide in the oceans. Alternatively, as discussed in Chapter 7, it may one day be possible to build nanotechnology-based greenhouse gas filtration factories to extract excess greenhouse gases from the atmosphere. Strategically located around the planet, such plants could potentially return greenhouse gas concentrations to pre-industrial levels. As yet another option, potentially the most ambitious climate change solution may involve building solar sails in space.

The level of solar radiation that bathes our planet is pretty much constant. Climate change is now starting to occur because an increased concentration of greenhouse gases in the atmosphere is causing the Earth to retain too much of this heat. To prevent this happening, all of the climate change mitigation measures discussed so far seek to control greenhouse gas levels. However, basic physics tells us that we could happily live with higher greenhouse gas concentrations if less solar radiation hit the Earth in the first place.

In theory, giant solar sails could be constructed in orbit to shade the Earth and stop us receiving so much solar radiation. While vast in area, potentially such sails would only have to be made from plastics or metals a few hundred atoms thick. Creating such sails may be impossible today. However, the developments in nanotechnology discussed in Chapter 7 do suggest that their construction may become a possibility sometime next decade.

A white paper presented by Kenneth I. Roy at the Space Technology and Applications International Forum in 2001 suggested that 100,000 square kilometres of solar sails may be sufficient to give humanity control of climate change. Such sails could also potentially generate electricity to be beamed down to Earth. Even with the best space access technology on the horizon, building such sails on the ground and launching them into orbit would probably be a non-starter. Indeed, according to Roy, 100,000 square kilometres of sail might weigh 40 million tonnes. Solar sails would therefore have to be constructed in space, and perhaps using raw materials mined from the Moon or the asteroids.

This kind of thing may sound incredible and massively expensive. But so did sending a human being to the Moon in the early 1960s, and that mission had no planet-saving ambition. The solar sail solution to global warming may at present be just an outlandish idea. However, in a few decades time it could turn out to be a more viable option than persuading billions of people to consume and travel far less in addition to making other radical changes to their lifestyles.

*   *   *

Learning to Care about the Future

Over the next few decades climate change will have an increasing impact on us all. For some the implications will be limited to higher food prices and occasional mild disruptions as a result of more extreme weather. However, for the less fortunate majority of the world's population, climate change will result in floods, drought and associated shortages of food and water. There can be little doubt that many people in poorer parts of the world will die as a direct consequence of climate change.

The difficulty humanity faces in responding to climate change is convincing far more people today to start caring about the global population of the future. John Maynard Keynes, the famous economist whose preachings dominated 20th-century capitalism, may have argued that 'in the long-term we are all dead'. His inference that businesses, governments and individuals can simply ignore the long-term consequences of their actions may also have proved convenient for many decades. However, what Keynes and his followers chose to ignore is the simple fact that in the long-term our children and their descendants will still be alive and will suffer the consequences of our current selfish folly. In tandem with the 2008 financial crisis, climate change ought therefore to provide another strong reason to junk the misguided and short-term economic logic of the heartless 20th-century men-in-suits. Reflecting this, one of the most startling opening statements in the UK government's Stern Review is an acceptance that 'climate change is the greatest and widest-ranging market failure ever seen'. The way that the review then proceeds to make proposals based on economic logic is then at best bizarre.

Along with Peak Oil, climate change is a physical certainty that will not go away and that we will have to do something about. Coupled with an expanding global population, both Peak Oil and climate change are also likely to have a significant impact on future agricultural production and fresh-water supplies. The next two chapters therefore address head-on possible future food shortages and the phenomenon called Peak Water.

3

PEAK WATER

Whether they believe in it or not, everybody has heard of climate change. And even if they do not know the term 'Peak Oil', most people understand that eventually we will run out of petroleum. However, mention the term 'Peak Water' in general company and the most common reaction is a vacant stare.

Peak Water refers to the point in time when we will reach the natural limit of available fresh-water supplies. Beyond Peak Water, demand for fresh water will then start to outstrip supply. According to the United Nations, by 2025 1.8 billion people will face a position of 'absolute water scarcity', with two-thirds of the world's population likely to be facing stressed or restricted fresh-water supplies.

Some regions of our planet are clearly more blessed with fresh water than others. Different parts of the world will therefore hit local Peak Water at different times. Already the United Nations believes that around 700 million people across 43 countries live with water scarcity. At present all such individuals reside in Africa, south Asia and other regions where droughts have always been common. However, parts of China and Europe are now also listed by the United Nations as facing 'moderate-to-high water stress'.

Water, Water Everywhere?

When they first learn about Peak Water, many people's initial reaction is one of disbelief. As they usually argue, over two thirds of the surface of the world is covered with water! Alone in the solar system, our Earth is sometimes even referred to as the 'blue planet'. Unlike oil and other fossil fuels, most water is also naturally recycled after it is consumed. How, then, can we possibly be running out of water?

Estimates suggest that there are about 1.4 billion cubic kilometres of water on the planet (or roughly 326 quintillion gallons). However, around 97 per cent of this water is salty and hence unsuitable for agriculture or human consumption. In addition, the majority of all fresh water is frozen in the polar icecaps. Most of the rest is in the soil or inaccessible very deep underground. The tiny percentage of fresh water that is available for human consumption and all other land-life therefore comes from lakes, streams, rainfall, snow melt, glacial melt and accessible groundwater aquifers. This global reserve is admittedly still very large indeed. However, it is also very unevenly distributed.

Almost all local fresh-water sources do naturally replenish over time. This occurs through the Earth's 'hydrologic cycle' of evaporation, precipitation, surface runoff and the transfer of atmospheric moisture from the sea to the land. However, in given climatic conditions, the rate of replenishment of any particular fresh-water resource is pretty much fixed. All sources of fresh water will therefore face their own production peak if they are drained beyond their natural replenishment level.

Figure 3.1 illustrates a potential Peak Water curve for a single water source such as a groundwater aquifer. As shown in the figure, the acquisition of water beyond the aquifer's natural rate of replenishment follows a bell curve,

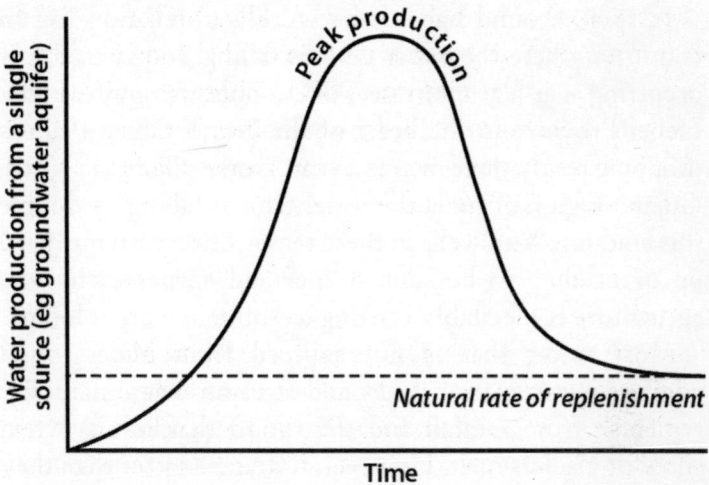

Figure 3.1: A Peak Water curve

with production beyond the peak inevitably falling to the natural replenishment level.

Some groundwater aquifers do recharge fairly rapidly. They may therefore have a natural replenishment level fairly high up Figure 3.1's vertical axis. However, other so-termed 'fossil groundwater' sources have been accumulated over many thousands of years and naturally replenish either very slowly or not at all. For example, the Ogallala aquifer in the United States and Saudi Arabia's Umm Er Radhuma aquifer have no effective natural replenishment and will eventually be pumped dry.

Many parts of the world are already experiencing or will soon face groundwater production peaks. For example Delhi, Rajasthan and many other parts of India rely on groundwater sources that are now being drained at almost twice their natural rate of replenishment. Other countries over-pumping their groundwater aquifers include China, Iran, Israel, Mexico and Spain.

In total, around half of the world's population live in countries where the water table is falling. In places this is occurring at an alarming rate. For example, the aquifer under Hebei Province in the heart of the North China Plain is dropping nearly three metres a year. Worse still, in the North Gujarat region of India the water table is falling by double this amount. With wells in these regions either having dried up or needing to be sunk deeper and deeper each year, agriculture is inevitably starting to suffer and crisis looms.

Most water that is not sourced from underground aquifers is taken from lakes and streams. These naturally replenish from rainfall and the runoff that results when snow or glaciers melt. However, if drained faster than they replenish, lakes and streams are still subject to a production peak as shown in Figure 3.1. Most open-water sources just have a natural rate of replenishment reasonably high up the vertical axis.

Water, Climate Change and the Environment

Humanity's increasing demand for fresh water is unfortunately not the only factor now putting more pressure on supplies. As detailed in the last chapter, climate change is also going to have an increasing impact. Even small changes in global temperatures are already altering the intensity and duration of rainfall, causing lakes to evaporate more rapidly, and so precipitating more droughts. Communities dependent on runoff water from glacial melt will in coming decades also face local Peak Water situations due to a loss of glaciers. As global temperatures lead to hotter climates, the demand for drinking water will also rise, as will the requirement for irrigation systems to grow crops that were previously watered naturally by the rain.

In some parts of the world, the quantity of water appropriated for human consumption, agriculture and industry is additionally starting to cause potentially irreversible environmental damage. In 2009, the Pacific Institute tried to highlight this danger by introducing the term 'Peak Ecological Water'. As its report on *The World's Water* pointed out, every new project that captures water for human use also 'decreases the availability of this water to support ecosystems and diminishes their capacity to provide services. The water that has been temporarily appropriated or moved was once sustaining habitats and terrestrial, avian and aquatic plants and animals'.

When regions consume water beyond the ecologically sustainable peak, the implications can be very serious indeed. For example, since 1900 half of the world's wetlands have disappeared. This has led not only to the extinction of many species, but also the increased flooding of many dryland regions in which people live. The draining of rivers to provide water for drinking and agriculture now also frequently causes natural vegetation to go short of water. In turn this leads to a loss of food and habitats for wildlife, and in time soil erosion.

During the 20th century, humanity's consumption of fresh water increased by a factor of nine. Some estimates suggest that we are now tapping almost half of all renewable and accessible fresh-water resources. If we continue to appropriate even more, there has to be a risk that the resultant damage caused to many ecosystems will seriously backfire.

Peak Water Implications

Peak Water is a future challenge with a very wide range of human and non-human implications. Around 8 per cent of the water consumed by human civilization is used for drinking and basic household purposes. In the majority of developed countries, this domestic supply may in future be more constrained but is not in danger. Nevertheless, in many regions the supply of the far greater quantity of water required for food production is far less certain.

At least 70 per cent of the water appropriated by humanity is used in agriculture. It takes, for example, about 1,000 tonnes of water to produce one tonne of grain, and a staggering 5,000 tonnes of water to grow one tonne of rice. In any region with insufficient rainfall, all or part of this water has to be supplied via irrigation. The current over-pumping of water in some key agricultural regions will therefore have significant future consequences.

For example, the World Bank has reported that the Hai river basin in China is being drained beyond its natural rate of replenishment. Once this water resource is depleted, a supply shortfall of about 40 billion tonnes a year is anticipated. In turn this means that the grain harvest in this region will fall by 40 million tonnes – or enough to feed around 120 million people. Across China more generally, both wheat and grain production peaked in 1997, with production of both staple foods now declining due at least in part to water shortages.

In India the situation is potentially even worse. For example, in Tamil Nadu in southern India falling water tables have already caused 95 per cent of the wells on small farms to run dry. Nationwide, intensive farming methods are still allowing India's total wheat and rice harvests to continue to increase. However, with the water table across most of the country falling, sometime this decade or next the loss of water for irrigation is likely to lead to falling yields. In a country where the margin between food supply and consumption is already precarious, this is likely to result in a humanitarian catastrophe.

As discussed in the next chapter, Peak Water is just one of the challenges that are likely to restrict future global food supplies. However, as water scarcity becomes more and more serious, it will inevitably have implications beyond agriculture. United Nations Secretary-General Ban Ki-moon has repeatedly warned that water scarcity will threaten economic growth, human rights, health and safety and national security within a couple of decades.

The potential health and safety implications of insufficient domestic water supplies are self-evident. So too are the implications of Peak Water leading to food scarcity. However, less obvious may be the broader industrial and hence economic implications of not having enough water.

A great many industrial processes are highly water intensive, with about 22 per cent of water use being industrial. For example, significant quantities of water are required in the production of metals, chemicals, paper products and electronic components. Water is also critical in the mining of coal, oil, natural gas and other fuels, as well as in the running of most power generation systems. Indeed, in the United States the fuel production and power generation sectors are second only to agriculture in their water requirements.

In March 2010, a survey of 1,200 sustainability experts conducted by GlobeScan and business think tank Sustain-Ability reported that future water shortages will 'prompt global industrial transformation'. As Jeff Erikson of SustainAbility noted, fresh-water scarcity will penetrate almost every aspect of business. For example, any company currently planning to locate a new plant in China now needs to consider the melting of the Himalayan glaciers that feed the country's most important rivers. Meanwhile, manufacturers in the United States may in future have to relocate plants from the increasingly dry south-west back to the water-rich Great Lakes region.

Peak Water Solutions

The term 'Peak Water' is increasingly being used to signal a scarcity situation to parallel that of Peak Oil. In some respects the adoption of the same terminology is useful, and not least when it helps to raise business and public awareness. However, it is also very important to appreciate that future oil and water scarcity are very different and will require somewhat different solutions.

Unlike water, the use of oil is almost entirely consumptive. In other words, with the exception of the recycling of some plastics, once we have used oil it has literally been burnt away and cannot be used again. In contrast, almost all uses of water are non-consumptive. Granted, some water may not be readily available for human consumption for hundreds or even thousands of years. However, given enough time and technological know-how, even the most industrially polluted water resources can potentially be used again.

While it is economic to transport oil from one part of the planet to another, the long-distance transportation of large quantities of water is never likely to be viable. This means that, in contrast to oil, water will become increasingly scarce in many locations while remaining plentiful in others. For many populations, the biggest consequence of Peak Water will therefore not be local water scarcity, but a reduced supply of food and other goods from parts of the world that become too dry. This could be a big problem for regions such as Europe that have become dependent on food imported from nations – such as India, South Africa and Ethiopia – that are already water-challenged. All of us will be impacted by Peak Water, but in somewhat different ways.

Most of our longer-term solutions to Peak Oil will involve the development and adoption of alternative fuels and manufacturing materials. Again in contrast, alternatives to fresh water are by-and-large not readily available. For those who live close to the sea, desalination plants will be an option as they already are in some regions. Currently desalinated water is very expensive. However, as discussed in Chapter 7, developments in nanotechnology may make desalination a far more cost-effective means of obtaining fresh water in the future.

What Peak Oil and Peak Water do have in common is a requirement for us to start using each resource far more efficiently. To this end, some of those who study Peak Water suggest that we need to adopt a 'softer path'. This would entail the development of a more integrated and sustainable approach for achieving those things that water makes possible.

For example, advocates of the softer path suggest that we find means of washing and sanitation that use less water, rather than continuing with our current 'hard path' approach of building ever-more dams, pumps, pipelines and treatment plants. In many countries there are also clear opportunities to start matching the quality of water needed with the quality of water used. For example, in countries with sufficient precipitation, houses can fairly easily be adapted to use rainwater to flush toilets and water gardens. Similarly, some agricultural and industrial water requirements could potentially be met from reclaimed wastewater rather than supplies that have been purified for drinking.

Peak Water on Our Doorstep
For most people in developed nations, any immediate, local impact of Peak Water may feel unlikely and rather distant. It is therefore worth being aware of the fact that water scarcity has already encroached well beyond traditionally drought-ridden regions. For example, in September 2010,

several news agencies reported that Cyprus had become the first country in Europe to experience Peak Water.

Situated in the Mediterranean Sea, Cyprus is home to about one million people, as well as being an annual tourist destination for millions more. Traditionally the island's water supplies have come from underground aquifers. However, these have become depleted, with some starting to take in seawater. The water from these aquifers has therefore become salty and unsuitable for drinking. Vegetation is also being severely affected, with 50 per cent of trees in some areas having died due to a lack of water. In turn, soil erosion is starting to take its toll on the land.

Following four years of drought, in 2008 the Cypriot government had to spend $39 million importing tankers of fresh water from Greece. Even so, household taps were rationed to a few hours a day. Across the island, a great many farm animals died.

As Sofoclis Aletraris, the director of the Water Development in Cyprus, told CNN, the 'water culture' in the country is now changing, with no Cypriot able to take water for granted as they very recently did. The Cypriot government is also now investing heavily in desalination plants, with a plan to source all of the drinking water required by Greek Cypriot cities from treated seawater. As this case shows, Peak Water is a real challenge, if with technological and attitudinal solutions that some nations are already having to put in place.

*   *   *

The Flow of Civilization
It is no coincidence that most successful early human settlements were founded on the banks of great rivers. Across history, civilization has always had to locate itself

in reach of adequate water supplies. In the future this is also unlikely to change. As a consequence, many of those currently reliant on over-pumped groundwater aquifers will sooner or later need to relocate. In the face of Peak Water, patterns of world trade are also likely to shift substantially. Peak Water may even have the power to influence the future dominance of the globe.

Talk to most business analysts and they will tell you that China and India are the Economies of Tomorrow. However, both of these nations are rapidly industrializing in part by exploiting their water supplies well beyond their natural rate of replenishment. The predicted rise of China and India to world domination may therefore turn out to be a misguided claim. Peak Water is already a significant future wild card that far too few analysts have on their radar.

Over the past 50 years, the developed world has allowed itself to become separated from many of the physical practicalities of living. But fairly soon the phenomenon of Peak Water could start to reverse this trend. Today, most people lucky enough to live in a developed nation still consider water to be a pretty much free resource. Many of us even waste enough fresh water each day to keep alive a thirst-stricken person elsewhere on the globe. Not that there is much we can do about this given that water is not en masse a transportable resource.

It is also worth reflecting on the fact that only half of the people on the planet currently obtain their water from a tap. Far from worrying if their tap will run dry, most people currently living in the regions of greatest water scarcity would simply like to have a tap in the first place. Nobody should therefore dismiss the provision of a sufficient, global water supply as anything other than a very major challenge. Not least this is because it is a challenge that global humanity has never before met.

4

FOOD SHORTAGES

By 2030 there are likely to be at least eight billion people to feed on Planet Earth. It is therefore highly significant that Peak Oil, climate change and Peak Water could all lead to a reduction in future food supplies. Specifically, more scare and more expensive oil will change the methods and economics of food production and transportation. Climate change is also already lowering agricultural yields, as well as reducing the ability of some regions to grow their current crops. An increasing scarcity of fresh water will additionally reduce crop yields further still and may prevent some regions harvesting any food at all.

In addition to Peak Oil, climate change and Peak Water, five other key challenges threaten future food security. Firstly, due to population expansion, more and more people will need to be fed from the same or a diminishing acreage of agricultural land. Secondly, as industrialization continues, the proportion of meat in the average human diet is increasing and this will stretch our agricultural resources further still. Thirdly, fish stocks are declining. Fourthly, we are witnessing a growth in so-called 'non-food agriculture', with more and more land being used to grow crops that are used to make biofuels and other petroleum substitutes. And last but by no means least, the productivity of a reasonable proportion of agricultural land is starting to decline.

Fortunately, it is already possible to identify several innovations that may enable us to produce sufficient food in the future. Such solutions include genetically modifying crops to increase their yields and quality (as discussed in Chapter 8), as well as vertical farming (as discussed in Chapter 10). Changes in diet, as well as a transition to more local food production, could also greatly help. This said, it is important to realize that food is likely to be in shorter supply in the coming decades and that our diets will need to alter as a result.

Peak Oil and Food

As noted in Chapter 1, every calorie eaten in a developed nation now requires the consumption of around ten calories of oil. To put this another way, the production and transportation of a 1 kg packet of breakfast cereal burns up roughly the equivalent of half a gallon of petroleum. Although many people may not realize it, Peak Oil threatens not just our ability to drive and fly, but also future food supplies.

During the 1950s and 1960s, world agriculture was transformed in a 'Green Revolution' that saw productivity improve by several hundred per cent. In part, this was achieved by developing new crop strains. However, also critical in increasing agricultural production were oil-fuelled farm machinery and irrigation systems, as well as oil-based pesticides and inorganic fertilizers. As the statistics highlight, food production today remains highly oil dependent. While we may not sit at the dinner table and pour petroleum on to our plates, most of us do fuel our bodies by indirectly ingesting oil.

At present the world could not feed itself if it had to stop using oil-based pesticides. However, in the future, genetically modifying crops to make them more resistant to disease may allow us to spray less oil on the land. It is also possible that organic nanotechnologies may be developed as an alternative to traditional pesticides. As yet another option, in the future small robots may scurry or fly over our fields to locate and destroy insects and other pests intent on consuming precious food.

Current irrigation systems and farm machinery are also essential if existing levels of food production are to be maintained. While these do not need to be fuelled by oil, we do need to start planning with some urgency how they will be powered by other means. Even more immediately, we also need to start producing a lot more of what we eat far closer to home. A great deal of our food now travels hundreds or even thousands of miles to reach our plate. It also often does so at least part-packaged in plastic. Reducing these particular aspects of our food-oil dependency should therefore be something that we urgently start to pursue.

Climate Change and Food

Every 1°C rise in average global temperatures is likely to result in roughly a 10 per cent decline in the global yield of corn, rice and wheat. Rising sea levels, coupled with the accelerated melting of ice sheets in Greenland and the western Antarctic, could potentially even lead to the flooding of every rice-growing river delta in Asia. Granted, in some parts of the world, intermediate rises in average temperatures may increase certain agricultural yields. For example, later this century some tropical fruit may be able to be grown in southern England. However, in aggregate, climate change will hinder rather than assist global food production.

As the UK government's Stern Review so starkly put it, 'climate change will increase worldwide deaths from malnutrition'. Every part of the world will to some extent suffer greater crop-loss and lower crop qualities as a result of the more adverse weather caused by climate change. However, in some nations the effects are likely to be catastrophic.

For example, Dr Rodel D. Lasco, the Filipino member of the Intergovernmental Panel on Climate Change, predicts that more frequent floods and droughts will significantly decrease the productivity of millions of acres of farmland in his country. There is also a risk that global warming may trigger the death of coral reefs. Once again, this is a matter of great concern in the Philippines, with almost all of its small island communities dependent on fishing the region's 27,000 square kilometres of coral.

Peak Water and Food

Around half of the world's population lives in countries where the water table is falling. Estimates also suggest that around 400 million people globally – including 130 million in China and 175 million in India – are currently fed from lands that are irrigated by over-pumping their water supplies. The average human consumes about four litres of water a day. But in addition, a typical person's daily food intake requires at least 2,000 litres of water to produce. Inadequate future water supplies are therefore very likely to contribute to future food shortages.

One of the nations where food production is going to be most starkly impacted by water shortages is Saudi Arabia. Almost all of the country's food production depends on land irrigated from non-replenishable fossil groundwater aquifers. For years Saudi used its oil wealth to subsidize the production of wheat that cost five times the world average.

However, as aquifers have been pumped dry, wheat production has fallen from its 1992 peak of 4.1 million tonnes to around 1.2 million tonnes in 2010. With its largest groundwater aquifer now having scant decades of water remaining, Saudi Arabia expects to phase out all of its wheat production by 2016.

Saudi Arabia provides the most extreme case of how Peak Water will curtail future food production. However, more generally the World Economic Forum has forecast that, if no action is taken, water scarcity could cut world harvests by as much as 30 per cent by 2030. This would be equivalent to removing all of the grain currently grown by India and the United States from the global food supply.

Fortunately, possibilities do exist for available water supplies to be used far more efficiently. Due to evaporation and runoff, many irrigation systems waste over 50 per cent of the water supplied to them. However, switching from high- to low-pressure sprinkler systems can reduce water wastage by 30 per cent, while drip irrigation can double the water efficiency of an irrigation system. By switching from a thirsty crop (like rice) to a less thirsty crop (like wheat), very significant increases in protein yields for a fixed level of irrigation can also be achieved. For this reason rice production around Beijing is now being phased out, while Egypt is also restricting rice production in favour of grain.

Our Growing Population

Every year there about 79 million more people to feed. Most of these new arrivals also live in regions where water is becoming more scarce and people are already going hungry. As the world's population further expands, short-ages of food and fresh water therefore threaten a humanitarian crisis.

Even if all of the other issues highlighted in this chapter

could be ignored, it is debatable whether the world's available agricultural land and current farming methods will be able to feed the eight billion people expected on Planet Earth by 2030. Beyond this, feeding the nine or more billion people expected to be alive by 2050 will be absolutely impossible without radical action to alter what we eat and how we grow it. Required changes will also take decades to implement.

Increasing Meat Consumption

Diets that are rich in meat are more resource intensive. This is because all animals bred for table have to be sustained from birth to the slaughterhouse. When we eat meat we are therefore indirectly consuming the quantity of food that our chosen animal has been fed in its lifetime.

The most meat-intensive diets in the world are at present those in Canada and the United States. To supply the beef, pork and poultry eaten in these nations requires about 800 kg of grain to be harvested per person per year. The vast majority of this grain is fed to animals that convert it to meat protein for human consumption. In contrast, in a poorer nation like India, the average diet requires less than 200 kg of grain per person per year. Almost all of this grain is then consumed directly as part of a largely vegetarian diet.

Fortunately, over 50 per cent of cattle worldwide are fed with grass rather than grain. The pastures they graze are also often too steep or arid to raise food crops on. Grazing cattle on such land is therefore an effective use of agricultural resources. However, suitable grasslands are finite. Grain is also still widely relied on to feed most poultry, as well as many pigs.

As nations industrialize, their people consume more meat. For example in China, while annual average meat consumption was 25 kg per person in 1995, by 2008 it had risen to 53 kg. To produce 1 kg of meat requires about 5 kg of grain. As a consequence, while the Chinese population increased only by about 10 per cent between 1995 and 2008, in this 13-year period grain consumption increased by a factor of four. The increasing demand for meat in China and other rapidly industrializing nations also shows no sign of slowing down. Indeed, the World Bank estimates that the global demand for meat is expected to rise by 85 per cent by 2030.

Even ignoring population growth, within a decade or two global meat demand will start to significantly outstrip global meat supply. Measures to limit climate change also ideally require a smaller rather than a larger global population of methane-expelling farm animals. Anybody who eats large quantities of meat should therefore expect to start eating a more vegetarian diet over the next 20 years.

Declining Fish Stocks

Unfortunately, we will not be able to offset an increased demand for a finite and potentially falling supply of farm animals by increasing our continual cull of the oceans. Three quarters of fish stocks are already being fished at or beyond capacity, or are having to be rested to recover from previous overfishing. In the future, fish will be in shorter and shorter supply. In fact, according to the ten-year *Census of Marine Life*, published in late 2010, unless something is done commercial fishing on a global scale will collapse entirely by 2050.

Quite simply, the world's oceans are currently being fished well beyond their natural rate of replenishment. If we do not stop doing this, then the natural rate of fish-stock replenishment is in danger of falling close to zero. In effect, we are already at or even beyond a situation of 'Peak Fish', and this will have very significant consequences for future global food supplies.

The *Census of Marine Life* established historical baselines for the abundance of ten groups of large marine species. These included diadromous fish (that swim between fresh and salt water), reef fish and deep-sea fish. The census discovered that most of these groups have now reduced in abundance by nearly 90 per cent. Chief among the reasons for this are overfishing and habitat destruction, with virtually no part of any ocean now unaffected by human activities. Many scientists believe that life in the oceans will soon be on the brink if it has not reached this point already. The oceans therefore unfortunately sit firmly in the 'problem' rather than 'solution' category when it comes to feeding humanity in the future.

Non-Food Agriculture

Just in case Peak Oil, climate change, Peak Water, population growth, increasing meat consumption and declining fish stocks were not enough, land is increasingly being sidelined for non-food agriculture. Most notably, vast and increasing quantities of land are being used for the cultivation of corn, rape, sugar cane and other crops for use in the production of biofuels. For example, according to the International Energy Agency, between 2001 and 2008 global biodiesel production increased tenfold to 10.9 billion litres per year. It is also anticipated to reach over 20 billion litres by the end of 2012.

Every acre of land used to cultivate a biofuel crop is inevitably one that was or could be used for food production. By the second half of this century, biofuels are likely to be essential in many industrial processes as the only viable substitute to fossil-fuel oil. The use of some agricultural land for biofuel production is therefore inevitable.

Burning a biofuel results in fewer carbon emissions than burning an equivalent fossil fuel. In theory, a switch to biofuels can therefore assist with efforts to lessen climate change. However, in practice, it is increasingly being recognized that the carbon emissions that result from the conversion of rainforests, peatlands and other areas for biofuel production far outweigh the final biofuel carbon savings. At least at present, biofuels are therefore only green if they are manufactured from crops grown on existing farmland. But if this is the case, any increase in biofuel production will inevitably reduce global food supplies.

The Ownership and Productivity of Land

For the many reasons already identified, viable agricultural land is becoming a scarcer and a more premium resource. It is therefore perhaps not surprising that businesses and governments in some developed nations are now spending billions to purchase land in other countries in an attempt to guarantee future food supplies.

Fields in Africa are already being used to grow food for UK supermarkets. This is despite the fact that Africans living near such farms continue to go hungry. Other countries that have purchased farmland in Africa include Qatar, Jordan, Kuwait, Saudi Arabia, South Korea and China. Libya has bought 250,000 acres in the Ukraine.

Foreign acquisitions remove not just land from poor host nations, but also other crucial natural resources. For example, any country that grows food on land purchased in Africa also imports a little of the thirsty continent's water with every fruit or vegetable harvest that is shipped out. As noted in the last chapter, very large quantities of water cannot be transported over long distances. However, any farmland acquisition in a foreign country does constitute an indirect water acquisition. How long it will be both possible and acceptable for rich nations to go on buying and farming large acreages overseas therefore has to be a matter of debate. Already Chinese deals to purchase land in the Philippines and Mozambique have had to be scrapped. So too was a plan by South Korea to purchase a very large quantity of land in Madagascar.

The value of many farmed areas is also diminishing, with soil erosion already decreasing the productivity of around 30 per cent of the world's agricultural land. With over-grazing, over-ploughing and deforestation now rampant in many rapidly industrializing regions, deserts are inevitably continuing to advance. Not least this is the case in China, where soil erosion has already forced around 24,000 villages to completely or partially abandon their farms. Many early human civilizations fell when they could no longer feed themselves in their native location. Unless they start to change their ways, a similar fate could in the relatively near future threaten many of today's greatest global powers.

On a more positive note, the productive potential of some agricultural land is starting to increase. Often this is being achieved by producing more than one crop a year from the same fields. Indeed, the tripling of world grain harvests between 1950 and 2000 was due to a reasonable extent to increases in multi-cropping across Asia. The genetic modification of crops – as will be discussed in Chapter 8 – may in future allow multi-cropping to increase further still. The creation in the lab of new breeds of crop that are more disease-resistant, as well as more tolerant of drought and cold, could also allow agricultural land productivity to rise. New or more tolerant crops strains may even allow food to be grown on land that was previously barren.

Food Glorious Food

Between mid-2006 and mid-2008, the price of rice, wheat, corn and soybeans roughly tripled. The global financial crisis in 2008 may have caused prices to briefly stabilize and even fall slightly. However, by early 2011 global food prices were rapidly rising again and continued to hit new highs. The surge in grain prices that occurred between 2006 and 2008 is therefore unlikely to remain unprecedented as the constraints on future food production outlined in this chapter come to bear. Bad harvests – such as that suffered in Russia in 2010 and in Australia following the floods in 2011 – are also already driving some nations to limit their food exports. Adequate food supplies have always been a massive issue in developing countries. However, within probably a decade at most, food supplies both at home and abroad will be an issue high on the agenda of every nation.

Technically it is quite probable that in the coming decades we could sufficiently feed every person on the planet. However, this would require substantial changes in the food we produce – including the widespread genetic modification of our food chain – as well as alterations in the diets of several billion. It is therefore in no way guaranteed that food shortages will not be widespread in the next decade or the one after that.

In recent years the number of hungry people in the world has been rising, with more than one billion human beings now undernourished. Every day about 16,000 children die from starvation. We should therefore not necessarily have any confidence that action to protect global food security will be taken in time. Indeed, as Lester R. Brown of the Earth Policy Institute argued in *The Futurist* in January 2010, 'food security will deteriorate further unless leading countries collectively mobilize to stabilize production, stabilize climate, stabilize aquifers, conserve soils, protect cropland, and restrict the use of grain to produce fuel for cars'.

Along with energy and most other resources, food is going to become more expensive. Most people will therefore have to spend a greater and greater proportion of their income on food. The current developed-nation luxury of being able to eat what we like when we like is also going to disappear for all but the extremely rich and the extremely selfish.

We can also be pretty certain that in future our food will travel less and will have to be grown more locally. What we eat is also likely to be subject to increasing genetic modification. Many in Europe may not like this idea. However, across the United States, and even parts of Africa, a genetically modified food chain is already a reality.

At the start of the second decade of the 21st century, there is the stark possibility that future food shortages will destabilize nations, topple governments, trigger crippling trade restrictions and even start wars. The challenge of achieving future global food security is therefore likely to bring with it a great deal of future grief. However, on the positive side, there is also the possibility that an increased focus on food and its supply will reconnect the populations of today's developed nations with the natural world. All of us depend for our survival on agriculture. In the future this is going to become more explicit and no longer something that millions can safely ignore.

5

RESOURCE DEPLETION

Like it or not, the Age of Plenty really is now coming to an end. In addition to oil, water and food, many other raw materials will become scarce in the coming decades. In particular, we face shortages of several metals currently vital in the production of electrical and electronic components. We will therefore have to get used to consuming a little less and valuing things a little more.

Humanity continues to expand in the face of a contracting natural resource base. If ignored, this increasingly precarious state of affairs is likely to breed future conflict on a global scale. We therefore need to change our approach to resource utilization if only to maintain today's relative global harmony. The alternative option of waiting until the cupboard is almost bare cannot be a sensible survival strategy.

In May 2011, a report from the United Nations Environment Programme (UNEP) made our position pretty explicit. As it explained, if left unchecked humanity's demand for natural resources is likely to rise to around 140 billion tonnes of minerals, ores, fossil fuels and biomass per year by 2050. This is three times our current rate of resource consumption and 'far beyond what is likely to be sustainable'. As UNEP's Executive Director Achim Steiner subsequently explained, we therefore need an 'urgent rethink' of the links between resource use and economic prosperity. Or, in short, we will have to start achieving more with less.

Peak Everything?

Most analysts expect that we will reach Peak Oil sometime between 2013 and 2030. In parallel, many of the other resources we currently extract from the ground are expected to peak within a fairly similar period. For example, zinc (used in the manufacture of many kinds of battery) and tantalum (also used in rechargeable batteries and in the production of capacitors and resistors) are both expected to peak between 2025 and 2035. Meanwhile antimony (essential in the production of semiconductors) will probably peak between 2020 and 2040.

Some key precious metals are potentially in even shorter supply. For example, indium – a vital element in the production of LCD flat screen displays – may be very scarce by 2020 unless new reserves are discovered. The price of indium also reflects this, having jumped from $40 per kilogram in 2003 to over $600 per kilogram in 2011. Supplies of gallium – currently essential in the manufacture of light-emitting diodes (LEDs) and some solar cells – are also potentially precarious. Even our reserves of copper and tin could cease to meet growing global demand not much after 2050. It is therefore perhaps not surprising that some people are now starting to use the term 'Peak Everything'.

All current initiatives intended to make us less reliant on fossil fuels risk making us more dependent on other resources that will themselves soon become scarce. For example, while we could replace coal power stations with conventional nuclear plants, these are currently fuelled by uranium. Unfortunately, viable uranium reserves will probably last no more than 80 years. A widespread uptake of electric vehicles (as discussed in Chapter 11) would also significantly increase our dependence on precious supplies of lithium, zinc, tantalum and cobalt as these are all used in the production of rechargeable batteries. Similarly, the uptake of conventional electrical solar cells (as discussed in Chapter 13) would increase our dependence on gallium, silver and gold.

Supplies of so-termed rare earth metals (REMs) are also likely to become critically scarce. REMs are a group of 17 metals on which we already depend and on which most next-generation energy technologies could rely very heavily indeed. For example, the REM neodymium is the world's strongest magnet, and therefore used in the production of electric generators and electric motors. Similarly, the REM dysprosium is relied upon to make electric motor magnets 90 per cent lighter, while the REM terbium is used to make electric lights far more efficient. Without a future supply of REMs, we will be unable to use conventional means to make electric cars, wind turbines, solar cells or low-energy light bulbs – not to mention lasers, computer memory, hard disk drives and smartphones.

What is most worrying for the West is that today China produces 97 per cent of global REM ores. China also engages in nearly 100 per cent of associated metal production and produces some 80 per cent of rare earth magnets. Already reports suggest that within a few years China's production of REMs will only be sufficient to meet its own internal demand. With the world demand for REMs having grown from roughly 40,000 tonnes to over 120,000 tonnes in the last decade alone – and China already only exporting about 30,000 tonnes a year – the development of many green technologies is therefore at significant risk.

REM reserves do exist outside of China. It is therefore hardly surprising that plans are already underway to construct REM mines in other countries. However, creating these mines is likely to take many years. REM mining is also exceedingly dirty and creates a great deal of pollution. Few if any communities will therefore welcome a REM mine on their doorstep, and this in turn will slow the growth of REM production in the West. At least a short-term shortage of REMs sometime before 2020 is therefore pretty much inevitable. Just one obvious consequence is that significant REM recycling initiatives will have to be introduced.

Achieving More with Less

We are eating our way through the Earth at a velocity that would shame our recent ancestors. There are, however, five things we can do in response to the many challenges of resource depletion. These options are to reduce consumption, to repair rather than replace, to increase recycling, to reduce wastage, and finally in the longer term to obtain resources from space. None of these options is likely to prove effective in isolation. We therefore need to adopt a collage response.

A decrease in the global demand for physical goods and energy would allow the finite supplies of our first planet to last a little longer. In the face of rising industrialization, achieving any such reduction may seem impossible. However, climate change is already shifting opinion and policy in many nations toward increased energy and resource efficiency. Practical measures are also starting to take hold. For example, energy-efficient light bulbs are becoming widespread, with energy-efficient computers not far behind. Indeed, as long ago as 2005, Intel pronounced the new mantra in computing to be 'performance per watt'.

Digital technology is also allowing more and more people to obtain services that consume far fewer resources. For example, the music industry has 'dematerialized' much of its output, with the sale of digital downloads now roughly equivalent to the sale of far more resource intensive CDs. By the end of the decade a great deal of text and video distribution is also likely to be digital. Already the Kindle e-book reader is the best-selling product on Amazon. In January 2011, it was even reported that Kindle e-books had started to outsell traditional paperbacks on Amazon.com.

A Return to Product Repair

Another way to lessen the impact of resource depletion will be to repair rather than automatically replace broken goods. This is, after all, what happened throughout human history until the arrival of a disposable culture in the second half of the 20th century. To allow this to happen, manufacturers need to start designing products capable of being repaired, with planned obsolescence becoming a thing of the past. As resource depletion grows, rising prices and a lack of raw materials may now also be starting to move some markets in this direction. However, in addition, government intervention will probably be required to force manufacturers to stop making things that are intended for very rapid disposal.

The electronics industry already demonstrates both the problem and the solution. Purchase a DVD recorder today, and when the drive mechanism goes wrong the whole unit has to be discarded. As a result a perfectly good case, tuner, remote control and power supply all end up in the bin. In contrast, if the DVD drive mechanism fails in a desktop or laptop PC then it is very easy to obtain a replacement mechanism as a standard part. The fact that not one DVD recorder manufacturer has yet chosen to include a standard, replaceable drive mechanism provides a stark demonstration of the shameful level of obsolescence designed into many current products.

With or without manufacturer or government action, many items will in the future become easier to repair. As discussed in the next chapter, one reason is that 3D printing will allow any spare part to be made available anytime, anywhere. So often today the breakage of a single piece of plastic or metal renders an entire item functionless and causes it to be discarded. However, in the future, 3D printers will allow almost any broken part to be easily replicated even if the manufacturer does not list a spare. Further into the future, developments in nanotechnology and synthetic biology (as detailed in Chapters 7 and 9) may even permit the creation of self-repairing machines. Once again, technological advancements will allow scarce resources to be saved.

Increased Recycling
A third response to resource depletion has to be increased recycling. In effect this will allow us to turn raw materials previously considered spent into fresh resources. Once again manufacturer action will be required. Already the term 'cradle to cradle manufacturing' is being used to refer to situations where the reuse or recycling of every component in a product is planned for at the design stage. Such developments are also likely to roll out hand-in-glove with far more routine product repair.

When I was a child my mother often told me that in the future people would mine our landfills. I am also certain that her decades-old prediction will turn out to be correct. Already it is cheaper to extract gold from certain types of scrap circuit board than from some gold ores. Tell most people that they are likely to have thrown gold away and they will be shocked. However, small quantities of gold are used on contacts in the computers, mobile phones and audio jacks that most people do still routinely discard.

We may soon even be recycling roadside dust. The catalytic converters now fitted in automobiles to reduce exhaust pollutants all use some platinum, which is one of the world's rarest and most expensive metals. As a result, roadside dust in the United Kingdom now contains as much as 1.5 parts per million of platinum. Research is therefore well underway to develop bacterial processes that will be able to efficiently extract our new urban precious-metal deposits.

Reducing Wastage
Fourth on our list of strategies for dealing with increasing resource depletion will be to reduce the volume of materials that we waste. This may also be achieved in several ways. For a start, as the price of many raw materials rises, companies are likely to reduce the quantity of materials discarded from their production lines. They are also pretty certain to reduce further the stock holding of items that may never be sold. As will be discussed in depth in the next chapter, 3D printing offers tremendous possibilities here as it will enable digital manufacture-on-demand. In turn this will reduce our need to fill warehouses and retail outlets with things that people may not want. Today, many shops are piled high with products that will never be sold. It is indeed sobering to walk around a bookshop pondering what proportion of the stock on display will end up being pulped. If companies learnt more about their customers and adopted on-demand production technologies, such waste-ful practices could fairly easily be reduced.

Another means of reducing wastage will be to use far fewer materials in product packaging. Many manufacturers have already started to pack their products in smaller, more sustainable and less resource-intensive boxes and cartons, and this trend is likely to continue. We may even return to an age in which many products are distributed and purchased with little or no packaging at all. Again this used to be common practice, with few people a century ago expecting to purchase fruit, haberdashery, clothing and many other items in shrink-wrapped plastic inside a box then placed in a bag. Implementing such a change would be difficult for large manufacturers, wholesalers and retail outlets as it would impact their whole distribution chain. Nevertheless, as the price of many resources spirals, packaging-free products could be significantly cheaper, so providing everybody with an incentive to work and shop in new ways.

Obtaining Resources from Space

Continual economic growth and constant population expansion is impossible within an effectively closed system like Planet Earth. Our ultimate and longest-term response to resource depletion will therefore have to involve obtaining raw materials from beyond our first planet. Across history our ancestors learnt to venture further and further from home in search of new lands and new riches, and there is no reason to believe that this will not happen again. Indeed, as I write these pages in mid-2011, NASA has just allocated another significant round of funding to private-sector organizations that are developing a first generation of commercial spacecraft. Google is also sponsoring a competition called the Lunar X Prize in which 29 private companies are competing to send a robotic craft to the Moon.

The only resource on which we can rely in the medium-to long-term is likely to be radiation from the Sun. All of the other things we currently consume are by definition finite. One day the cupboard will therefore be bare. As will be discussed when we look at space travel in Chapter 15, we therefore need to plan ahead for that day or accept our gradual extinction.

* * *

Future Challenges and Future Solutions

Peak Oil, climate change, Peak Water, food shortages and wider resource depletion are all natural inevitabilities. However, as I argued at the start of Chapter 1, they ought not to be used as the weapons of a doom-monger. Granted, in the future these five key challenges will catalyse fundamental changes in both individual lifestyles and the broader patterns of global civilization. This said, time and again across history we have seen periods of actual or potential adversity give rise to great and fundamental innovation.

Like most futurists I live with a daily sense of schizophrenia. On the one hand I have a constant awareness of the challenges – such as resource depletion – that may limit our future achievements. But I am also equally aware of those many, many bleeding-edge innovations that could alter and improve our lives in so many ways.

Fairly soon global civilization is going to start hitting some practical resource constraints. Yet in the face of this challenge, it equally remains the case that we stand on the brink of exponential and converging technological progress. In a sense, human civilization must therefore now learn to evolve by leveraging its increasing wisdom in the face of diminishing physical opportunity. This is also the challenge that every person has to face as they grow older and is consequently not something to be feared.

Due to the scant years they have lived, most teenagers know relatively little. However, most young people more than make up for this due to the near-boundless energy afforded to them by a recently created body with excellent recuperative capacities. Sadly, by the time most people reach 30 – and certainly by the time they hit 40 – such health and vitality will have started to deteriorate. It is therefore fortunate that by this age most people have garnered considerable knowledge and experience. While the passing of youth may be lamented, most people in their 30s and 40s nevertheless still look forward to the remaining years of their life even though they know that they have passed their physical peak.

In comparison to a human being, I would suggest that human civilization is now somewhere in its early 30s. The boundless resources and attainable folly of our collective youth is therefore now well and truly behind us. While this may be a little sad, it in no way has to imply the pending demise of civilization or that we are in any way doomed. Life will be different and perhaps very different as we start to trade more in wisdom and less in physical resources. This said, 'different' may turn out to be at least as good as today and potentially somewhat excellent.

Like most young people, human civilization to date has forged ahead with much energy but little control. Yet this is now starting to change. Indeed, the majority of the following 20 chapters deal with topics that will give us very significant abilities to manipulate the world in which we live. Increasingly, we will be able to manufacture just what we want, make use of a far wider range of energy sources, craft new forms of intelligence, and re-engineer our very selves. Against a rising backdrop of resource depletion, more human control is what the future will therefore be about. Whether this is a good thing – not least for all other life on the planet – is something to be legitimately questioned. However, once opened, the Pandora's box of technological possibility is unlikely to be closed. Whether we are advocates or sceptics, we therefore all have good reason to learn more about those many technological innovations that lie ahead.

Part II

THE NEXT INDUSTRIAL WAVE

6

3D PRINTING

Many times across history, new technologies have altered how things are produced. For example, steam power, production lines and computers all transformed the industrial landscape. Today, we stand on the brink of many similar industrial revolutions. The following five chapters therefore examine those cutting-edge technologies that are set to alter manufacturing and farming over the next couple of decades.

Increasingly, manufacturers will be able to produce products with atomic precision using the fledgling science of nanotechnology. A revolution in the biosciences is also on the horizon. This will allow farmers and industrialists to take control of life itself, and in the process to create genetically modified plants and animals, as well as next generation biofuels and bioplastics. Due to advances in a new field called 'synthetic biology', we may even start to cultivate entirely new forms of life that will be artificially created purely to produce certain chemicals. We may even begin to produce food and other agricultural products in our cities within vast, glass skyscrapers called 'vertical farms'.

Nanotechnology, genetic modification, synthetic biology and vertical farming – as covered in later chapters – are all likely to alter many of today's standard production methods. However, they all still require very substantial development and public acceptance. In contrast, a fifth new manufacturing revolution called 3D printing will be with us far sooner. This will enable plastic and metal components and even entire products to be printed out using devices similar to the inkjet and laser printers that we currently use to output documents and photos. 3D printing is also being born out of computing sector. It is therefore the child of a well-established industry that is experienced in the rapid delivery of practical, game-changing innovation. 3D printing therefore has to be a technology to watch.

The Future in 1984

The first 3D printer was built by Charles Hull in 1984. At the time the inventor was working with specialist ultraviolet lamps that were used to harden liquid plastic resins called photocurable polymers. Hull realized that the potential existed to solidify only certain parts of a container of liquid plastic, hence allowing a 3D object to be created.

After many long nights and weekends, Hull developed an apparatus that could computer-control an ultraviolet laser beam. He then used this to trace out and solidify a single layer of an object on the surface of a vat of photocurable liquid plastic. A perforated platform just below the surface of the liquid then lowered a fraction of a millimetre, so submerging this first layer just a little. The computer-controlled laser beam next traced out the second layer of the object, the platform lowered again, and so on. This process repeated until Hull had created a small, blue plastic cup.

Hull named his 3D printing process stereolithography. He also quickly obtained a patent for it and founded a company called 3D Systems to develop the first commercial 'stereolithography apparatus'. By 1988 a second-generation stereolithographic printer was offered to the mass-market.

At present stereolithography is the most widely used 3D printing technology. It will probably also remain popular for the foreseeable future. Stereolithography may be limited by the fact that it is fairly slow and can only create single-colour objects out of certain plastic resins. Nevertheless, as a form of 3D laser printing, stereolithography is an extremely accurate process. Stereolithographic printers now also come in all manner of sizes, ranging from those with 5×5 inch build areas, right up to monster machines with 20×60 inch platforms.

Once printed, objects created by a stereolithographic printer need to be detached from their printing platform. They usually also need to be set absolutely solid by placing them under a strong UV light for an hour or so. After this has taken place, objects can then usually be sanded, primed, painted or plated as required. While early stereolithographic printers could only output fairly brittle plastics, a wide range of photocurable resins has now been developed. These have made it possible to produce both very hard and fairly flexible objects.

Stereolithographic 3D printing already has a wide range of applications. Most commonly, it is used to create functional prototypes of new products. In many industries, stereolithographic printing is therefore often referred to as rapid prototyping. For example, an automotive engineer may test-print parts for a new gearbox to check how everything fits together. Some designers now also use stereolithography to create concept models. For example, a marketing agency may use a stereolithographic printer to create a mock-up of a new shampoo bottle.

Stereolithographic printers are also increasingly being

used to create the mould masters from which final production moulds are taken and end-use plastic or metal parts are then cast. It is therefore very likely that you already own some products that had their original mould master created by a stereolithographic printer.

Following the development of improved photocurable resins, a few companies have even started to use stereolithographic printers directly to manufacture final production components. When maybe only a few hundred items need to be produced, this is usually far more cost-effective than tooling-up a traditional production line. It can also allow for highly customized manufacturing as each part can be 3D printed to order.

A Range of Processes

Alongside stereolithography, in the late 1980s and early 1990s a number of other 3D printing or 'additive manufacturing' technologies were developed. The first was 'fused deposition modelling' (FDM). This builds up objects in layers by extruding a hot thermoplastic from a moving print head. FDM was created by Scott Crump in 1988. A year later he set up a company called Stratasys to develop and sell FDM 3D printers.

Like stereolithography, today FDM 3D printers are increasingly used to create concept models, product prototypes, mould-masters and even final components. One of the advantages of FDM is that it creates 3D objects using the same types of thermoplastics used in injection moulding. The material properties of FDM printed parts are therefore exactly the same as those produced by a traditional manufacturing process.

A third 3D printing technology is 'selective laser sintering' (SLS). This was developed by Carl Deckard at the University of Texas in the 1980s, although it was not commercialized until 1992. SLS 3D printers create objects by laying down successive layers of powder. Each object layer is then selectively solidified – or 'sintered' – by fusing the granules of the powder together using a high-temperature laser. An alternative and very subtle variant of SLS is called selective laser melting (SLM). This uses a laser to fully melt the powder granules that form the printed object, rather than just heating them enough to fuse them together.

By using different cocktails of powder, SLS or SLM 3D printers can output objects in a wide range of materials. These include polystyrene, nylon, glass, ceramics, steel, titanium, aluminium and most recently sterling silver. It is therefore not surprising that SLS 3D printers are increasingly being used not just for rapid prototyping, but to produce final components. 3D Systems is now a major supplier of SLS 3D printers, having acquired Deckard's patent in 2001.

A final mainstream technology is a 3D version of the 2D inkjet printing process used in most home and office colour printers. This uses an inkjet print head to spray a liquid glue or 'binder solution' on to successive layers of powder. The process was developed in 1993 at the Massachusetts Institute of Technology (MIT) and subsequently licensed and commercialized by a company called Z Corporation. By 2005 Z Corporation (often known as Z Corp) had launched its groundbreaking Spectrum Z510. This was the first 3D printer capable of outputting high definition objects in colour – a feat achieved by using an inkjet print head to spray four different colours of binder solution on to successive powder layers.

Six years later, Z Corporation is selling a range of monochrome and colour 3D printers. These floor-standing items connect to a standard PC, print at up to 600 dpi and have up to 1,520 print nozzles. Current Z Corporation 3D printers can produce objects up to 10 × 15 × 8 inches in size and are fed supplies using snap-in cartridges.

On the Brink of a Revolution

The technology behind 3D printing is only just starting to mature. Many companies – including 3D Systems, Stratasys, Z Corporation, Solid Scape, Fortus and Desktop Factory – now sell 3D printers. However, browse any of their websites and you are likely to be both amazed and yet at the same time a little disappointed.

Current 3D printers are amazing because they allow 3D computer models or digital scans to be printed in a range of materials and sometimes even in colour. However, on the disappointing side, it currently takes many hours to print most objects out. Following stereolithography, printed objects also have to be cured, while following all processes it is usually necessary to remove support structures or excess materials. Current 3D printers are already capable of printing objects with interlinked parts like a set of working gears. This said, 3D printers that can combine a wide range of materials to print out almost anything are still many years away.

Today, most companies with 3D printers still use them to create prototypes and mould masters. While this may not sound that radical, it can nevertheless lead to some very impressive results. For example, the Gas Turbine Research Establishment (GTRE) in India used 3D printing to substantially reduce the time and cost involved in designing its Kaveri fighter jet engine. A prototype was built from around 2,500 components that were 3D printed in just 30 days. This compares to the year that would have been required to make the prototype engine using conventional techniques.

As another example, the creators of a new hybrid vehicle called the Urbee used 3D printing to produce all of the parts required to build a drivable, working prototype of their new automobile. As both of these examples demonstrate, just one future implication of the pending 3D printing revolution is that it will allow complex products to be tested and brought to market far more quickly.

Using 3D printers to gain efficiency improvements is one thing. However, the 3D printing revolution will not take hold – much less capture the public imagination – until many final products are routinely 3D printed. Such 'direct digital manufacturing' (DDM) is also now more than science fiction, with several pioneering organizations already pushing traditional manufacturing boundaries. In fact, in February 2011 *The Economist* reported that already about 20 per cent of 3D printed outputs are final products.

Direct Digital Manufacturing

One of the most significant DDM initiatives is a project called MERLIN. This involves a consortium of six leading aero engine manufacturers coordinated by Rolls-Royce. MERLIN's aim is to use additive manufacturing processes in the production of civil aero engines. This will reduce the cost of tooling to zero. It will also result in environmental savings as 3D printing methods waste far fewer materials than most traditional manufacturing processes. MERLIN commenced in January 2011 and is expected to complete by December 2014.

While MERLIN may allow DDM to be used in the manufacture of aero engines in a few years time, some companies are already 3D printing final components and even entire products. One example is Mercury Customs, a manufacturer of high-end custom motorcycles and components. The company is using a Dimension FDM printer from Stratasys to manufacture a unique cycle fender called the Prolite. This features integrated LED lights and would have been impossible to create solely with traditional injection-moulding techniques.

A second motorcycle manufacturer pioneering DDM technology is Klock Werks Kustom Cycles. The company designs custom components in a 3D modelling package called SolidWorks. These are then sometimes printed out in polycarbonate using FDM, rather than being machined from aluminium or injection-moulded in plastic.

For one build, Klock Werks had just five days to produce a custom motorcycle to take part in a TV show. To achieve this timescale, the company's engineers 3D printed the bike's gauge pod, fork tube covers, headlight bezel, floorboard mounts, floorboard undercovers and wheel spacer cover. The finished bike then went on to set an American Motocyclist Association land speed record, so proving once and for all the durability of 3D printed parts.

Riding motorcycles at high speed can be dangerous. It is therefore perhaps fitting that another DDM pioneer – Bespoke Innovation – is using 3D printers to create custom casings for prosthetic limbs. In the future, the company is also planning to 3D print entire artificial arms and legs. By employing a 3D scanner, exact measurements will be taken from amputees and used in the design of a custom prosthetic. The resultant 3D printed artificial limb will subsequently be far more comfortable than an off-the-shelf, one-size-fits-all traditional model. It will also cost about 90 per cent less.

Several web-based companies – including 3Dproparts. com, Sculpteo.com and Shapeways.com – already allow anybody to have their own designs 3D printed. This in turn is permitting individual designers to bring products to market without ever having to tool up factories or invest in stock. For example, a lone designer called Jeff Bare has started selling a flexible iPad cover called the Canvas Wrap that is 3D printed and distributed via Shapeways.

At present, the company that has most greatly exploited the manufacturing potential of 3D printing is Amsterdam-based Freedom of Creation. Set up by entrepreneur Janne Kyttanen in 2000, this pioneering design and research firm uses 3D printers to manufacture products sold in 25 countries, with its merchandise including table lights, wall lights, trays, tables, chairs, bags, earrings, necklaces, shoes, hat racks and iPhone cases.

Freedom of Creation and the other aforementioned organizations use off-the-shelf 3D printers to create relatively small components and final products. However, in the future, custom 3D printers may be used to create very large things indeed. For example, a team at Loughborough University in the United Kingdom are currently developing 3D concrete printers that may potentially be used to print building parts and even entire buildings. At present the team is working on a technology capable of printing concrete components up to $2 \times 2.5 \times 5$ metres in size. These could then be assembled into larger structures.

In the future, the direct digital manufacturing of buildings could remove many of the constraints inherent in traditional construction methods. For a start, it would allow almost any shape to be created. Concrete printers could also save materials and improve insulation by allowing the creation of honeycombed or otherwise partially hollow concrete walls.

Digital Transportation, Storage and Replication
Later this decade or sometime next, 3D printing is going to become a mainstream manufacturing process. This will allow new products to be delivered to market far more quickly, as well as permitting a much higher level of product customization. However, in addition and perhaps even more significantly, mainstream 3D printing will also

facilitate widespread digital transportation, storage and replication.

Today, many things are manufactured thousands of miles from their point of sale. As a result, around one seventh of the price paid for most products goes directly or indirectly on transportation. Shipping products around the planet also consumes a great deal of oil and other diminishing resources. It would therefore be beneficial if we could start to move products around digitally rather than physically.

The idea behind digital transportation is very simple. Rather than transporting physical items, manufacturers instead use the Internet to transfer digital files to local 3D printing bureaus where they are printed out as close to their point of sale as possible. The aforementioned 3D printing pioneer Freedom of Creation has for ten years been embracing the principle and benefits of digital transportation. As its founder explains on its website, 'at Freedom of Creation we believe in a future where data is the design product, and where products are distributed in the same way that images and music travel through the Internet'.

Digital transportation has the potential to spark a manufacturing revolution. In the future, most towns and cities may have their own 3D printing bureaus to which manufacturers will direct digital data. Groups of manufacturers may also form consortia to run such facilities. Small products may even be digitally transported directly from websites to home 3D printers. Alternatively, larger retailers may opt to receive most of their stocks digitally for printout in store. Everybody with a 3D printer would still need to take delivery of 3D printing supplies. This said, 3D disassemblers may be created to recycle old 3D printed products or parts thereof into fresh materials. Genetic or nanotechnologies – as covered in the next three chapters – may even allow 3D printing supplies to be cultured, grown or otherwise farmed and manufactured locally in almost any part of the world.

Closely related to the digital transportation of products will be their digital storage. Today the number of products that any retailer can offer is limited by available showroom and warehouse space. However, once products can be 3D printed, their digital designs may be stored either on local computers or out on the Internet. Any retailer with a 3D printer could therefore effectively offer any number of products and would not have to maintain a significant physical inventory. Objects stored digitally would also never go out of stock, nor would their retailer run the risk of having to dispose of surplus inventory when a product ceased to be in demand. Already today, digital presses and e-book readers mean that no book ever has to go out of print, while simultaneously enabling publishers to reduce their inventory levels. In the future, 3D printers could do the same for both entire products and spare parts.

Digitally stored products and spare parts may become critical in situations where very limited storage space is available. NASA has already tested a 3D printer on the International Space Station, and recently announced its requirement for a high resolution 3D printer to produce spacecraft parts during deep space missions. The US Army has also experimented with a truck-mounted 3D printer capable of outputting spare tank and other vehicle components on the battlefield.

Coupled with 3D scanners, future 3D printers will allow the digital replication of almost any damaged component. Today many items with a single broken part have to be discarded entirely because a spare is not available. But as we have seen, pending resource depletion will soon require us to abandon this wasteful practice. We are therefore likely to see repair outlets opening up on every high street. With

3D scanners and 3D printers available, craftspeople and technicians in these facilities will be able to scan broken components, repair them digitally in a computer and print replacements. Anybody will also be able to take in any item and say 'can I have three of these please, in this material, in this colour?' Maybe only a decade from now, getting an object replicated will be as easy as dropping in some documents to Xerox in a copyshop.

These developments will start to raise all sorts of questions and possibilities. For example, today when we buy a product we cannot choose the quality of the material it is made from, but in future this may well be the case. The concept of an 'original' item will also come into question. Already sculptor Bathsheba Grossman uses 3D printers to create her artworks, with the possibility existing to mass-produce originals. The authenticity of works of art and other items is therefore going to become harder and harder to verify. When Grossman produces a statue, every one is printed out as an identical masterpiece. But so too would be a duplicate statue created from a scan of her work, let alone a 'fake' artwork 3D printed from a copy of her digital files. In the future, ownership of a work of art may therefore equate to ownership of the digital data from which it was or could be created.

In the future, museums could print out exhibits as required from their own digital collection, or indeed from a global archive of artworks scanned from long-lost or too-delicate-to-display originals. Already archaeologists have scanned mummies and printed out their skeletons without having to rip apart millennia-old bandages. This may all be found fascinating and highly beneficial; however, such scanning and replication could make intellectual property rights management a nightmare. Already the media industries have been thrown into turmoil by the digital distribution and copying of music and video. Quite how traditional artists and manufacturers will react when we can routinely scan and endlessly replicate objects will therefore be interesting to observe.

Building Your Own 3D Printer
Most 3D printers currently cost many thousands of dollars, with the majority of models in the $10,000 to $20,000 bracket. However, for enthusiasts without such deep pockets, an alternative route to owning a 3D printer is already available.

For those with time to invest, it is now possible to build your own 3D printer using designs developed and made freely available by open-source online communities. Two such initiatives currently exist, called respectively RepRap and Fab@Home.

RepRap – or the self-replicating rapidprototyper – is a self-build 3D printer capable of printing plastic objects up to 8 × 8 × 5 inches in size. This means that RepRap can print many of its own components. Once one person has built a RepRap they can therefore create the parts from which a friend can construct another. It costs around $500 dollars to purchase the materials necessary to build a RepRap. You can find out more at reprap.org.

Fab@Home is an alternative open-source, 3D printing initiative with the somewhat ambitious goal of 'changing the way we live'. More specifically, Fab@Home 'is a platform of printers and programs which can produce functional 3D objects'.

Self-built Fab@Home printers create objects in layers using syringe tools that enable the use of multiple materials. These build substances potentially include silicone, cement, stainless steel, cake frosting, ice and cheese. Finished products created by the Fab@Home initiative include a battery, a torch, a bicycle sprocket, toy parts and various food products. It costs $2,400 to build a 'Model One' Fab@Home, although plans for a forthcoming 'Model Two' are expected to reduce the component costs to around $1,300. For more information browse on over to fabathome.org.

*   *   *

The Age of the Santa Machine

3D printing is already a very real and a very useful technology that is developing exceedingly quickly. The gulf between today's 3D printers and future 'Santa machine' devices capable of printing out almost anything we can dream up may still be very wide. However, it is worth remembering that only 20 years ago a black-and-white 2D inkjet printer was very much a novelty. Even ten years ago, it was not possible to use a desktop printer to output a photograph of comparable quality to a traditional photo-chemical print. Given that photo-quality printing at home is now run-of-the-mill, it is therefore not unreasonable to anticipate very significant developments in 3D printing over the next 10 to 20 years.

Even before 'build anything' 3D printers are created, enormous possibilities exist for the exploitation of current 3D printing methods across a range of industries. For example, in the past few years dentists have begun to get in on the act, with 3D printers just starting to be used to create wax-ups directly from 3D scans. This is already allowing better quality dental appliances to be created far more quickly than with traditional methods. The day when a dentist can scan your mouth and print a new plastic or metal crown while you wait cannot be that many years away.

Talking of teeth, we may soon be rotting them away with customized food that is printed to order. As noted above, the self-build Fab@Home printer can already make things out of cake frosting, ice and cheese. In July 2010 two graduate students at the Massachusetts Institute of Technology also put together plans for a 3D printer or 'personal food factory' capable of printing food from a number of refrigerated canisters.

Future food printers could allow those without any culinary skills to produce magnificent, edible creations. A few master chefs aside, it is also unlikely that anybody will strongly object to the manufacture and sale of food printers. The same, however, may perhaps not be the case when it comes to the development of 3D bioprinting. This bleeding-edge technology has already resulted in the 3D printing of living tissue, and will in time lead to the creation of customized human body parts and even wound-free surgical techniques. Already the first commercial bioprinter is on the market. So radical is this particular 3D printing development that it is discussed all by itself in Chapter 22.

By allowing digital data to be 'atomized' back into reality, 3D printers effectively provide a bridge between the real world and the online realm. In the future, any means of making things better, cheaper and more customized is also likely to be in great demand. As a future technology that will permit the digital transportation, storage and replication of any spare part, 3D printing is particularly likely to be welcomed as raw materials become scarcer. This said, as the next few chapters will demonstrate, 3D printing is just the tip of the iceberg of a wide range of innovative new manufacturing techniques.

7

NANOTECHNOLOGY

Every physical object is made from atoms. You, me, the fridge in your kitchen and even the tortoise that ambles around the garden. However, when a fridge is manufactured, its atoms are moved into a fridge-like configuration in a pretty crude manner. In fact, current manufacturing methods – including casting, cutting, pressing, welding, screwing and gluing – have been likened to building things out of Lego while wearing boxing gloves. In other words, although current manufacturing methods do allow us to move collections of atoms around, they do not enable us to position the individual building blocks of matter with any level of atomic accuracy.

Enter nanotechnology or 'nanotech' – the science of understanding and manipulating materials on a nanometre scale. A nanometre is just one-billionth of a metre, or the length of a few atoms placed end-to-end. To put this in a more everyday context, a human hair is around 50,000 nanometres in diameter, while most pieces of paper are about 100,000 nanometres thick.

Any manufacturing or other process that works at a level of precision of between 1 and 100 nanometres can be described as nanotechnology. This means that nanotech is an incredibly diverse field. Indeed, the Consumer Products Inventory maintained by the Project on Emerging Nanotechnologies already lists over 1,000 products that are in whole or part dependent on nanotechnology. Produced by nearly 500 companies across 24 countries, such everyday items include microprocessors, batteries, car paints, textiles, medicines and cosmetics.

The Science of Opportunity

Nanotechnology was first brought to public attention in 1986 when pioneer Eric Drexler published his ground-breaking book *Engines of Creation*. This seminal work effectively established the field of nanotechnology, and in 2007 was updated as a free, 21st anniversary e-book.

The future promise of nanotechnology is the creation of all manner of new and improved materials and products. In recognition of the potentially incredible opportunities, in 2001 the US government established the National Nanotechnology Initiative (NNI) to coordinate the work of 25 federal agencies in fostering nanotech development. This 25-year project has already invested over $14 billion, and is just one indication of the significance being placed on nanotechnology at the highest levels. As the NNI explains:

> The power of nanotechnology is rooted in its potential to transform and revolutionize multiple technology and indus-try sectors, including aerospace, agriculture, biotechnology, homeland security and national defense, energy, environ-mental improvement, information technology, medicine, and transportation.

As the NNI also notes, 'the ability to image, measure, model, and manipulate matter on the nanoscale' will 'impact virtually every sector of both our economy and our daily lives'. Increasingly, nanotechnology is going to be used to make things that are stronger, lighter, cheaper, faster, more energy efficient and more environmentally friendly. Indeed, Drexler confidently predicts that future nanofactories will be able to 'convert simple chemical feedstocks into large, atomically precise products cleanly, inexpensively, and with moderate energy consumption'. Already nanotechnology has enabled a billion and more transistors to be put on a microchip, plasma TV screens to be strengthened and made thinner, sunscreens to provide better UV protection, and fabrics to become more wear resistant. However, the true nanotech revolution is still waiting in the wings.

Theoretically at least, nanotechnology could give humanity control over all forms of matter at the atomic level. In the future, nanotechnology could therefore allow us to make and achieve almost anything we can imagine. Drexler for one is also confident that a fundamental nanotechnology revolution may be on the near horizon. As he explains:

> The last 50 years have shown the incredible dynamism of technologies in the microworld. While cars, aircraft, houses, and furniture have changed only moderately in their capabilities and costs, DNA and microelectronic technologies have exploded, expanding their basic capabilities by factors of more than one billion. [Beyond a certain threshold] ... these developments will burst forth from the microworld to transform technologies on a human and even planetary scale.

The Ways to Tinker with Atoms
The manipulation of matter at the nanoscale can be achieved in two different ways. The first or 'top-down'

approach involves the manipulation of conventional materials to either alter their composition at the nanoscale or to produce nanoscale structures on their surfaces. The second or 'bottom-up' approach is alternatively based around the assembly of nanostructures from individual atoms and molecules.

Almost all current nanotechnology developments are based on the top-down approach. Most widely this is typified by the technology used to make silicon chips. This uses an ultraviolet photographic process known as nanolithography to etch microprocessors and computer memory on to silicon wafers. Employing this technique, for several years Intel's latest fabrication plants have been manufacturing microchips with components only 32 nanometres wide. The company has also recently invested about $8 billion in fabrication plant upgrades to allow it to produce a new generation of chips with components only 22 nanometres across.

Other common top-down processes mix tiny, nanoscale particles into conventional materials to create so-termed 'nanocomposites'. For example, nanotech sunscreens are produced by adding nanosized particles of titanium and zinc oxide into conventional lotions. Nanoparticles of silver are also increasingly being added to medical and cleaning products. These prove very effective in killing a range of bacteria due to silver's antimicrobial properties.

One of the most common nanocomposite additives are carbon nanotubes. These are hexagonal lattices of carbon atoms bonded into tiny tubes about one nanometre in diameter. They are also incredibly strong. In fact, carbon nanotubes are about 117 times stronger than steel, and probably one of the strongest materials theoretically possible. As a consequence, carbon nanotubes are already being added to a range of conventional materials –

including glass, steel and plastics – in order to improve their strength.

Many companies have now developed complex chemical processes that allow them to mass-produce carbon nanotubes. The nanotubes they produce can be up to a few centimetres in length and typically sell for several hundred dollars per gram. Some companies – such as Bayer – now have plants that can each produce 30 or more tonnes of carbon nanotubes a year. By the end of the decade the annual global market for carbon nanotubes is expected to be worth several billion dollars. This is due not only to their use to reinforce other materials, but also their potential application in next-generation nanoelectronics.

The Nanoscale Factory of the Future

While manipulating conventional materials at the nanoscale is already going mass-market, the 'bottom-up' manufacture of things from individual atoms or nanoscale components is far less advanced. This said, bottom-up nanotech is an active research area that could one day allow almost anything to be turned into almost anything else. Not least, with bottom-up nanotechnologies widely available, all 'pollution' and 'waste' would become just gatherings of atoms waiting to be rearranged into something of value.

Nanostructures may be constructed from individual atoms or molecules in one of two ways. The first is known as 'positional assembly', and involves the use of larger tools to move individual atoms or molecules around. The second method is called 'self-assembly' and is where nanoscale objects themselves construct or manipulate other objects on a nanoscale.

Experiments in positional assembly have already taken place. For example, back in 1989 an IBM Fellow called Don Eigler became the first person to controllably manipulate individual atoms. Eigler took a scanning tunnelling micro-scope (STM) and used it to push around 35 xenon atoms. By the time he had finished he had managed to spell out the letters 'IBM', so creating the smallest ever company logo.

Pushing atoms around with an STM may be difficult to get your head around. If so, self-assembly, bottom-up nanotechnology may sound like pure science fiction. Indeed, for several decades the idea of using 'nanobots' or 'nanites' to create and repair things on an atomic scale has been a popular staple of futuristic novels, films and television shows. However, nanotech self-assembly is no fantasy. Not least life itself it based on the process, with all biology relying on molecular self-assembly techniques.

Nobody has yet created the self-replicating nanobots of science-fiction fame. However, there have already been several successful experiments in so-termed 'molecular self-assembly'. This technique employs DNA molecules to assemble shapes using chemical rules. For example, in October 2010 it was reported that two research groups at New York University and Columbia University had built prototype 'DNA robots'. These incredibly tiny machines were constructed out of strands of DNA molecules and 'programmed' to perform simple functions.

For example, New York's DNA robots have already managed to assemble gold particles in eight different patterns. Meanwhile, the Columbia research team has programmed its DNA robots to start, stop, turn and move. Their 'DNA walkers' have three or more legs made from a string of genetic enzymes. Each leg is able to move forward based on its chemical attraction to a sequence of biochemicals laid down as a program of chemical-command stepping-stones. In theory these and other developments may one day lead to the creation of molecular factories capable of manufacturing chemical compounds and even nanoscale computers.

Nanoelectronics

It is far too easy to get carried away with nanotechnology's potential promise. However, it is equally possible to be too dismissive of nanotechnology's already proven application and potential. According to Lux Research in Boston, products incorporating nanotechnology are likely to be generating total sales of about $2.5 trillion by 2015. The next few pages will therefore showcase where nanotechnology is realistically headed in the next decade or so.

As already mentioned, nanolithography is currently used to make state-of-the-art silicon chips with components as little as 22 nanometres in size. Such 'complementary metal oxide semiconductor' (CMOS) chips are fabricated with layers of metal oxide only 0.9 nanometres thick. We will therefore soon reach the miniaturization limits of CMOS technology. Beyond 2020, the constant performance improvements we have come to expect in computing will subsequently have to rely on other technologies.

Research teams around the world are now focused on the challenge of developing post-CMOS nanoelectronics. For example, back in 2007 a team at IBM created the first flawless, single-molecule switch, so paving the way for building computing components at the molecular scale.

Future nanoelectronic devices will also exploit the superconductive properties of carbon nanotubes. Because these very tiny conduits conduct electricity in a different way to normal metals, they do not scatter electrons around. This means that carbon nanotube wiring may potentially be used to make operable electronic circuits at a far smaller scale than possible with current silicon manufacturing techniques.

Alongside carbon nanotubes, another nanomaterial with many possible future applications is graphene. This is made up of a single layer of carbon atoms arranged in a honeycomb, and has quite spectacular strength, flexibility, transparency and electrical conductivity. Although graphene was discovered in 1962, until recently it was impossible to produce except in very small flakes. However, in 2010 researchers at Samsung and Korea's Sungkyunkwan University managed to produce a continuous layer of pure graphene on the top of a flexible, see-through, 63 cm-wide polyester sheet. Due to this accomplishment, in the future graphene may well be used to produce highly flexible displays and touchscreens. Graphene may also be used in the production of future solar cells.

Nanomaterials and Nanocoatings

Increasingly nanotechnology will be used to improve the properties of many materials. Already nanocoated textiles that can repel dirt and water are fairly common. Some buildings are also starting to be glazed with nanocoated 'self-cleaning' glass that similarly prevents dirt sticking to the panes. These developments may seem fairly rudimentary. However, they are likely to be taken very seriously by window cleaners and detergent manufacturers!

The addition of carbon nanotubes to certain traditional materials is also already leading to some rather novel developments. For example, scientists at chemical manufacturer Battelle are developing a heatable paint to prevent ice building up on planes. This incorporates carbon nanotubes, and in the near future is expected to be applied to the wings and other important flight surfaces of aircraft. The pilot will then 'energize' the paint in cold conditions using the plane's electrical systems. Scientists at Battelle believe that nanotech heatable paint will be a game-changing de-icing development. Not least this is because an application of their ingenious coating will be 100 times lighter than any comparable de-icing solution.

In the plastics industry, the introduction of nanoscale additives into conventional materials will also increasingly lead to the development of new nanocomposites. These will allow improvements in strength and surface properties, yet at lower cost. For example, some car bumpers are already being manufactured with nanoclays composited into the plastic to improve impact resistance. Nanocomposite foams have also already been created that look the same as solid plastics, yet are much lighter. Such foams are therefore likely to be widely adopted in the production of items including disposable cups and fast food containers, packaging, home insulation, carpet backings and cushions.

Yet another potential nanomaterials development is bonding on demand. In the future, this should allow metals and plastics to be fused together with secure joints that may years later be atomically 'deactivated' to enable easier recycling.

Nanomedicine

The adoption of nanotechnology in medicine is a very logical next step. For hundreds of years doctors have been developing surgical techniques that have enabled them to perform operations with a greater and greater level of precision. Taking medicine to the nanoscale is therefore a natural evolution that may lead to the fusion of surgery and pharmacy.

In June 1999, Nobel laureate and nanotech pioneer Richard Smalley testified before the US House of Representatives in one of several hearings that led to the creation of the National Nanotechnology Initiative. At the time Smalley was undergoing chemotherapy. However, he predicted that this 'very blunt tool' then ravaging his own body would be obsolete within 20 years. Smalley's belief was that nanoscale drugs would be developed capable of targeting mutant cells with minimal side effects for the patient. He concluded with the assertion that cancer of the type he had would become a thing of the past.

Smalley died of his cancer in 2005. However, several teams are now developing nanorobots or 'nanobots' to enable the future targeted delivery of cancer drugs. One such project is running at the École Polytechnique de Montréal. As explained by Sylvain Martel, the director of its nanorobotics laboratory, this will have a 'huge impact' on cancer therapy as nanorobots will one day be able to deliver therapeutic agents directly to a tumour through the bloodstream.

The nanobots being developed by Martel's team consist of magnetic drug carriers coupled with flagellated bacteria motors. The team use magnetic resonance imaging (MRI) to feed information to a controller that steers the nanobot through the patient's blood vessels. This enables them to deliver drugs to areas inaccessible via traditional catheterization techniques. In September 2009, Martel predicted that it would take three to five years to perfect the computer-control of the nanobot's steering mechanism. A second project at Carnegie Mellon University is also working on similar programmable nanoscale robots for targeted drug delivery.

Another research initiative hoping to use nanobots in medical practice is led by Bradley Nelson of the Institute for Robotics and Intelligent Systems at the ETH Zürich science and technology university in Switzerland. One of Nelson's projects is the development of nanobots for use in retinal surgery. This, he believes, may even be possible sometime this decade. Indeed, as he explained in an article in 2009, 'with sufficient resources and energy and the backing of doctors and business people, retinal therapies using nanobots will be possible within five years'.

Meanwhile, a team under Aristides Requicha, director of the Laboratory for Molecular Robotics at the University of Southern California, is hoping to overturn current medical paradigms entirely. Requicha's aim is to focus on prevention rather than cure by creating swarms of nanobots that will constantly roam the bloodstream to seek out and kill pathogens before patients exhibit any symptoms. Requicha's long-run ambition is 'to build artificial and preferably programmable cells'. We will return to the potentially profound implications of creating this kind of artificial, nanotech immune system when we look at life extension in Chapter 24.

While nanorobot swarms to patrol our bloodstreams may be many decades away, several other nanotech health developments are far closer to practical application. For example, a project funded by the European Union and based at the University of Bath is developing a smart nanotech bandage. This fights infections by releasing antibiotics from nanocapsules. However, the really clever part is that antibiotics are only released if disease-causing pathogenic bacteria are detected by the bandage. In turn this reduces the risk of patients receiving unnecessary medication to which they may develop a resistance.

Another health-related development is the use of nanotechnology in water purification. As part of the Hope Project in South Africa, researchers at Stellenbosch University's Water Institute are developing a revolutionary water filtration system incorporated into a conventional teabag. Expected to cost around half a cent, these contain activated carbon and nanofibres bonded to thin films of biocides. The user simply installs a teabag into a container and adds dirty water. As the water filters through the bag, the activated carbon removes unwanted chemical compounds and impurities, while the biocides on the nanofibres destroy harmful microbes. Dirty water can therefore be made safe to drink on the spot.

Small Science, Big Future Solutions

Nanoelectronics, nanomaterials, nanocoatings and nano-medicine are likely to transform many industrial sectors and numerous lives. In addition, some of the most fundamental, global challenges identified in Part I of this book may also have nanotech-related solutions. For example, there are potentially several ways that nanotech-nology could be employed to tackle climate change. As noted in Chapter 2, one solution may involve the construc-tion of vast solar sails out in space. These could potentially curtail global warming not by reducing the level of greenhouse gases in the atmosphere, but by shading the Earth from just a little of the Sun's heat.

Vast solar sails would of necessity have to be extremely thin. They would therefore almost certainly have to be manufactured in space using either top-down or bottom-up nanotechnology. In turn this would present the challenge of getting the required materials into Earth's orbit. One mooted solution is to mine minerals from the Moon or the asteroids. However, another possibility may be the con-struction of a space elevator that could carry materials into orbit without the requirement to launch a single spacecraft.

A space elevator is a theoretical future lift that would climb up a very long cable stretching from the ground to a space platform in geostationary orbit. Such a device could therefore greatly ease access to space. However, it would also present many tremendous construction challenges. Not least these would include the production of a very strong cable many thousands of miles in length. If such a cable were to be made from any current material then it would collapse under its own weight. However, in the future carbon nanotubes could potentially be used to create a space elevator cable. As will be discussed in Chapter 15, due to nanotechnology a space elevator is therefore now at least a theoretical future possibility. Should we choose to try to curtail global warming by shading the Earth with solar sails, a space elevator may also prove essential.

Another grand-scale alternative for tackling climate change could involve the construction of atmosphere filtration plants around the globe. As Eric Drexler describes in the 2007 edition of *Engines of Creation*, future nanotechnology could potentially be used to extract greenhouse gases from the atmosphere. This he accepts could take ten years, not to mention several terawatts of power that he suggests would have to be provided by vast solar arrays. However, Drexler is nevertheless convinced that future nanotechnology developments will make it both possible and affordable to remove and store the excess carbon dioxide that has been accumulating in the atmosphere since the Industrial Revolution.

In the more immediate future, nanotechnology is also likely to assist with the challenge of Peak Water. It could do this by enabling low-cost and low-energy water desalination. Already the US Department of Energy's Lawrence Livermore National Laboratory has found a way to remove the salt from seawater using nanotechnology. This uses carbon nanotubes to filter out or 'reject' the ions that make up common salts. If this technology can be developed further then it could help to greatly increase available fresh water supplies in coastal regions. In turn this could help prevent pending global food shortages.

Given that future nanotechnologies could potentially allow almost anything to be constructed atom-by-atom, it is theoretically possible that they may help solve future fuel and food shortages. This said, for the very foreseeable future, it is far more likely that new fuels and food stocks will result from developments in genetic modification and synthetic biology, as detailed in the next two chapters.

Nanotechnology is, however, likely to have a major role to play in the future energy and transportation sectors. Possibilities include nanotech solar panels, as well as the use of nanotechnology in the production of new battery technologies for future electric vehicles.

Tomorrow's Asbestos?

Nanotechnology may offer a great many advantages. Yet, as with any other revolutionary new technology, there are already those who suggest that we are meddling with things we do not understand. Some simply believe that mucking around with matter is a violation of the natural order. While very few take this extreme view, far more people are raising more mainstream nanotech safety concerns.

Following the popularization of nanotech in the late 1980s, the idea spread that out-of-control nanotechnology could result in the end of the world. This became known as the 'grey goo scenario' and was based on the idea that future self-replicating nanobots could potentially turn all matter into some kind of lifeless sludge. For some years Prince Charles and many other naysayers espoused the grey goo scenario. However, today, even most of those who object to nanotech now accept that there is no risk of us all becoming grey goo. To fear the creation of things that can endlessly turn dirt into copies of themselves may appear rational. However, this is exactly what potatoes do and we tend not to worry about getting overrun by spuds.

The above noted, nanotechnology may raise significant safety concerns. For example, several bodies – including Friends of the Earth – have warned that we need an 'immediate moratorium' on the use of carbon nanotubes if we are to avoid a repeat of the asbestos tragedy. It is certainly the case that some nanomaterials have been brought to market way before their potential long-term impact on human health and the wider environment has been established. Quite how the human body may rid itself of unwanted nanoparticles is, for example, far from known. Research in this area is therefore needed, and not least because some toxic effects of nanoparticles at the pulmonary, cardiac, reproductive, renal and cellular levels have already been reliably documented.

Nanotech advocates suggest that the nanosized particles that have already been added to many everyday materials present no danger to human health. This means that there are no health risks associated with the carbon nanotubes now present in many car paints and plasma TV screens. However, taking an opposing view, others point out that loose nanotubes easily permeate the skin and may cause cancer. One thing is fairly certain: by the end of the decade we will have found out who is right.

Around the world the debate surrounding nanotech safety is rising. At the very least, more comprehensive toxicity testing may therefore slow the roll out of some new nano products in the same way that opposition to GM crops has significantly prevented their roll out across Europe. Some nano-safety initiatives are also starting to emerge. For example, in 2008 an accreditation scheme called AssuredNano was introduced to promote the responsible and proactive application of good nanotechnology health and safety practices. You can find out more at assurednano.eu.

* * *

The Promise of the Future

As you may have gathered, of all the things highlighted in this book, nanotechnology may have the widest future potential. Many of our remaining chapters will therefore return at some point to nanotechnology. However, given than nanotech is basically the study and manipulation of matter at its most basic level, its application in so many areas of future technology development ought to come as no surprise.

In the 1980s, microelectronics kick-started the current industrial wave of computing and digital communications. While the technologies of the Internet Age are not going to disappear anytime soon, it could well be that nanotechnology and perhaps 3D printing will create a new wave of almost limitless manufacturing possibility. This new wave may also be the first to sustainably champion repair and recycling alongside new production methods. In common with most previous industrial waves, mainstream nanotechnology will also bring with it a vast cacophony of choice.

One of the world's most renowned nanotechnology researchers is Ralph Merkle, a faculty member at the highly future-focused Singularity University in the United States. Merkle has frequently spoken of the manufacturing possibilities that will exist when self-replicating nanobots can turn a supply of atoms into anything we can dream up. In one such recent lecture (available for free on YouTube), Merkle drew a circle to illustrate all of the possible things that could ever be made. Within this ring he then represented with a very small dot all of those products that have been manufactured to this point in history. His contention was quite simply that nanotechnology will allow us to create that vast array of other things that are physically possible, but which we have not figured out how to make yet.

Many futurists believe that the period from 2020 to approaching 2050 will be an era of relative scarcity. This does not mean that we will have run out of everything, but that there will be widespread global shortages of many raw materials including oil, water, food and some minerals. In the face of this challenge the human race will learn to live in new ways. However, by around 2050, it may well be that developments in nanotechnology, genetic engineering, synthetic biology and space travel will herald a new Age of Plenty. If this proves to be the case it will be because these new technologies – and in particular new bottom-up nanotechnologies – will have caught up with our needs.

Even without the acquisition of new resources from space, the Earth has a plentiful enough supply of atoms to enable ten or more billion people to live comfortable lives. All we therefore require is the technology to enable the right atoms to be rearranged into those resources and products that we need or otherwise demand. In the long term, that is the promise of nanotechnology. It is therefore a promise that we have a very great incentive to pursue and at some speed.

8

GENETIC MODIFICATION

The dominant sciences of the 20th century were physics and chemistry. In the 21st century physics and chemistry will remain very important as new developments like 3D printing and nanotechnology rise to the fore. Nevertheless, we should increasingly expect physics and chemistry to be overshadowed by the biosciences. For a start, advancements in traditional botany and zoology are likely to lead to new agricultural practices and production methods. More prominently, the Bioscience Revolution will also encompass the genetic testing and genetic modification of both ourselves and other organisms. The most radical bioscience developments will even give rise to the artificial genesis of entirely new living things.

Future bioscience developments are far too broad to be covered in just one chapter of this book. The next few pages will therefore focus solely on the genetic modification of existing plants, animals and microscopic organisms. The following chapter will then explore the creation of entirely artificial biological creations, as well as the radical redesign of existing biological systems. In aggregate, the role of this chapter and the next is to consider how bioscience developments will change farming and manufacturing.

Human genetic testing, 'pharmacogenetics' and gene therapy will then be looked at separately when we consider genetic medicine in Chapter 21.

Manipulating Life

The intentional manipulation of living things has been taking place since agriculture began. As just one example, for centuries buds have been grafted between apple trees. This allows different branches of the same tree to bear different varieties of fruit. So successful is this technique that today some hybrid trees grow over 100 different kinds of apple.

Cutting a bud from an apple tree and grafting it to another is an age-old means of introducing foreign genetic material to a host plant. But more recently, the new science of genetic modification has started to allow us to exchange and manipulate genetic material in far more fundamental ways. To some people's alarm, in the future this may give humanity control over all living things.

The characteristics of all forms of life are determined by their complete genetic code or 'genome'. This information is stored in deoxyribonucleic acid (DNA) using four different chemicals called adenine, cytosine, guanine and thymine. Abbreviated to the letters 'A', 'C', 'G' and 'T', these so-termed 'bases' are coupled together to form the linkages or 'base pairs' that hold together the two spirals found in every DNA molecule.

Genetic engineers study and manipulate DNA by altering specific portions of its base pair sequence known as genes. So, for example, a human DNA molecule contains about three billion base pairs that may be subdivided into approximately 20,000 to 25,000 genes. Figure 8.1 provides an indicative representation of the relationship between a DNA molecule and its genes and base pairs.

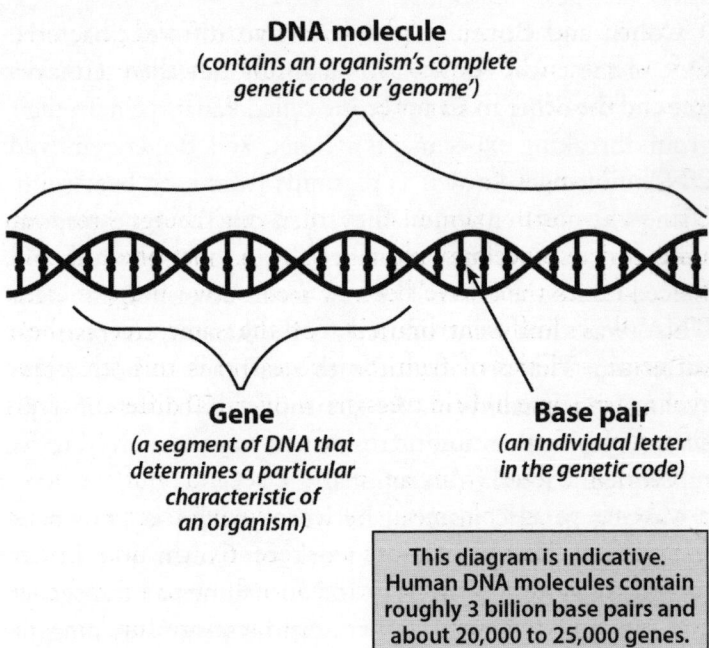

DNA molecule
*(contains an organism's complete
genetic code or 'genome')*

Gene
*(a segment of DNA that
determines a particular
characteristic of
an organism)*

Base pair
*(an individual letter
in the genetic code)*

This diagram is indicative.
Human DNA molecules contain
roughly 3 billion base pairs and
about 20,000 to 25,000 genes.

Figure 8.1: DNA, genes and base pairs

DNA was first discovered in 1869 when Swiss chemist
Johann Friedrich Miescher extracted a substance then
called nuclein from white blood cells. By the early 1900s
nuclein was being referred to as DNA, with its four
different chemical bases having been identified. In 1944 a
team lead by Oswald Avery at Rockefeller University first
demonstrated that genes consisted of distinct portions of
DNA. The double-helix structure of DNA was then
determined by James Watson and Francis Crick in 1953.

Genetic modification (GM) introduces genes from one
species into the DNA of another. The first genetically
modified organism (GMO) was a novel *E. coli* bacterium
created by Stanley Cohen and Herbert Boyer in 1973. Their
work also kick-started the new science of genetic engineering.

Cohen and Boyer started with two different bacteria. One of these was resistant to an antibiotic called tetracycline and the other to an antibiotic called kanamycin. In their groundbreaking experiments, Cohen and Boyer removed DNA molecules known as plasmids from each bacterium. Using chemical enzymes, they then cut the gene responsible for tetracycline resistance from one plasmid and spliced it into the other. The new mash-up of 'recombinant DNA' was then reintroduced to the kanamycin-resistant bacterium. This provided it with resistance to both tetracycline and kanamycin. As the modified bacterium replicated, this dual antibiotic resistance was transferred to its subsequent bacteria generations.

Moving genetic material between species is known as transgenics. The pioneering work of Cohen and Boyer subsequently paved the way for all manner of transgenic innovations, with many other scientists soon learning to create GMOs that contained genes from other species. For example, in 1974 researcher Rudolf Jaenisch created the first transgenic animal when he introduced leukaemia genes into mice embryos.

In 1976 Herb Boyer co-founded a company called Genentech with the goal of using GM to create new medicines. Only two years later Genentech had managed to produce human insulin by inserting the appropriate gene into E. coli. By 1982 this first genetically engineered drug had been approved by the US Food and Drug Administration (FDA) and went on sale for medical use.

Genetic modification has now been used to create a wide variety of transgenic plants and animals. Genetically modified bacteria are now also being employed to manufacture not just medicines like insulin, but also biofuels and bioplastics. Over the next few decades the manipulation of DNA therefore holds the potential to trigger an agricultural and manufacturing revolution. To explore further where this may take us, the following sections consider in turn the development of GM plants, GM animals and GM biotech factories.

GM Plants

One of the first and most famous GM plants was created at the University of California in 1986. Here scientists took the luciferase gene from a firefly and inserted it into tobacco DNA. The result was a GM tobacco plant capable of emitting a glow. This experiment was intended to help scientists track the successful transfer of genes between species and across subsequent generations. Nobody ever intended to market glowing tobacco plants. However, at the time the transgenic tobacco-firefly hybrid very much captured the public imagination as it indicated the future promise or menace of GM.

The first commercial GM plant was the Flavr Savr tomato. Created by a company called Calgene, this was licensed for human consumption by the FDA in June 1994. The Flavr Savr was genetically modified to stay firm after harvest, so allowing it to be ripened for longer without the risk of the fruit being crushed on the way to market. Calgene achieved this by using so-termed 'gene-silencing' or 'antisense' technology to shut down the gene that causes tomatoes to rot and release their seeds.

Following in Calgene's controversial footsteps, from 1995 Monsanto was the first company to introduce a range of corn and other GM crops. Initially plants were modified to be resistant to particular pesticides, so enabling farmers to kill weeds more easily without harming their harvests. In turn this allowed smaller amounts of less-selective pesticides to be sprayed less often, so lowering agricultural costs.

Several staple crops – including corn, cotton, soybeans, sugar beet, canola and rice – have now been genetically modified. Changes have been made not only to make plants resistant to pesticides, but also to increase their resistance to pests and viruses. GM has also been used to improve particular crop qualities like sucrose content.

Today, around 90 per cent of the corn, cotton and soybeans planted in the United States are GM. China also grows large quantities of GM corn, rice, tomatoes, tobacco and cotton – and is investing billions in GM development. Brazil, Argentina, Canada, Paraguay and South Africa also grow significant quantities of GM crops. Across these nations large increases in yields have been obtained. For example, GM cotton has shown yield increases of up to 80 per cent due to its greater resistance to bollworm infection. Meanwhile, following public protests, most countries across Europe have yet to allow any GM produce to be grown in their fields.

While GM crops remain contentious, in the face of Peak Oil, climate change and Peak Water they may be the only alternative to widespread food shortages. For example, Monsanto claims that it is about to launch a drought-resistant GM corn. Scientists working in the John Innes Centre in Norwich also believe that they have isolated the gene that controls how plants sense and adapt to changes in temperature. In the future, this may allow the creation of GM crops that can be grown in any climate. We are therefore en route to GM crops that will be resistant to the impact of global warming.

GM crops are also being engineered to provide health and medical benefits. One such 'nutraceutical' is Golden Rice, a species of rice that has been genetically modified to produce beta-carotene in its grain as a source of vitamin A. According to the World Health Organization, a deficiency of vitamin A causes somewhere between 250,000 and 500,000 children to go blind every year. Vitamin A deficiency is also thought to compromise the immune systems of about 40 per cent of children aged under five in the developing world, often with serious health implications.

The future humanitarian potential of the Golden Rice project is very significant indeed. The first Golden Rice field trial was harvested way back in 2004; however, regulatory hurdles abound, environmentalists continue to campaign against the crop and Golden Rice is therefore still not available for human consumption. Best estimates suggest that people may actually start eating and benefiting from Golden Rice sometime in 2012. As and when they do, the way the world views GM crops may also start to change.

In the future, nutraceutical GM crops engineered with medicinal properties could potentially be used to immunize entire populations against diseases that currently kill millions. In developing nations this may also provide the only realistic method of mass immunization. Imagine the potential of rice, soybeans or corn genetically modified with a future AIDS or malaria vaccine. Such possibilities may lie decades into the future. The mass use of any such 'immunization crop' would also undoubtedly raise widespread ethical debates. However, given that many developed nations add fluorine to drinking water just to improve dental health, it is likely that future governments will readily sanction the mass delivery of nutraceutical vaccines in our food even if some people object strongly to the practice.

GM Animals

Potentially even more contentious than GM crops are GM animals. The first GM animal was a transgenic mouse with leukaemia genes spliced into its DNA. Since this was created in 1974, many other rodents have also been genetically modified. Perhaps most notably, in the 1980s researchers at Harvard created a transgenic mouse with a foreign oncogene that can trigger the growth of tumours. This made their Oconomouse very susceptible to cancer and hence a useful test subject for cancer research. The Oconomouse also earned the distinction of being the first animal to have the intellectual property encoded in its DNA legally protected. This occurred in 1988 when the United States Patent Office granted a patent for 'a transgenic non-human mammal whose germ cells and somatic cells contain a recombinant activated oncogene sequence'.

Like it or not, made-to-order transgenic animals are already a reality, with the creation of transgenic mice for medical research now very routine. For example, in Perth, Australia, a company called Ozgene has been producing GM mice and rats for a wide range of clients for nearly 20 years. At ozgene.com the company even has a very cheery website that uses cartoon mice to illustrate how its GM rodents are taking part in projects around the planet. As the company explains, it provides clients with a complete 'design and construction service' for GM rodents. These include mice that have been 'humanized' with functional human genes.

Creating GM rodents for scientific research is one thing. However, genetically modifying those species that we farm and may eat is something else. The first major news story involving a GM farm animal was the successful cloning of a sheep called Dolly at the Roslin Institute in Scotland in 1996. While Dolly was a GM animal, she was not a transgenic creation as no genetic information crossed the species barrier. Rather, the intention of the scientists at

Roslin was to demonstrate the potential to create an exact copy of an animal from just one of its cells.

Cloning is defined as making one or more copies of a gene, cell or entire organism. Before Dolly was created, recombinant DNA technology had been used to clone genes in bacteria. California-based Genentech, the first ever biotechnology company, was also using this method commercially to create insulin and other proteins. However, the scientists at Roslin were the first to clone a living, breathing creature.

As shown in Figure 8.2, Dolly was created by removing an udder cell from the sheep to be cloned. An egg cell was also removed from a donor sheep and its nucleus discarded. The udder cell nucleus from the sheep to be cloned was then transplanted into the donor sheep's 'empty' egg cell. Next, the resultant hybrid cell was stimulated with an electric shock to make it start dividing. Finally, the resultant embryo was implanted into a third sheep that acted as a surrogate mother and grew Dolly in its womb.

The creation of Dolly was not an easy process. In fact, it took the scientists at Roslin 277 attempts to create a viable embryo. Since Dolly was born, reproductive cloning has been used to create copies of pigs, horses and dogs. In the future, while the technology will almost certainly continue to be refined, it is very unlikely that cloned animals will ever be raised for table. Nevertheless, the creation of transgenic animals for human consumption is now on the cards.

At the time of writing, although many animals around the world eat GM feedstocks, no GM animal is in the human food chain. However, the FDA is considering the potential sale of a new transgenic salmon called the AquAdvantage. Created by AquaBounty Technologies, this fish has had ocean pout and chinook salmon genes

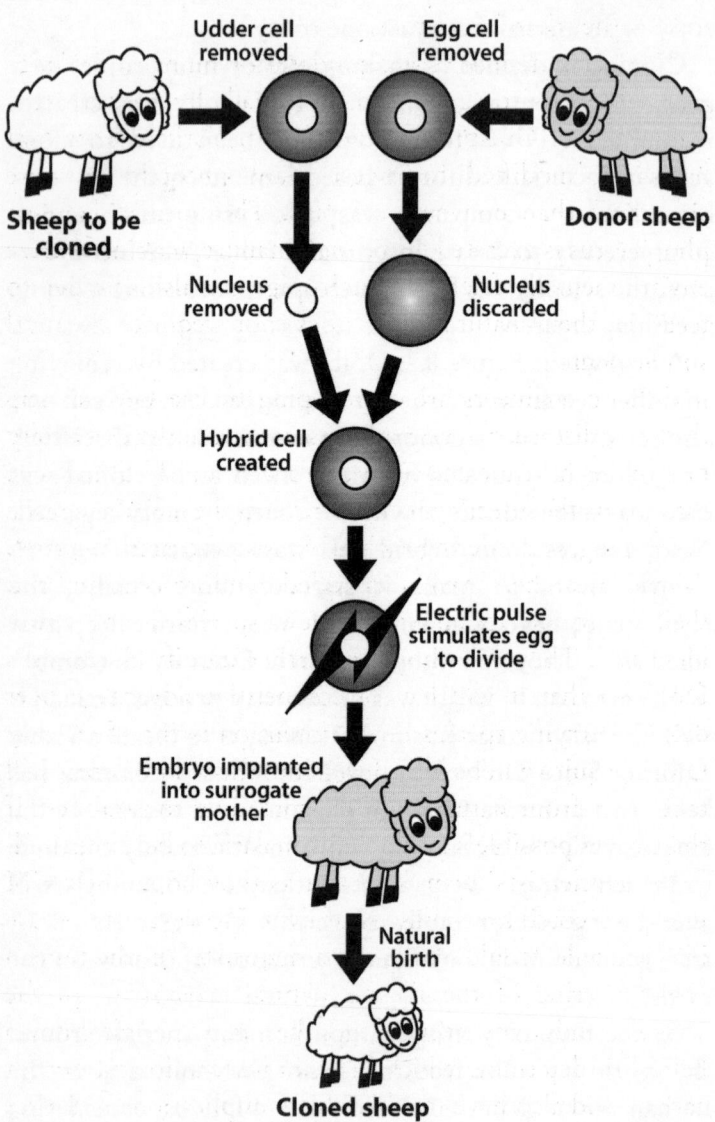

Figure 8.2: How to clone a sheep

spliced into its DNA in order to make it grow to full size in 18 rather than 36 months.

Another potential GM candidate for human consumption is the Enviropig. Created in Canada by a team at the University of Guelph, this is a type of Yorkshire pig that has been modified to digest plant phosphorus more efficiently than conventional pigs. This means that less phosphorus is excreted in the pig's manure, making it more environmentally friendly. Enviropigs are also cheaper to feed as their natural diet does not require chemical supplements.

Genetic engineers are also hoping to use GM to help eradicate disease. For example, researchers at the University of Arizona have created a mosquito with an additional gene that affects the insect's gut. This prevents the malaria parasite developing, so rendering their GM mosquito malaria-proof.

The researchers have also added a fluorescent tag into their mosquito to allow the new species to be easily identified. They even hope to further modify the insect's DNA so that it will have a competitive advantage over disease-carrying species. Their intention is that their new GM mosquito will be introduced into the wild where it will take over from natural, disease-spreading mosquitoes. If this proves possible it could allow malaria to be eliminated.

If the scientists' plans turn out as they hope, their GM mosquito could save millions of lives. However, its release into the wild would also mark a major step in the human re-engineering of the Earth's natural ecosystem. In the wrong hands, any technology that may permit human beings to determine which diseases insects do and do not carry could also have terrible future implications if it were ever to be used as a biotechnological weapon.

It is not unreasonable to predict that by next decade GM animals are likely to become both highly controversial and a very big business. With pending food shortages and an increasing demand for meat, the world is very unlikely to reject technological developments that may lessen hunger, maintain and improve diets, and potentially improve human health.

Some people may even welcome GM creatures into their lives as companions. Already a range of GM pets called GloFish is on sale. Available in 'electric green', 'starfire red' and 'sunburst orange', these contain a fluorescence gene. In the future it may well be that children will complain if the fish they win at the fairground does not glow in the dark. We may also develop a fondness for fluorescent felines, or maybe GM dogs engineered for improved temperament or intelligence.

GM Biotech Factories

As we have seen, genetic engineering began with the modification of just a few, humble bacteria. Since that time GM plants and animals may have managed to garner most of the attention. However, some of the most significant GM advancements and applications continue to involve microscopic organisms.

Biotechnology uses living things to produce products and is already a global industry worth over $200 billion a year. For centuries natural fermentation processes have been used to produce foods such as cheese, beer and yogurt. However, since Genentech started to commercially produce human insulin using *E. coli* bacteria, high-tech biotechnology has been embracing genetic modification.

Another early GM product was a synthetic version of an enzyme called chymosin. This is used in the making of cheese, and in 1988 became the first enzyme from a GM source to be approved for use in food production. Three such GM enzymes – each produced from modified yeast or bacteria – are now approved in the United States and most European countries. Indeed, even in the United Kingdom, the majority of hard cheese is now made using GM chymosin rather than a natural protein taken from the stomach of a calf or other animal.

Future biotech factories are likely to produce a wide range of products from genetically modified micro-organisms. In addition to insulin and chymosin, these already include human growth hormones, biofuels, some bioplastics, and chemicals for cleaning up oil spills and other contamination. In 2008 scientists at the University of California modified *E. coli* bacteria to synthesize a high yield of several biofuels from glucose. In the future, this and related developments could allow petroleum substitutes to be obtained in large quantities not just from grains, but also from weeds and marine life.

Future GM biotechnology may also provide us with new fabrics. For example, in 2002 Canadian pioneer Nexia Biotechnologies managed to produce artificial spider silk by genetically modifying goats with a spider gene. The resultant transgenic animals produced an appropriate protein in their milk which could then be spun into spider silk fibres. Unfortunately, Nexia never cracked mass production. However, in 2010 a team from Notre Dame University, the University of Wyoming and the private Kraig Biocraft Laboratories in Michigan managed to genetically modify silk worms to produce spider silk. With spider silk being much stronger and more flexible than natural silk and other materials, this 'natural nylon' may find a wide range of medical and textile applications.

While some GM biotech products are already in common use, GM biofuels and bioplastics are currently more expensive than their conventional counterparts and often have poorer chemical properties. However, as we shall see in the next chapter, developments in the fledgling science of synthetic biology are about to take industrial biotechnology to the next level. Many a factory of the future may therefore be a biotech plant, with a greater and greater proportion of industrial output relying on organic rather than inorganic raw materials.

But is GM Safe?
The cultivation of GM plants and the biotech production of other GM materials are already widespread. GM animals are also sooner rather than later going to enter the human food chain. In the future, further GM developments offer the potential to significantly increase food production, to fight disease and malnutrition, and to enable us to wean ourselves off petroleum. This said, concerns about the long-term implications of manipulating DNA continue to exist. For a start, some people simply consider any form of GM to be just plain wrong.

Across history human beings have been afraid of the unknown. Not least, in medieval days people feared magic and burnt suspected witches at the stake. It is hopefully some time since a potential sorceress has been cremated alive. However, even in the early 21st century, many people continue to reject what they consider to be unnatural practices. Chief among the opponents of GM has been Greenpeace, which believes that genetic modification could seriously threaten human and environmental health. The organization therefore continues to argue that genetically modified organisms should not be released to 'contaminate' the natural environment until there is an 'adequate scientific understanding' of their long-term impact. Of course, what is meant by an 'adequate scientific understanding' is open to much debate.

Once GM crops start to be cultivated commercially it is

extremely difficult to prevent a cross-contamination of non-GM strains. This was shown in 2010 when a team from the University of Arkansas surveyed canola plants growing across North Dakota. The team found that GM transgenes were present in 80 per cent of wild plants. Greenpeace is therefore almost certainly right to suggest that the lid will never be able to be put back on the GM box.

There is also a little evidence to suggest that GM crops could harm animal health. For example, in January 2010 Monsanto was forced to release toxicology studies that had been carried out on some of its GM corn. These showed 'unusual concentrations of hormones and other compounds' in the blood and urine of rats fed on it for three months. By the end of the trial, some female rats also had elevated blood-sugar levels. None of this provides any proof of acute GM toxicity. However, those with concerns over GM crop safety nevertheless point out that the results in no way preclude potentially negative long-term health implications.

Nobody can tell you than GM is absolutely safe. However, Americans have been eating GM plants in bulk for over a decade with no apparent ill effects. Without GM food it is also almost certain that millions if not billions of people in the future will die from starvation. We should also not forget that the continuous modification of genes is a natural process. DNA is constantly being transferred within and between species. This is, after all, how evolution works and how every species prevents genetic degeneration.

I really do not want to dismiss too lightly the concerns of those who oppose GM. The ethical issues surrounding genetic screening and genetic medicine – together with the potentially wider implications of using other technologies to change the human race – will therefore be explored in Part V of this book. However, what does need to be appreciated is that attitudes toward non-human GM are now starting to change.

For example, in his 2010 book *Whole Earth Discipline: An Ecopragmatist Manifesto*, veteran environmental campaigner Stewart Brand argues that the green movement has done a great deal of harm by opposing genetic engineering. As Brand emphatically states, the actions of environmental activists have 'starved people, hindered science, hurt the natural environment and denied our own practitioners a crucial tool'. Grafting buds between apple trees has always been accepted as a reasonable agricultural procedure. In the relatively near future, the use of GM now also looks likely to be accepted by the majority right around the globe.

* * *

The Next Information Revolution

The 1980s saw the beginning of an information revolution centred on new computing and telecommunications technologies. That revolution is still far from over. But in parallel, another information revolution is now also taking hold. This is the advancing Bioscience Revolution, and is based on the understanding and manipulation of the genetic information or 'genome' stored in the DNA of all living things.

The first complete genome to be mapped out was the *Haemophilus influenzae* bacteria. Since this was decoded in 1995, the genomes of over 100 other organisms have now been sequenced. These include the genetic code of ourselves, which was sequenced by the Human Genome Project between 1990 and 2003.

While sequencing a genome is a complex process, more complex still is understanding the role of its individual genes in determining an organism's characteristics. As we have seen in this chapter, over the past few decades scientists have begun to understand the role of a few genes in the DNA of some species. Further, such knowledge has already been used to allow the creation of transgenic micro-organisms, plants and animals with useful properties. This said, at present our understanding of genetic information is incredibly limited. The Bioscience Revolution is therefore barely out of its infancy, and perhaps akin to where the first information revolution was before the invention of the personal computer.

A currently pubescent revolution may be both exciting and frightening. On the exciting side, over the coming decades we are likely to witness an explosion of new opportunities. However, in parallel there is the frightening possibility that we will make mistakes with GM that will have serious and irreversible implications.

Greenpeace is probably wrong about GM crops being a long-term risk to human health. However, it is almost certainly right to suggest that a few large companies already have far too much control over the GM agenda. Until only a few decades ago, life got on with altering the organic world, with Big Businesses limited to the creation of new inorganic technologies. However, with the rise of GM, the business world may come to dominate both the inorganic and organic frontiers. Personally I am not too concerned that scientists with noble goals – such as those creating Golden Rice – are now playing with life. However, I do worry about very large, for-profit organizations increasingly taking genetic control of a greater and greater proportion of organic matter. Already many biotechnology companies have been allowed to patent human genes and even entire GM plants and animals. The fact that companies now own part of the information contained in at least some human cells really is a most disturbing development.

The way in which we risk handing control of life itself to the madness of the market ought to be raising far more debate. Economists and their flawed systems of decision-making are very unlikely to make good guardians of the natural world. This is also something that needs to be rapidly addressed given that – as we shall explore in the next chapter – we have recently witnessed the birth of artificial life.

9

SYNTHETIC BIOLOGY

Inventing and building new technologies is usually difficult. Any ideas and components that engineers can borrow from the natural world are therefore extremely useful. As explored in the last chapter, genetic modification is increasingly being used to re-engineer plants, animals and micro-organisms. However, this is just the beginning of the Bioscience Revolution.

The cutting edge of biotechnology will soon extend significantly beyond the splicing of an extra gene or two into an existing organism. To this end, a brave new discipline called 'synthetic biology' has already started to emerge. Sometimes also referred to as 'biological engineering', this assembles the components of life in new ways, and will take genetic engineering to the next level.

As explained at syntheticbiology.org, synthetic biology is the 'design and construction of new biological parts, devices and systems', together with 'the re-design of existing, natural biological systems for useful purposes'. In essence this means that synthetic biology applies an engineering mentality to biology. As detailed in the last chapter, traditional genetic modification involves the transfer of individual genes between existing species. In contrast, synthetic biology is dedicated to the assembly of novel living systems from a set of standardized but not necessarily natural genetic parts.

To provide a more pragmatic comparison, let us imagine how either genetic modification or synthetic biology could be used to make an improved wooden building. On the one hand, a genetic engineer may decide to genetically modify an acorn to grow into a better oak tree. This tree would then be felled to make the joists and planks from which the final wooden house would be constructed. On the other hand, a future synthetic biologist may simply decide to artificially reprogram an acorn's genetic code so that it grew directly into their intended biobuilding. This far more radical approach – wherein the natural organism of the acorn is biologically altered to perform a different function – would thereby remove the need for traditional felling, sawing and other construction hassles.

Given that an acorn can grow into a tree, there is at least a theoretical possibility that it could be artificially reprogrammed to grow into some sort of wooden building. Granted this quite literal tree house would probably take a very long time to grow and would therefore not constitute a very practical construction solution. However, what this hypothetical example hopefully illustrates is the clear divide between genetic modification and synthetic biology. While the former alters existing life, the second rearranges the components of life to its own and entirely new ends.

Milestones in a New Science

You may be starting to think that this chapter is a work of pure science fiction. Let me therefore quickly bolt us back to reality with a brief routemap of some early synthetic biology successes. The discipline may well be very new indeed, with 2011 seeing only the Fifth International

Meeting on Synthetic Biology. This said, the GM tools on which much of synthetic biology relies have been in development since the 1970s.

One of the most significant pioneers of synthetic biology is the J. Craig Venter Institute (JCVI). In 2003 this private, non-profit research organization built the world's first synthetic chromosome. In 2007 the company then developed DNA transplantation methods to transform one kind of bacteria into another. Following this, in 2008 JCVI went on to create the first synthetic bacterial genome. This it named *Mycoplasma genitalium* JCVI-1.0.

In progressing through all of the above steps, JCVI was perfecting the range of genetic transplantation, synthesis and assembly processes necessary to create a fully synthetic, living cell. In May 2010, JCVI scientists subsequently brought all of their knowledge and experience to bear when they created the first ever entirely synthetic life form. Technically called 'JCVI-syn1.0' (if nicknamed Synthia), this self-replicating, single-celled organism was based on an existing *Mycoplasma capricolum* bacterium. However, at Synthia's core was an entirely synthetic, 1.08 million base pair genome created in the JCVI laboratory.

To highlight its achievement, JCVI developed its own alphabetic code based on the four DNA base pair letters A, C, G and T. It then used this code to write watermarks into JCVI-syn1.0's DNA. The JCVI scientists have even invited anybody who can crack the code to contact them using an e-mail address that is apparently written into the DNA of their new life form.

The research process that led to the creation of JCVI-syn1.0 occupied 20 scientists for more than 10 years and cost an estimated $40 million. The synthetic life form's creation was also very controversial. Not least, following its announcement, President Obama immediately asked the

Commission for the Study of Bioethical Issues to investigate the matter. This body rapidly reported back with the view there was no need to halt synthetic biology research and that synthetic biologists should continue to self-regulate their own actions. Some may still argue that JCVI ought never to have placed God-like powers in human hands. However, the fact remains that they have, with a launch pad now existing for the construction of a very wide range of things from an ever-expanding toolkit of living Lego.

Building with BioBricks

Already, engineering terms and an engineering mentality are starting to creep into the biological realm. Synthetic biologists talk of 'booting-up' cells and refer to 'modules' of genes assembled to perform a particular function. Indeed, fundamental to synthetic biology is the identification and creation of biological parts that can be consistently assembled using standardized tools and interfaces.

Already, there are public websites that provide a catalogue of synthetic biology components. For example, point your browser to partsregistry.org and you will be welcomed to the Registry of Standard Biological Parts. As the site explains:

> The Registry is a continuously growing collection of genetic parts that can be mixed and matched to build synthetic biology devices and systems. Founded in 2003 at MIT, the Registry is part of the Synthetic Biology community's efforts to make biology easier to engineer.

Some of the components used in synthetic biology are now referred to as 'BioBricks'. These are biological parts and associated usage information that meet the technical and legal standards laid down by the BioBricks Foundation (BBF). Founded by researchers from the Massachusetts Institute of Technology (MIT), Harvard and the University of California, the BBF is a not-for-profit organization committed to promoting open standards in synthetic biology. In particular, the BBF is committed to developing BioBrick legal standards and educational resources. More information can be found at BioBricks.org.

In addition to catalogues of approved and standardized parts, online synthetic biology toolkits are now also available. For example, from openwetware.org anybody can now download *Bio Building Basics: A Conceptual Instruction Manual for Synthetic Biology*. For $235, New England BioLabs even sell a 50-reaction BioBrick Assembly Kit. This company also sells an extremely wide range of genetic parts via its online store. Need some Tma Endonuclease III DNA repair proteins? Then visit www.neb.com and you can buy 500 units for $64.

One of the things that surprised many people when JCVI created synthetic life was that they obtained some of the DNA sequences they needed from the web. Already, skilled synthetic biologists can design new living systems at their keyboards and obtain the parts they need in the same manner that the rest of us purchase online groceries. As synthetic biology continues to advance, the creation of designer life may therefore become as easy as mashing a few web services or installing a Facebook app.

Future Biohealthcare

In common with nanotechnology, synthetic biology will be applied across a wide range of industries. Already a great many research undertakings are in full swing. The next few pages will therefore highlight just a few of the most significant.

Given that synthetic biology involves living systems, it will almost inevitably find a great many healthcare applications. As just one example, synthetic biology may well help in the future treatment of malaria. This disease has now become resistant to the early medications introduced in the 1960s. However, a combination therapy using several different drugs called artemisinin derivatives is now proving nearly 100 per cent effective as a malaria treatment.

Artemisinin derivatives are obtained from a plant called *Artemisia annua*. Unfortunately, cultivating and harvesting artemisinin from this natural source is very labour intensive and expensive as the plant grows slowly and yields are low. Life-saving antimalarial therapies are therefore largely unaffordable to the most vulnerable populations.

An initiative called the Artemisinin Project is planning to use synthetic biology to help manufacture a low-cost, semi-synthetic version of artemisinin. The team is assembling a pathway of genes taken from the *Artemisia annua* plant and other sources. This artificial gene sequence will then be spliced into the DNA of micro-organisms. The hope is to produce high qualities of artemisinin at low cost using industrial fermentation processes already common in the biotechnology industry. If this goal is reached then millions of lives may be saved.

The Artemisinin Project highlights how synthetic biology will be used to help make vital drugs more widely available. In the Netherlands, a company called DSM is also pursuing a similar goal, and has already used synthetic biology to produce a lower-cost version of the synthetic antibiotic Cephalexin. DSM is also applying synthetic biology in the manufacture of vitamin supplements. Potentially in the future, synthetic biology may even be applied to improve the nutritional quality of staple foods eaten by malnourished billions.

Also on the biohealth frontier, synthetic biology may allow the development of new biocosmetics. Already some cosmetic products – such as the Ayurvedic Beauty Care range from Indian beautician Shahnaz Husain – include stem cells from plants to help regenerate the wearer's skin. As with artemisinin derivatives, such treatments are currently very expensive. However, synthetic biology may one day allow similar, synthetic biocosmetics to be produced in bulk at low cost. In ten years' time, synthetic biology could therefore be helping to keep millions of people wrinkle free.

Future Biochemicals
Alongside its role in healthcare, synthetic biology will also assist in the production of many chemical compounds and raw materials. Chief among these may be improved bioplastics. At present one of the most promising alternatives to oil-based plastics is polylactic acid (PLA). Manufactured from corn or sugar cane, this can be industrially processed like existing thermoplastics and is safe enough to use in food packaging. PLA is also biodegradable.

Currently PLA has to be manufactured using a two-stage process. Firstly, the agricultural ingredients are fermented with bacteria to produce lactic acid. A second chemical, post-processing stage is then needed to link the short lactic acid molecules together into long polymer chains. However, a team from the Korea Advanced Institute of Science and Technology have now succeeded in producing PLA directly in a single process. They have done this by redesigning an *E. coli* bacterium with a set of synthetic genetic pathways that do not exist in nature. Once this process is commercialized, it will allow large quantities of PLA to be produced as a cost-effective substitute to petroleum-based plastics.

In a similar vein, a company called OPX Biotechnologies is using synthetic biology to develop a bioacrylic. Traditional acrylics are used in a wide range of products including paints, adhesives, detergents and clothing, and are another petroleum-based product. Bioacrylics will therefore be a very welcome development.

Using what it terms 'EDGE' (efficiency directed genome engineering), OPX Biotechnologies is designing a microbe to manufacture its new bioacrylic from corn, sugar cane or any other form of cellulose. Already, the company has a pilot plant in operation, together with a target for a full-scale production facility by 2013. OPX Biotechnologies' long-term strategy is to produce bioacrylic for the same price as its petroleum-based counterpart.

Other companies intent on using synthetic biology in future biochemical production are Genencor and Goodyear. These two organizations are working together on artificial gene sequences that will allow crops other than rubber plants to be a future source of isoprene. This will enable the production of synthetic rubber from nonpetrochemical sources. Once again a significant potential exists to use synthetic biology in response to the challenge of Peak Oil.

Future Bioenergy
Micro-organisms modified with synthetic DNA sequences are also going to be used to create new and improved biofuels. In fact, following the creation of the first synthetic bacterium by JCVI, several patents to this effect were filed by one of its commercial sister companies, Synthetic Genomics. The plan is to engineer new forms of synthetic algae that produce hydrocarbons which can then be converted into petroleum substitutes.

The most widely used liquid fuel is diesel. At present

almost all diesel is produced from oil. Biodiesels do exist – such as NExBTL from Neste Oil. However, these are produced from palm or other natural organic oils and are therefore never likely to be produced in sufficient quantities to replace their fossil fuel rivals.

Using synthetic biology, a Californian biotechnology company called LS9 is developing a synthetic *E.coli* bacterium that can convert natural carbohydrates to one of two diesel alternatives. In the future, this could enable the fermentation of diesel from wood chips, corn stalks and other agricultural waste products including faeces.

Several projects are also now using synthetic biology in the creation of second- and third-generation bioethanol. Already, some cars and commercial vehicles run on a first-generation bioethanol produced by fermenting grains such as corn and sugar cane. However, as we saw in Chapter 4, non-food agriculture is placing a significant pressure on available farmland. Traditional bioethanol therefore cannot hope to provide a realistic, widescale substitute to fossil fuels.

Second-generation bioethanols are now starting to be produced from weeds and woods. However, far more significant will be the use of synthetic biology to help create third-generation 'advanced bioethanol' from algae rather than traditional land-grown crops.

Appropriate algae have the significant advantage of producing ethanol from sunlight (using photosynthesis) and even extract carbon dioxide from the atmosphere in the process. Microalgae can be grown in ponds, hanging pods or even in vertical tubes in the home. A Mexican company called BioFields is planning to start commercial production of an algae-based biofuel in 2014.

Third-generation bioethanol will also be produced from seaweeds or what scientists call 'macroalgae'. Already a team from Tokyo University, Mitsubitshi and several other private-sector firms is planning a 10,000 square kilometre biofuel seaweed farm at Yamatotai, a shallow fishing area in the middle of the Sea of Japan. In the future, and thanks to synthetic biology, a great deal of liquid fuel production may therefore come to depend on 'aquaculture'. This may also provide a new line of business for trawlermen as fish stocks dwindle.

Synthetic Biofutures?

Most scientists – including practitioners of genetic modification – work with existing things that they discover. In contrast, engineers build new things from parts that they usually invent. A century ago the discipline of electrical engineering grew out of physics. In the same way, synthetic biology is now emerging out of the traditional biosciences. As the new discipline matures, we should also expect its practice to move far beyond the introduction of artificial DNA sequences into micro-organisms that will in turn produce substitutes for traditional medicines, plastics and fuels.

Fairly soon we are likely to be drinking from bioplastic bottles. But why stop there? Why settle for micro-organisms that manufacture a bioplastic that we then have to turn into bottles in a traditional, energy-guzzling factory? In the long term it would surely make more sense to use synthetic biology to engineer synthetic plants capable of growing finished bottles on the vine. And why even stop there? If a future species of synthetic plant can grow a bioplastic bottle, then why not go the whole hog and create an entirely new plant that grows bottles already filled with a soft drink? In a similar vein, why stop at a plant capable of producing isoprene when we could engineer one from which we could directly harvest car tyres, knicker elastic or synthetic rubber bands?

Synthetic plants that grow complete products could be an excellent complement to future 3D printers and nanotech factories. In fact, in a few decades' time, species of synthetic plant may well be developed to provide low-cost, widely available 3D printing and nanotech manufacturing raw material supplies. Future 3D printers are likely to become the most appropriate technology for producing most customized consumer products and spare parts. In parallel, nanotechnology is in future likely to be used to make our most expensive, sophisticated items, including many medical technologies. However, alongside 3D printing and nanotech, synthetic plants are likely to have the edge when it comes to the mass manufacture of basic supplies and everyday items such as pre-packaged food. Bananas already come in an organic wrapper that they grow themselves. It would therefore be logical to apply synthetic biology to let more plants manufacture their own protective outer wrapping.

Synthetic biology may also enable the development of bioelectronics. All biological organisms absorb and digest various metals and minerals. The opportunity therefore exists to use synthetic biotechnology to create micro-organisms and plants capable of revolutionizing the manufacture of electronic components. Future synthetic animals may even be designed to function as living micro-processors.

Researchers from Japan's Nagoya University have already demonstrated the use of DNA in the production of the thin-film transistors used in liquid crystal display screens. So-termed 'DNA nanophotonics' is also starting to be developed to improve the brightness of organic light-emitting diode (OLED) displays.

The marriage of synthetic biology and electronics is also likely to assist in the development of biosensors with an artificial sense of taste and smell. A UK company called Presearch is already developing 'e-Tongue' and 'e-Nose' sensors, while Nanogen in the United States has developed its 'NanoChip' poison detector. Future synthetic biosensors may one day even allow food labels or supermarket shelves to smell and taste produce to check that it remains suitable for consumption. Sell-by dates could therefore become a thing of the past, so reducing food waste. Synthetic biosensor technologies may even allow future aircraft to be built with rivets that could sniff out explosives and glow if any are present.

The possible future developments outlined above may sound like pure fantasy. After all, how could a plant possibly grow a filled bottle of cola or a car tyre? However, when you think about it a little more, this would still be a lot less miraculous than a few cells growing into an earthworm, a cow or a brand new human being. Biological systems have evolved to be intensely good at storing information and using it to manufacture all manner of things from very basic raw materials. Developing toolkits and knowledge to allow human beings to manufacture things in just the same manner is also exactly what synthetic biology is all about.

*   *   *

Building with Things that Mutate

All natural living things continually refine themselves via a process of constant mutation and genetic exchange that we call evolution. For synthetic biology this may also present a challenge. After all, when Intel creates a new microprocessor it expects the one millionth off the production line to be just like the first. Within predefined tolerances, engineers can currently take design and production stability for granted. However, with synthetic biology this may well not be the case.

Biological systems survive by not being entirely stable. Different members of the same species are subsequently a little bit different for very good reason. We may therefore be about to enter a world in which we purchase a computer processor or a pair of shoes of a particular species, rather than an item identical to that owned by our neighbour. Some future products may even slowly evolve into the next model, in part directed by their industrial designers, but also as a consequence of being manufactured by and even as living things.

As this chapter has outlined, synthetic biology may soon place in our hands a wide variety of future possibilities intertwined with a great variety of challenges. After all, routinely creating new life for commercial purposes is not something that everybody is going to be comfortable with. Or as Nancy Gibbs wrote in a *Time Magazine* article on synthetic biology in June 2010:

> The path of progress cuts through the four-way intersection of the moral, medical, religious and political – and whichever way you turn, you are likely to run over somebody's deeply held beliefs. [JCVI's] bombshell revived the oldest of ethical debates, over whether scientists were playing God or proving he does not exist because someone re-enacted Genesis in suburban Maryland.

Alongside the ethical dilemmas, the mainstream adoption of synthetic biology also raises another far more practical challenge. As we have seen in this chapter, many medium-term synthetic biology developments are likely to involve the use of micro-organisms to convert existing agricultural crops into medicines, fuels or other chemicals.

Others will require the cultivation of new plants for yet more non-food purposes.

This would be all well and good were it not for the fact that agricultural land is under pressure as never before. Ethics aside, the major constraint on the development of synthetic biology could well be a shortage of available land. It is therefore fortunate that, as we shall see in the next chapter, some visionaries are already planning to increase available agricultural acreages by building vertical farms.

10

VERTICAL FARMING

Over the coming decades we will start to produce many things in new ways. 3D printing will allow custom digital manufacturing, while nanotechnology will increasingly enable us to manipulate materials and engineer products on an atomic scale. In tandem, genetic engineering and synthetic biology will trigger a new wave of GM crops and transgenic animals.

By changing production methods, all of the aforementioned developments will start to alter the kinds of things we produce. This said, they are less likely to change traditional production locations. Since the Industrial Revolution, the majority of products have been manufactured in towns and cities, while food has been the principal product of rural areas. However, over the coming decades, this will probably change.

Finding new ways to produce building materials, clothing, electronic items and medical supplies is all very well and good. However, by far the most important thing that we need to produce is food. Unfortunately, in the face of Peak Oil, Peak Water, climate change and an expanding population, current methods of agriculture will simply not be able to feed the world. We therefore need to start pursuing some radical new food production solutions.

The genetic modification of plants and animals is likely to significantly improve farming yields. However, just producing more food in old locations will not solve food shortage problems if we cannot get this sustenance to where it is needed. Remember that every calorie we eat often consumes about ten calories of oil. To feed ourselves in the future, more food will therefore have to be produced relatively close to where most people live. To achieve this we will need to start growing a lot of food in urban areas. At least some future farms will therefore have to be skyscrapers rather than fields.

Farming in the Sky
Vertical farms are multistorey buildings used for growing crops or rearing animals. The basic idea is to produce food without soil in specially constructed skyscrapers. This would help cities to become more self-sufficient in a variety of ways. Vertical farms therefore have the potential to be one of the greatest innovations of the 21st century.

All of the future solutions explored in this book are being developed by great scientists and visionaries. However, at the time of writing, vertical farms are popularly associated with a single, influential advocate. His name is Dr Dickson Despommier, and he has been sowing the seeds of vertical farming since the mid-1980s.

This chapter features more than Dr Despommier's ideas. This said, his work is inevitably to the fore. Despommier runs an excellent website called verticalfarm.com. In 2010 he also published an amazing book called *The Vertical Farm*. Already a modern classic, if you want to read another future studies book after this one then I would heartily recommend Despommier's tome as your next mind-opener.

In theory, almost any kind of crop could be grown in a vertical farm. Today, food products that are regularly grown indoors include tomatoes, lettuce, spinach, peppers, strawberries and green beans. However, there is no reason that we could not grow wheat, rice, corn, potatoes and other staple foods on the many floors of future urban skyscrapers. Poultry and fish could also be reared, although Despommier does not think it right to raise cattle, pigs, sheep or other four-legged animals indoors. Aside from food, vertical farms may also cultivate future bioplastics, biomedicines and other off-the-vine bioproducts.

Vertical Farming Advantages

One of the most obvious benefits of vertical farming is that it will free farmers from the constraints of the seasons. Any crop will be able to be grown anytime and anywhere. Many foods will also not have to be stored, let alone frozen. Rather, crops will be grown to order, with 'on-the-vine inventory' becoming a real possibility. Vertical farmers will also not have to pray for rain or sunshine. Nor will they live in fear of hurricanes, floods or droughts. As our climate changes, an increasingly large proportion of the food we try to grow is damaged by freak weather or a lack of rain. However, by farming indoors, the risk of such crop damage may be practically eliminated.

By adopting technologies and techniques developed for hospital intensive care units and microchip fabrication plants, vertical farms will be built to keep out weeds, insects and disease. Within such secure, totally controlled environments, pesticides will therefore not be required. Traditional fertilizers will also not be needed as crops will be grown using pure water supplemented with a very precise balance of nutrients.

The amount of water required by vertical farms will also be far lower than in traditional farming. With Peak Water looming and traditional agriculture already using around 70 per cent of available fresh water, this is very significant indeed.

Vertical farms will use less water by relying on either hydroponics or aeroponics. Hydroponics grows crops without soil by feeding the plants a water and nutrient mix that is slowly circulated through pipes. This results in water savings of around 70 per cent compared to traditional farming methods. However, aeroponics can improve matters further still as it reduces water usage by up to 95 per cent. Here small nozzles spray a nutrient-laden mist on to the roots of plants. This technique was invented in 1982 and has already been used successfully on the International Space Station.

Another major benefit of vertical farms is that they will not create agricultural runoff. Current irrigation systems cause excess water to drain off the land, and this is usually contaminated with a highly pollutant cocktail of silt, fertilizers and pesticides. This runoff then ends up in rivers and estuaries where it contaminates the food chain.

In the United States, agricultural runoff is now the primary cause of pollution. It has even created so many 'dead zones' in rivers and coastal waters that 80 per cent of the country's seafood now has to be imported. The fact that vertical farms will be able to recirculate their water and will only ever add to it the exact level of nutrients required is therefore another of their killer benefits.

If food can be grown within cities then it will not have to be transported for hundreds or even thousands of miles. As Despommier states, in future 'the amount of travel between the tomato and your plate will be measured in blocks, not miles'. In turn, this will result in significant oil and other transport-resource savings, so also helping to reduce climate change. We will also reap the benefit of eating food that is fresher and tastes better as it will not have festered for weeks or months on its way to our table.

Vertical farming also has the potential to improve food safety. Especially in Africa, contaminated food is a major source of disease. However, vertical farms built to keep out pests and micro-organisms that are harmful to plants will prevent our food from being contaminated with things that are harmful to humans.

A final key benefit of the vertical farm will be its ability to purify water. All cities create large quantities of so-termed 'black-water' – or in other words, water contaminated with faeces, urine, bathwater, runoff from storms and other contaminants. Once solids are filtered out, the resultant 'brown water' then needs to be processed. New York, for example, needs to process around one billion gallons of brown water every day.

One future solution will be to feed the plants in some vertical farms with brown water. Via the natural process of transpiration, these plants will remove the nutrients from human and other waste, so purifying the water for drinking. Plants used for water purification will not be able to be eaten due to potential health risks. However, they could be used to manufacture biofuels, bioplastics or the organic raw materials required by the 3D printing machines housed in the direct digital manufacturing facility next door.

Vertical Farm Logistics

The previous section has outlined eight key advantages of vertical farms. However, making agriculture work in a skyscraper will not be easy. Indeed, as I was asked in a radio interview a little while ago, 'if we can't keep the grass growing in the new Wembley Stadium, how can we build a viable vertical farm?'

The designers and engineers of vertical farms will have to work out how to provide plants with sufficient light. They will also need to create and power heating and water delivery systems. Effective barriers to protect plants from all forms of biological hazard will also be required. In addition, future vertical farmers will face the tricky issue of generating an adequate return on any land devoted to growing crops or rearing animals in a city.

To grow happily, plants basically require just water, nutrients and sufficient light. In a vertical farm, light will come either from the Sun or from artificial sources. The former will obviously be preferable, although problems will exist getting sunlight to crops stacked on the floors of a building. In part this may be addressed via innovative architecture and the use of transparent building materials. However, in addition, parabolic mirrors and fibre optics are also likely to be used to capture sunlight and direct it to where it is needed. Such technologies are also already available. For example, a company called Sunlight Direct sells a range of products for tracking the Sun, capturing and concentrating its rays, and distributing them via fibre optic bundles to 'hybrid luminaries' that then diffuse the light within a building.

While noting the above, at least parts of some vertical farms will need to be artificially lit. At first this may seem ludicrous. However, we must remember that plants use only a relatively narrow spectrum of the energy that exists in sunlight. Conventional light bulbs also emit 95 per cent of their energy intake either as heat or across a far broader light spectrum than required by plants. Lighting vertical farms artificially will therefore be nothing like filling them with conventional light bulbs. Indeed, if we can develop artificial lighting solutions that emit only that narrow spectra of radiation required by plants for photosynthesis, then artificially lit vertical farms will become a realistic possibility.

Progress in developing such lights is now also being made. Already LEDs have been designed exclusively for growing plants. As noted by supplier LedGrow-Lamps.co.uk, these are nearly 98 per cent efficient in providing the light necessary for plants to produce chlorophyll. Future flexible thin-films of organic LEDs or OLEDs will also be orders of magnitude more energy efficient than current LEDs and could even be wrapped around individual plants.

Energy, Security and Productivity

Regardless of where their light comes from, ideally vertical farms will not draw any power from their local electricity grid. Those artificial energies required to run their hydroponic or aeroponic systems, as well as to heat and light them if required, ought therefore to be self-generated. Several options exist, including the use of rooftop wind turbines (as discussed in more depth in Chapter 12) or solar energy (as discussed in Chapter 13).

Vertical farms may also use ground source heat pumps to extract heat from the Earth by circulating fluids through deeply buried pipes. As yet another option, Despommier proposes that 'the roots, stems and leaves of crops, and the entrails of fowl and fish, all need to find their way back into the energy grid'. His suggestion is that these non-edible by-products of food production ought to be incinerated, as this is far more energy efficient at scale than rotting them to obtain methane. Despommier's proposal is that vertical farms ought to incorporate plasma arc gasification (PAG) devices. These use electricity to create a high-energy plasma arc to which waste material is introduced in a powdered format. The heat so generated then powers a steam turbine to create electricity, with six times more power being created than used to power the plasma arc.

Even with light and energy requirements taken care of, vertical farmers will face the very significant challenge of keeping their controlled environments free of anything that may harm their crops. Buildings will need to be airtight, with a positive pressure atmosphere maintained to prevent pests or micro-organisms being sucked in via doors and vents. All incoming air will also have to be filtered – much as it is today before entering a microchip fabrication plant – and workers will need to change clothing on entry and observe strict sterile procedures. It is also likely that workers will require regular medical checkups to prevent them introducing salmonella, giardia, cyclospora or other infections into the building.

As Despommier suggests, 'canary plants' could potentially be created to act as pest and disease early warning systems. These would glow if their modified genetic structure detected any danger. As we saw in the last two chapters, slightly modifying existing plants for this purpose – or indeed building new organisms almost entirely from scratch – will in the future be a very real possibility. As in several other instances, a great many of the innovations covered in this book will reinforce each other as they develop hand-in-hand.

Technical challenges aside, vertical farms will have to produce enough agricultural outputs to be commercially viable on available urban land. Initially at least, this could prove quite a barrier to their construction. Potentially vertical farms could be built in the run-down areas that sadly exist in most inner cities. Vertical farm projects may therefore become a source of urban regeneration that will provide not just food or other bioproducts, but also restaurants, water treatment facilities and even indoor parkland. As Despommier hopes, 'because vertical farms will by their nature be things of beauty . . . neighbourhoods will take great pride in welcoming them into their midst as stunning and nurturing parts of the local scene'.

Regardless of the type of city land they are built on, vertical farms do have the potential to be very productive and so justify their occupancy of prime real-estate. Current methods of stacking crops have already proved the potential for significant indoor crop yields. For example, some strawberry farmers have already managed to produce the equivalent of 29 acres of fruit from just one acre of greenhouse by using plastic containers called Hydro-Stackers to elevate many levels of hydroponically grown crop. Productivity improvements over existing agricultural methods will additionally result from year-round production, zero weather damage, not having to pay for pesticides, and near-zero transportation and storage costs. The return-on-investment from every acre of cityscape devoted to vertical farming may therefore in time prove attractive to at least some long-term investors.

Ecosystem Restoration

In short, vertical farms will allow us to produce in a highly controlled manner more food and future bioproducts than we can reliably harvest today. They will also bring food manufacture closer to the point of final consumption, and will decrease significantly the reliance of agriculture on dwindling petroleum and fresh-water supplies. If this were not enough, the large-scale uptake of vertical farming may also result in broader environmental benefits.

Few can deny that the rise of human civilization has been at the expense of our wider environment. Biodiversity continues to be threatened by human action, and more species become extinct every year. However, if vertical farming causes a sufficient enough volume of future agriculture to move into the city, then a potential does exist for ecosystem restoration.

Despommier is insistent that vertical farming can allow the ecological footprint of an expanded world agriculture to actually shrink. As he calculates, for every acre of produce grown in a vertical farm, about 10 to 20 times the acreage could be converted back to hardwood forests or other forms of wilderness. The most immediate benefit would be to lessen and even reverse the impact of climate change as increased forest acreage would soak up more carbon dioxide. More broadly, the human race could benefit from improved biodiversity. It is currently both sad and ironic that we continue to let so many plants and animals die out just when we are developing the skills to build useful things from their unique DNA.

The biosphere of our first planet keeps us all alive. It is also rather good at repairing itself when we give it a chance. Should humanity withdraw from some of the land currently used for agriculture, it is therefore very likely that nature would thrive there once again in only a few decades. Consider, for example, how the town of Chernobyl has already become a wildlife haven now that humans have fled. In Costa Rica, those few areas of rainforest once cleared for farmland and now abandoned have also already started to restore themselves. A future vertical farming revolution may therefore provide the added bonus of allowing the rejuvenation of some parts of the natural world.

Getting from Here to There

Vertical farms will not be built overnight. The construction of such future 'agritecture' will also be held back more by traditional mindsets than a lack of skills and resources. Vertical farms are indeed a radical idea. However, the first steps are now starting to be taken. Or as Majora Carter argues in her foreword to *The Vertical Farm*, 'if the skyscraper farm is like a 747 jetliner, we are now at the stage of the Wright Brothers'.

Nobody has yet built a vertical farm, and even Despommier admits that several years of prototyping will be needed before we get to full-scale, purpose-built urban agricultural facilities. However, many smaller-scale developments in indoor plant cultivation and urban agriculture do signal a clear direction of travel.

For example, a UK company called BioTecture already runs a business designing and implementing so-called 'green walls'. These feature plants that cover the inside or outside wall of a building. As the company explains, 'plants are grown vertically in a unique, patented, modular hydroponic system designed for precise low water usage and low maintenance'. BioTecture has already created green walls in countries around the world. Some of these installations are many storeys high, including the one now growing inside the Zizzi Restaurant in Gateshead, United Kingdom.

Another pioneer is Valcent Products who have developed a vertical crop-growing technology called VertiCrop. This indoor, multi-tier hydroponic system can yield 20 times the production volume per square foot of land than possible with traditional agricultural techniques. As the company explains:

The VertiCrop system grows plants in a suspended tray system moving on an overhead conveyor system. The system is designed to provide maximum sunlight and precisely correct nutrients to each plant. Ultraviolet light and filter systems exclude the need for herbicides and pesticides. Sophisticated control systems gain optimum

growth performance through the correct misting of nutrients, the accurate balancing of PH and the delivery of the
correct amount of heat, light and water.

VertiCrop's 10-foot-tall motorized growing trays were first
installed in Paignton Zoo. Here a 395 square foot greenhouse now provides 800 lettuce heads a week for the
animals. It also only consumes around 20 per cent of the
water that would be required if these greens were grown
via conventional methods.

For individuals keen to embrace a new trend, the
Windowfarms Project has even developed a personal,
vertical hydroponic farming system. This modular, low-
energy and high-yield system allows anybody to grow food
on the inside of any window, and often using recycled
materials. The project aims to 'empower urban dwellers to
grow some of their own food inside year-round'. As well
as selling Windowfarm kits, the project is a community for
the collaborative innovation of vertical, indoor growing
methods. You can find out more at windowfarms.org.

*   *   *

Toward a More Sustainable City?

As much of the world has industrialized, so our cities have
evolved into sophisticated mechanisms for keeping civilization alive. However, as a consequence, all cities now rely
on a supply of food, water, energy and other resources that
is very unlikely to be sustainable in the long-term. Having
long since become accustomed to consuming more than is
locally available, cities do not currently even attempt to live
within their means.

In the face of Peak Oil, Peak Water and broader resource
depletion, over the next few decades our cities will need to

become at least partially self-sustaining. As has been discussed in this chapter, vertical farming could allow future cities to grow some of their own food and clean some of their own wastewater. Vertical farms are therefore one possible solution for reducing the environmental impact of cities. They may even start to reconnect the urban landscape and urban living with the natural world.

City life is currently lived at the expense of the biosphere. But this does not have to remain the case. As Despommier so passionately argues:

> The vertical farm is the keystone enterprise for establishing an urban-based ecosystem . . . Establishing vertical farming on a large scale would be the start to a complete remake of urban behaviour centered around the concept of doing no harm to the environment. Ultimately it is about creating a healthier lifestyle for anyone living anywhere in the city, making the built environment an ideal place to raise children, and about improving the overall environment of the planet.

By now some readers may be dismissing Despommier as an idealist. However, as I argued back in the Prologue, we do need to construct the future in our heads before we craft it with our collective hands. In the face of the future challenges outlined in Part I, technically informed visionaries like Despommier are therefore required in spades. To make our lives and our cities more sustainable – and indeed to enable the best aspects of our current way of life to even survive – we therefore need to promote and back the work of people like Despommier even when their visions may currently seem so far from reality.

Part III

FUELLING THE THIRD MILLENNIUM

11
ELECTRIC VEHICLES

All forms of life and all other machines consume energy. None of us can therefore work or play without using some kind of power. For a couple of centuries, most of the energy used to run artificial mechanisms has been produced by burning fossil fuels. However, as we saw in Part I, fairly soon a fossil fuel economy will no longer be sustainable.

With the exception of some solar or ground-source heating systems, it is pretty much certain that within 50 years practically every machine will either consume electricity or digest organic material. We have already seen how future organic technologies and the new farming methods required to sustain them are likely to develop. The next four chapters therefore focus on our future sources of and uses for electricity. Chapter 15 will then quite literally take us further by considering how we may one day obtain energy and other resources from space.

The Rise of Electric Transportation
It is around a century since Henry Ford built his first production line and started to churn out the Model T. Over that hundred years, automobiles fuelled by oil have become the dominant means of carrying people and things from A

to B. The gradual transition to electric vehicles will therefore be one of the most obvious changes that most of us will experience in the next few decades.

Take a conventional car, remove the engine and fuel tank, replace them with an electric motor and a battery, and you have an electric automobile. OK, so there is a bit more messing around than that, and ideally the whole thing wants to be designed for electrical locomotion from scratch. However, at a basic level, electric cars are not that radical an innovation. Even so, the benefits of switching from petroleum-powered to electric transportation will be considerable.

The most obvious benefit of any electric vehicle (EV) is that it does not burn oil. The development of EVs is therefore both critical and inevitable given that oil will soon start to become scarcer and more expensive. Because they are not powered by oil, EVs also have the advantage of not generating any greenhouse gas or other emissions. This said, we do need to remember that electric vehicles are only really a zero-carbon form of transport if the electricity that powers them is not produced by burning fossil fuels.

Another major benefit of EVs is that they are very energy efficient. A conventional internal combustion engine only manages to transform about 15 per cent of the fuel it burns into locomotive force. The remaining 85 per cent is simply wasted heating the engine block. In comparison, electric motors are about 90 per cent efficient in producing locomotive force. Even accounting for energy losses in electricity generation, transmission and battery charging, EVs will therefore allow us to use our available energy resources far more efficiently.

EVs also only consume energy when they are actually moving, and hence are more power efficient than oil-powered vehicles when sitting in traffic jams. Yet another advantage of EVs is that they contain far fewer moving parts than conventional cars. They are therefore likely to prove more reliable, last longer and require less maintenance.

Just before we risk becoming too evangelical, a few EV drawbacks do also have to be noted. Chief among these is the distance any EV can travel on one battery charge. Totally electric cars are also only just starting to become available. A mass transition to electric vehicles will also require the mass roll out of an appropriate public infrastructure. This said, it is far easier to build a network of electrical charging points than it is to transport, store and dispense liquid or gaseous fuels.

From Hybrids to Plug-ins

Over the past few years many hybrid electric cars have received a great deal of attention. These include the Toyota Prius (launched in its first generation in September 2000) and the Chevrolet Volt (launched in November 2010). Each of these vehicles includes both an electric motor and an internal combustion engine. However, their approach and technologies are very different.

The Toyota Prius uses a 'power split device' to link an internal combustion engine, an electric motor and electrical generator. These linked components allow the car to transition from electrical to petroleum power on-the-fly. So, for example, the Prius always uses electrical energy to start moving, but engages its internal combustion engine as it starts to go faster.

The Prius has low emissions and is more power efficient than a traditional car. However, current Prius models charge their batteries solely from their internal combustion engines when the car is running on petroleum. They are therefore not at present a form of plug-in electric car. This point noted, in January 2010 Toyota announced that it was building 100 prototype plug-in hybrid vehicles (PHVs). These are currently being tested, with a production model expected to go on sale in late 2012.

In contrast to existing Prius models, the Chevrolet Volt from General Motors is already a plug-in hybrid EV. Although it includes both an electric motor and a petrol engine, the wheels are only powered electrically. The internal batteries are also charged directly from an electrical outlet. A Volt can be fully charged in four or ten hours depending on the mains voltage and type of charging point available. The car can then travel between 25 and 50 miles. Beyond this range, the petrol engine is used to generate electricity to run the electric motor. In practice this means that for many commutes and other local journeys the Volt is an all-electric vehicle. For longer journeys it then functions as a hybrid.

While the Volt is a major leap forward, pure plug-in electric vehicles are also just starting to become available from major manufacturers. Most notable at the time of writing is the Nissan LEAF. This is powered solely by an electric motor that obtains power from a battery. The LEAF is also charged from an electrical outlet. If driven at 38 mph in ideal driving conditions, the LEAF can travel 138 miles on a single battery charge. Around town with the air conditioning on, this quickly drops to a range of 62 miles. At a public charging station, the car can be quick-charged to 80 per cent capacity in about half an hour, although charging in this manner seriously diminishes battery capacity if done on a regular basis. The preferred charge option is therefore an eight-hour full-charge from a standard electrical socket. The LEAF features a smart on-board navigation system that works out if a driver can reach their destination, and if not where charging stations are located. Perhaps not surprisingly, the LEAF also comes with three years of complimentary roadside assistance.

While both the Volt and LEAF have a rather limited range on one battery charge, electric vehicles that can travel far further are now in production from non-mainstream manufacturers. Most notably, the Tesla Roadster sports car was released in 2008. Produced by Californian start-up Tesla Motors, this has a range of over 200 miles, although it does cost well in excess of £80,000. Over 1,200 Roadsters have already been sold in more than 30 countries. Tesla Motors also intends to launch its new Model S family electric vehicle in 2012. This will come with a 160, 230 or 300 mile battery pack that will quick-charge in 45 minutes.

Over the next few years, plug-in EVs will become available from most major automobile manufacturers. Even Rolls-Royce has shown off an EV prototype. BMW expects to launch its Megacity Electric Vehicle in 2013, and is currently conducting UK field trials of an all-electric MINI E. In 2012, the Vauxhall Ampera Extended-Range Electric Vehicle is also expected to hit the market. Similar to the Chevrolet Volt, this plug-in car includes an internal combustion engine to provide electricity beyond its 40-mile battery range.

Renault is also developing a range of electric vehicles in a new zero emission (ZE) range. These comprise the Fluence ZE family saloon (expected in 2012), the Kangoo ZE van, the Zoe, and a wacky, single-seater 'heavy quadricycle' called the Twizzy. Ford also plans to launch five fully electric or hybrid vehicles by the end of 2012, including a commercial electric van called the Transit Connect. Honda and Mitsubishi also have electric cars in the pipeline. It is therefore certain that by the middle of the decade a large number of EVs will be available and that competition to sell them to us will be intense.

Extending the Range

Many people associate electric cars with golf carts or milk floats. However, the idea that EVs have to be slow and ugly is now starting to be challenged. As the Chevrolet Volt, Nissan LEAF and Tesla Roadster already demonstrate, electric cars may be stylish and can perform as well as many an oil-fuelled vehicle. The only major issue that demands attention is therefore the distance that EVs can travel.

Future EVs will increasingly be constructed out of lightweight composites. This will decrease their weight and so increase their range. For example, BMW's Megacity will be the first mass-produced vehicle to incorporate a passenger cell made from carbon fibre reinforced plastic. However, even when using future nanotechnologies, there will be a limit to how light a vehicle can be made. After all, no car can be lighter than the weight of its occupants and other cargo. Developments in battery technologies or alternative charging arrangements will therefore be needed before EVs can truly go mass market for long-distance travel.

All of the electric cars mentioned in this chapter use or are expected to use lithium-ion batteries. Models like the Tesla Roadster can travel further simply because they include more battery cells and do not have family car dimensions. The race is therefore on to improve lithium-ion battery performance.

Several potential battery innovations involve the use of nanotechnology. For example a team at the US Department of Energy's Pacific Northwest National Laboratory is working with a company called Vorbeck Materials to use graphene in lithium-ion battery electrodes. As explained in Chapter 7, graphene is a one-atom thick sheet of carbon. The use of this material in electrodes could potentially allow lithium-ion batteries to recharge in minutes, rather than hours. While the range of EVs would not be directly extended by this technology, drivers would only have to call in to a charging station for a short period when running short of power.

Other research teams are trying to use nanotech materials to improve the capacity of lithium-ion cells. For example, a team at the Georgia Institute of Technology is working on a self-assembling nano-composite technique that could allow lithium-ion battery electrodes to be made out of high-performance silicon structures. In theory, this could increase battery capacity fivefold. Yet another team at the Massachusetts Institute of Technology (MIT) is trying to improve the capacity of lithium-ion batteries by making their electrodes out of carbon nanotubes.

Alternative power storage technologies are also a possibility. One of these involves the use of ultracapacitors. Conventional batteries store electricity electrochemically. In contrast, a capacitor is a common electronic component that stores a static electric field between two plates. The larger these plates, the more power the capacitor can store. In most traditional capacitors the plates are wound together in a spiral and are a fraction of a millimetre apart. However, nanotechnology is now permitting the construction of ultracapacitors with plates that are only a few nanometres apart. This significantly increases the plate area that can be accommodated in a capacitor of a certain size, so in turn also increasing the charge that it can store. One day ultracapacitors may therefore replace conventional batteries.

Ultracapacitors have the advantage of being able to charge up extremely quickly. A future EV with an ultracapacitor rather than a conventional battery could therefore fully charge in only a few minutes. At present, ultracapacitors have a far lower capacity than lithium-ion cells. This said, Intel and others are trying to develop ultracapacitors with a storage capacity to rival conventional batteries.

Although they can charge very quickly, ultracapacitors currently also discharge rapidly and suffer from considerable leakage. This means that they cannot hold their charge for long periods, and potentially no longer than a few hours. There is therefore some way to go before ultracapacitors replace lithium-ion batteries. However, in the near-term, significant possibilities exist to use both lithium-ion batteries and ultracapacitors to power electric cars. The inclusion of an ultracapacitor would allow the rapid recovery of energy when the brakes were applied – a system known as regenerative braking – and would also provide an excellent battery supplement in quick-charge situations on long journeys.

Future EVs capable of charging rapidly may even be able to top up wirelessly. For example, we may see the roll out of inductive charging plates in some car parks or even under some stretches of road. These would add charge to an EV's battery or ultracapacitor when they were parked or driven over them. Future users of toll roads may therefore be paying in part for the electrical power they will obtain from the road surface.

The range of EVs is also likely to be extended by including solar cells to constantly top them up. Already the Nissan LEAF has a solar panel in the rear spoiler that provides a little bit of extra energy for essential systems. Future nanopaints may even allow the entire body of a car to become a solar panel.

Toward a Better Place?
Another way to extend the range of EVs will be to fit them with rapidly swappable batteries. Drivers taking short, local trips will continue to charge their EVs at home or at

initiatives are intent on developing EVs and EV infrastructures as a means of shaping a greener, cleaner future. For example, a hybrid EV called the Urbee is being developed by a team of volunteers over at urbee.net. Their vision is to create an environmentally sustainable vehicle that can efficiently store and use exactly the amount of solar and wind energy that can be collected on a one-car garage in one day. For drivers who need to travel further than this energy quotient, the Urbee also includes an ethanol-powered engine. (You may remember from Chapter 6 that all of the components used to build the first Urbee prototype were manufactured using a 3D printer.)

Researchers at MIT even have plans to use new electric car designs to help shape the environment of future cities. As they note, current automobiles are very heavy (typically 20 times heavier than a single driver) and occupy significant real estate when parked. The MIT researchers therefore envisage far lighter, smaller and hence more energy-efficient EVs. To this end they have designed a two-passenger EV called the CityCar. This features in-wheel electric motors – or 'Wheel Robots' – that incorporate drive, suspension and braking in one unit. They also allow the CityCar to turn on its axis. The CityCar can fold from 100 to 60 inches in length for parking, and then use its zero-turn radius to park at right angles to the kerb. This allows three CityCars to park in one conventional parking space. Just in case you are wondering, occupants exit by opening the large, front windscreen when the car is in its folded position.

In designing the CityCar, the MIT researchers are suggesting that today's vehicles are 'over-engineered for most practical purposes in the city'. Why have a large vehicle with a range of several hundred miles when most journeys involve moving only one or two people and a little cargo for less than a 40-mile round trip? And come to that, why have EVs in private ownership when fleets of CityCars could be more efficiently utilized in shared-usage schemes?

Some researchers at MIT and elsewhere also expect most future EVs to be autonomous. In other words, they expect the cars of tomorrow to drive themselves! The logic is that autonomous vehicles will be able to optimize their energy efficiently and contribute to road safety. Quite possibly this will in part be achieved by connecting all EVs to a computer network so that the overall performance of entire car swarms will be able to be optimized en masse. While such an idea may sound crazy, it is worth noting that in October 2010 Google revealed that it has secretly been building and testing robot cars that drive themselves.

Google's autonomous vehicles rely on video cameras, radar sensors and a laser range finder to 'see' other traffic. They also utilize Google Maps. With an operator on board for safety, such vehicles have already logged over 140,000 miles on public roads. This has included driving themselves along Hollywood Boulevard, across the Golden Gate Bridge and down the Pacific Coast Highway. By the time most cars are powered by an electric motor and a battery or ultracapacitor, we should therefore not necessarily expect human beings to always be at the wheel.

Planes, Boats and Trains

When I was growing up in the 1970s and 1980s, the conventional wisdom was that nothing electrically powered could possibly fly. I therefore smiled the first time I went into a toyshop that sold a flying electric helicopter that proved this conventional wisdom wrong. I smiled further when, in July 2010, a full-size electric aircraft powered by photovoltaic cells flew non-stop for over 26 hours. The team responsible consider their Solar Impulse plane an 'ambassador of the future'. They are also planning to fly it non-stop around the world.

It will take a major step-change in battery and solar technologies before conventional airliners and cargo planes can become EVs. Nevertheless, decades hence electric jumbos remain a possibility. Such future places may perhaps have next-generation ultracapacitors for wings and be coated all over in a nanosolar photovoltaic paint. However, even before such a day dawns, safe, helium-filled airships propelled with electric motors may be constructed.

Leading airship manufacturer Aeros is already working on a next-generation airship called the Aeroscraft ML866. With a 3,100-mile range and about 5,000 square feet of cabin space, this 'new paradigm in air transport' will be electrically powered and could function as anything from a private sky yacht to a cargo carrier or even a flying conference centre.

Back on the ground, while electric trains are hardly a novelty they will become more and more common as supplies of oil diminish. Although most future electric trains will continue to travel on rails, we may also see the development of magnetically levitated vehicles, otherwise known as maglev trains. These float over a guideway of superconducting magnets that can propel them at hundreds of miles per hour.

The world's first commercial, high-speed maglev train commenced public service in China in January 2004, and connects Shanghai Pudong International Airport to central Shanghai. This train operates at 268 miles an hour, although in tests it has reached 311. Many countries have considered and even started to develop proposals for high-speed maglev rail links. For example, a 269-mile maglev to link California and Nevada was in various stages of development for over 20 years before the funding was finally diverted elsewhere in 2010. However, as mass aviation becomes less viable and far more expensive, maglev may well be an EV technology yet to have its day. It is even possible that a future conventional or maglev electric train could one day travel in an underground transatlantic tunnel connecting Europe with the United States.

Completing our roundup, some future EVs will travel on water. Electric boats have been available for decades from manufacturers including the Duffy Electric Boat Company. Greenpeace's new flagship, the 58-foot *Rainbow Warrior III*, also uses an electric propulsion system that can draw at least some of its power from photovoltaic solar cells.

While the market for electric boats is currently tiny, again in the face of Peak Oil more manufacturers are likely to consider the electric option. Electric sailing craft also have far more opportunities than electric cars, trains and aircraft to power themselves from solar panels. We may, for example, in future see hybrid wind-and-electric ships that feature cloth sails coated in an electricity-generating, photovoltaic nanocoating.

* * *

Making the Transition

There are currently estimated to be about 800 million cars in the world – with over 250 million of these in the United States alone. Approximately 70 per cent of adults in developed nations own a vehicle, with 20 per cent car ownership in other parts of the world. Economic development in China, India, Russia and Brazil is also expected to increase the world's fleet to over a billion vehicles by 2020. In the face of Peak Oil and climate change, a transition to personal EVs is therefore needed and quickly. A global society that relies on petrol vehicles is simply not a future possibility.

November 2010 saw the first ever Brighton to London Future Car Challenge. Over 60 eco-friendly vehicles took part in this rally, many of which were either fully electric cars or part-electric hybrids. Most major car manufacturers were represented, and even if many of their vehicles were pre-production models, the event did provide a strong signal that electric motoring is about to come of age.

As this chapter has hopefully demonstrated, electric cars are no longer a whimsical idea. By 2015 many models will be on the market from major automobile manufacturers. People wanting to join the EV revolution will therefore not be constrained to the conversion of an oil-powered vehicle or the risky purchase of a newfangled design from a little-known start-up.

Two scenarios exist for the future uptake of electric cars. One could see relatively few such vehicles being driven for a decade or more, with people only transitioning to EVs when petroleum-powered vehicles become unaffordable for most people and organizations. In other words, the EV revolution may not occur until people have no choice in the matter. On the other hand, there is a more hopeful scenario that will see EVs gaining in popularity and reaching mass market before the end of the decade. However, for this second scenario to come true, several things will need to happen and fairly fast.

Most significantly, an early, controlled transition to EVs will require an appropriate infrastructure of public charging points and battery-swap stations to be established. High-power charging points will also need to be installed in many homes and potentially also in many workplaces. Recognizing this, a report from the UK's Royal Automotive Club (RAC) in 2010 suggested the compulsory inclusion of EV charging points in all new buildings. However, before any required legislation can be enacted, standards for EV connectors, charging regulators and battery styles will need to be agreed industry-wide. We really have no time for a VHS/Betamax-style format battle.

Even with an appropriate investment in infrastructure, an early mass-update of EVs will only happen if car makers and governments can convince the public that EVs will serve them just as well as traditional cars. Drivers will also have to adjust to a new form of motoring. Already most EV drivers are reported to suffer from 'range anxiety' as they constantly fear running out of charge. Drivers will also have to adjust to cars that do not have gears and which handle differently to petroleum-powered vehicles.

How rapidly we transition to EVs will also depend on the development and promotion of other alternatives to petroleum-fuelled vehicles. In recent years, cars powered by hydrogen have been heavily promoted in some quarters. Such vehicles either burn hydrogen in an internal combustion engine or use a fuel cell to convert hydrogen and oxygen into electricity that then powers an electric motor. Either technology generates low emissions and is greener than petroleum.

Unfortunately, what advocates of hydrogen-fuelled vehicles tend to miss (or otherwise conveniently ignore) is that there is no natural source of hydrogen on the Earth. Rather, hydrogen to power fuel-cell or direct hydrogen vehicles either has to be sourced from methane or other fossil fuels, or else needs to be extracted from water using electrolysis. The latter process itself uses electricity which would be better used to directly power future EVs. Add to this the fact that putting in place a supply infrastructure for hydrogen would be far more cumbersome and dangerous than creating a network of EV charging points and battery-swap stations, and the case for future hydrogen-fuelled vehicles disintegrates. In a similar manner, any case for putting in place an infrastructure to fuel vehicles from the fossil fuel natural gas is equally blinkered. But sadly, as we all know, the human race has a rich history of doing stupid things. We can therefore only hope that advocates of EVs will get their arguments in order before we start putting in place any mass infrastructure for non-sustainable, gaseous fuels.

In the very short term, electric cars with range-boosting petrol generators – such as the Chevrolet Volt and the Vauxhall Ampera – are most likely to drive the EV revolution. These vehicles will allow many people to drive cleaner cars that will not require petroleum most of the time, but which will still be capable of long journeys and refuelling at any roadside station. In the longer term, as battery and ultracapacitor technologies develop and as public and private infrastructure is put in place, fully electric vehicles are likely to become the norm. The next question to be answered therefore has to be where the electricity to power future EVs and most other machines will come from. But fear not! The next three chapters will now address that issue head-on.

12

WIND, WAVE AND KINETIC POWER

The wind, tides and other natural water flows have been exploited by human beings since the beginning of civilization. Cattle, horses and human muscle power have also been used to work the land since agriculture began. Obtaining energy from things that naturally move is therefore nothing new. However, in the past couple of centuries, a smaller and smaller proportion of humanity's energy requirement has been met from naturally locomotive sources.

Since the Industrial Revolution we have come to rely very heavily indeed on an abundant supply of fossil fuels to power industrial machines. For a great many decades, in developed nations there has therefore been comparatively little interest in the invention of new engineering methods capable of taking our oldest forms of power to the next level. Today, however, in the face of Peak Oil and climate change, the pendulum is starting to swing back in favour of 'renewable' or 'alternative' energy sources. This chapter subsequently examines how the exploitation of naturally locomotive power is about to come full circle.

The New Energy Landscape

We are now in need not just of new energy production methods, but also new energy attitudes. In part, all of us need to become more energy conscious and to embrace a more energy-efficient lifestyle. However, just as importantly, we also need to understand that the future energy landscape will be a collage of many different methods of both large-scale and small-scale power generation.

Most people in developed nations have only ever known a large-scale or 'macro' national electricity infrastructure. For decades, huge coal, oil, gas or nuclear power stations have successfully churned out all of the electricity demanded by millions. For most people, electrical energy generation has therefore always been somebody else's problem.

In the future, national electricity infrastructures will continue to exist. Indeed, as we transition to electric vehicles, national infrastructures will in some senses become even more important. This said, large-scale electricity networks will increasingly be supplemented by local and even personal methods of so-termed 'micro' power generation.

Today, many people continue to dismiss local, small-scale alternative energy sources. For example, household wind turbines are often shunned on the basis that they will 'not be able to generate enough power'. Anybody hoping to power their home from one small wind turbine is indeed very likely be disappointed. However, the 'all-or-nothing' attitude to local and domestic energy generation is precisely what needs to be changed.

In the relatively near future, we will need to harness every possible form of power. No longer will a handful of large-scale power generation technologies prove sufficient to meet global energy needs. Even technologies that can only generate a few per cent of our energy requirements will therefore have to be embraced.

Already, smart electricity networks are starting to allow some individuals and companies to become both energy users and energy suppliers. Local, micro-generation technologies – such as domestic wind turbines or solar panels – are therefore starting to make more and more sense. In the relatively near future, a partly decentralized, two-way electricity grid fed by a myriad of generating mechanisms both large and small is likely to become the norm. Most individuals, homes and businesses will also directly generate at least a little of their own electricity to power appliances that are never connected to the mains. As we explore alternative means of power generation in this chapter and the next, it is therefore extremely important to keep this changed energy landscape in mind.

The Power of Moving Air

Since ancient times people have been harnessing the power of the wind. The Ancient Egyptians were travelling the Nile in wind-propelled boats over 5,000 years ago, with the earliest record of a sailing ship depicted on an Egyptian pot dating back to 3200 BC. By around 200 BC, windmills had also been invented and were being used to pump water in China.

During the Middle Ages, windmills became established in the Middle East as a means of grinding grain and powering machines. In the 11th century, merchants and crusaders then began to carry windmill designs back with them to Europe. By the 14th century, the Dutch had further refined windmills and were using them to drain areas of the Rhine River delta. The first electricity-generating windmills were built in Denmark as early as 1890.

Since the oil price rises of the 1970s, interest in wind

power has been growing. By late 2010, almost 2 per cent of the world's energy was being generated by the wind. This compared to just over 1 per cent in 2007. Alongside solar, wind is now one of the two fastest growing parts of the global energy sector. The intermittent pattern of wind flows, coupled with the fact that the wind tends to blow harder at night, can make wind a difficult power source to rely on. This said, as we saw in the last chapter, battery technologies to allow the storage of electricity generated by the wind are continuing to improve. Several studies have now also shown that there is potentially enough wind energy in the atmosphere to meet current daily global energy demands many times over.

Electricity is generated from the wind using a wind turbine. Most commercial turbines have three or more rotor blades up to 80 metres in diameter. When the wind blows, the blades revolve around a horizontal hub. The hub is in turn connected to a gearbox and generator that are mounted in a nacelle on the top of a tower. The gearbox is necessary to allow a hub that typically rotates at between 10 to 30 revolutions a minute to turn a high-speed generator. This said, major manufacturers Siemens and GE are now planning more efficient wind turbines with large, low-speed generators that will dispense with gearboxes entirely. Typically today, most wind turbine towers are somewhere between 25 and 85 metres high. The power output of commercial wind turbines then ranges from a few hundred kilowatts to many megawatts.

Commercially Farming the Wind

Wind farms that produce electricity using many wind turbines are now common around the globe, with the wind industry consistently growing at more than 25 per cent annually. In 2007, the Worldwatch Institute reported that wind power represented 40 per cent of newly installed electricity-generating capacity in Europe and 35 per cent in the United States. According to the World Wind Energy Association, in mid-2010 the world's total wind turbine capacity was 175 gigawatts, with this figure expected to reach 240 gigawatts by 2012. Such a capacity will enable wind power to provide about 3 per cent of the world's energy requirement.

The first major onshore wind farms were constructed in California in the 1980s and 1990s. Major US wind farms also continue to be announced. These include the $1.2 billion project that will see Terra-Gen Power build a further four Californian wind farms with a total capacity of 3 gigawatts. In October 2010, the US government also approved the 130 turbine Cape Wind Project as the nation's first offshore wind farm.

While the United States has been the dominant wind energy player for many years, by the end of 2010 it was overtaken by China. The growth of wind power generation in China is also remarkable. In mid-2010, the country had about 34 gigawatts of wind generation capacity and was adding an extra 1.2 gigawatts every month. Some estimates suggest that China's wind generation capacity could reach 230 gigawatts by 2020 – or the equivalent of around 200 coal-fired power stations. Five of the world's top 15 wind turbine manufacturers are now Chinese.

For most European countries, offshore wind farms offer the most potential. The world's largest offshore wind farm is now operating in the North Sea, off the coast of Thanet in the United Kingdom, and is capable of powering around 200,000 homes. A consortium of 11 Spanish companies and 22 research centres is also planning to construct the world's largest offshore wind turbine. This single, 15-megawatt monster is intended to be brought online by 2020.

Current offshore turbines are built on towers that are fastened to the seabed. This makes them immobile and restricts them to waters no more than about 50 metres deep. However, floating and semi-submersible platforms are planned as the mounts for some future offshore wind turbines. Like many oil rigs, these will be tethered rather than fastened to the sea floor. They will therefore be able to be moved around and positioned far out at sea where the wind is strong and steady and nobody on land can see them.

One of the safest predictions in this book is that we will continue to see a very significant expansion of large-scale onshore and offshore wind farms. Already, even non-energy companies are starting to invest in wind-power projects. For example, in October 2010 Google announced that it was investing $200 million in the $5 billion Atlantic Wind Connection. The goal of this project is to build an underwater network to carry electricity from wind farms off the mid-Atlantic coast to US homes.

Supplementing with Small Wind

In addition to acres of commercial wind farms, we should also expect small-scale and domestic wind turbines to become far more common. Known in the industry as 'small wind systems', these typically produce up to 15 kilowatts of power at a low voltage, and may be connected via a transformer and inverter system to the mains for 'on grid' use. Alternatively, small wind systems may be used 'off grid' to charge batteries that are in turn used to run appliances.

Regardless of how they are connected, small wind turbines are most likely to supplement rather than replace electricity obtained from the mains. So, for example, as the use of very low power LED lighting becomes common over the next decade, it will become possible for many households to power all of their lights from a small rooftop turbine that charges a set of batteries whenever the wind is blowing. Special 48-volt immersion heaters are also already available to allow domestic wind turbines to heat hot water. These can also allow excess energy from small wind turbines to be 'dumped' into hot-water tanks rather than wasted when battery packs are fully charged.

In any setting, wind turbines currently have a reputation for being both ugly and noisy. Aesthetically the options are limited given that turbines by their nature need to be mounted high-up with blades of a reasonable size. However, a few quiet small-wind turbines are now becoming available. For example, QuietRevolution sell a very-low-noise wind turbine. This features three vertical, 5 metre helical blades that resemble a spinning DNA molecule. Mounted on a 9 metre tower, the system costs £20,000 plus installation and will quietly produce about 7 kilowatts of power in a good wind location.

Generating Power from the Oceans

For thousands of years it was common to locate a mill or other workplace near a river so that its machinery could be powered by a water wheel. Since the Industrial Revolution, this practice has all but died out in the developed world. However, the art of damming a river and using its falling water flow to generate electricity has been perfected and applied in a great many locations. For example, the Three Gorges Dam was completed in China in 2011. This is the world's largest hydroelectric undertaking and can produce over 80 terrawatts of power. Similar hydroelectric generating facilities include the Itaipu Dam on the border between Brazil and Paraguay, the Churchill Falls Generating Station in Canada, the Chief Joseph Dam in the United States and the Dinorwig Power Station in Wales.

While hydroelectric dams undoubtedly provide a great source of clean energy, their further development is inevitably geographically constrained. On the other hand, generating electricity from the ocean presents an enormous, untapped opportunity. Although wave power technology is still in its infancy, many projects are now off the drawing board and out at sea. Wave power therefore has the potential to become a significant source of electricity generation in the future.

Several different technologies may be used to generate energy from the oceans. The most straightforward is to build a tidal barrage. These dam a natural estuary to contain water at high tide and release it through flood gates at low tide to generate energy using turbines. The first such facility was built on the estuary of the River Rance in France and opened in 1966. Here the flow of the tidal waters turns 24 turbines, so generating up to 240 megawatts of electricity. Several other tidal barrage power stations are currently under construction, including one at Sihwa Lake in South Korea. The possibility of building a massive tidal barrage across the Severn Estuary in the United Kingdom has been muted with little action for decades.

Like hydroelectric dams, tidal barrage power stations can only be constructed in a limited number of suitable locations. More widely applicable tidal power technologies therefore use turbines to extract energy from ocean currents, or employ wave energy converters to harness the motion of individual waves.

A company called Atlantis Resources is currently developing submerged ocean current tidal generators. Some of these feature three-blade propellers on pylon mountings that are anchored to the sea bed. Others have a great many 'Aquafoil' blades on a rotating conveyor loop and are more suitable for shallow waters. Depending on the size,

individual ocean current generators are expected to produce between 100 kilowatts and 2 megawatts of electricity.

The state of Gujarat in India is currently constructing a
new tidal power station using Atlantis Resources tidal
current generators. Due for completion sometime in 2013,
this is initially intended to produce about 50 megawatts of
power from 50 turbines positioned on the seabed. However, there are already plans to add more turbines to
increase the total capacity to more than 250 megawatts.

While ocean current generators can be installed in many
more places than dams and tidal barrages, they are still
limited to suitable seabed locations. A great deal of research
is therefore going into the development of wave energy
converters that can generate electricity anywhere on the
surface of the ocean from the motion of individual waves.
Mechanisms for achieving this vary greatly, with all
systems still very much in development. However, some
promising technologies are now reaching commercial
application.

One of the first wave energy converter generating plants
is the Coos Bay Wave Park. This is being constructed 2.7
miles off the coast of Oregon by a company called Ocean
Power Technologies. When completed, the farm will
feature an array of 200 floating 'PowerBuoy' generators
that will capture and convert wave energy into electricity.
Each PowerBuoy is effectively a floating ring with a
central, vertical plunger. The plunger rises and falls with the
ebb and flow of the waves, so driving a hydraulic pump
attached to an electricity generator. Each PowerBuoy in the
farm will be connected to one of 20 underwater substation
pods, and from which cables will carry electricity to land.

The PowerBuoys in the Coos Bay Wave Park will each
generate 500 kilowatts, hence giving the total array a 100
megawatt capacity. Several prototype PowerBuoys have

already been built and tested out at sea in locations ranging from Spain to Hawaii to the Orkney Isles off Scotland. These smaller prototypes have been capable of generating 40 or 150 kilowatts of power, and over several years have demonstrated the viability of the technology.

Another pioneer is Pelamis Wave Power. Their 'Wave Energy Converter' (WEC) is a semi-submerged, articulated, snake-like structure built from cylindrical sections linked by hinged joints. In the sea, the cylindrical sections ride the waves, so causing the joints between them to move. Hydraulic rams use this joint motion to pump high-pressure fluid through hydraulic motors. These then drive electrical generators to produce electricity.

Current Pelamis WEC production models are 180 metres long, 4 metres in diameter and feature four power conversion modules per machine. The power output of a WEC is 750 kilowatts, meaning that each machine can potentially provide sufficient power for several hundred homes. In 2008, three of these units were installed off the Atlantic coastline of northern Portugal and successfully exported power to the national grid. Several other Pelamis wave farms are also in various stages of development in the waters around Scotland.

Once again, Google is taking an interest in the development of such pioneering alternative energy solutions. Specifically, in April 2009, the Internet giant was awarded a patent for a floating data centre that would be powered by Pelamis WECs. If such ships ever get built, then once again machines requiring power will be located next to sources of water-based energy just as they were centuries ago.

Yet other methods of extracting energy from the sea are also in development. For example, Green Ocean Energy is working on its 'Wave Treader'. This fits on to the foundation of an offshore wind turbine, and features two paddle-like floats that ride the waves. As these rise and fall they force pressurized fluid through hydraulic cylinders, with the mechanism in turn generating electricity. The idea is to allow even more power to be generated from new or existing wind farms without a significant investment in additional infrastructure.

Other future wave power devices may use 'oscillating water columns' to generate electricity. These would be hollow cylinders with their capped upper portion in the air and the remainder of the device in the sea. Waves would enter via an aperture at the bottom and rise up the tube. This would pressurize the air in the upper part of the cylinder, which would then be released to spin a turbine.

Other possible wave power generators may even be based on giant, rubber, underwater 'snakes'. These would be filled with water that would be squeezed by each wave, so producing a bulging pressure that would travel the length of the snake and turn an electrical turbine at its end. Already scale models of such contraptions are being tested at the University of Southampton.

Personal Kinetic Power

Most future alternative energy systems will generate power from large or very large moving things. There are, however, also significant future possibilities for individuals to generate a little of their own electricity from their everyday activities. Kinetic power generation is the broad term to describe the creation of energy from objects in motion, and such items can include human beings. For example, for many years some people have worn kinetic watches. These use natural wrist movements to swing a rotor that in turn winds a spring or charges a battery.

One of the great pioneers of kinetic power is British inventor Trevor Baylis who, in the early 1990s, invented the first clockwork radio. Like a traditional clock or wrist-watch, this stores energy in a spring that is wound up by hand. By 1997, Trevor's clockwork radios were in commercial production and were capable of running for up to an hour after only 20 seconds of winding. Today, clockwork radios and torches can be purchased on most high streets. Wind-up mobile phone chargers are also on the market, while wind-up laptops have been prototyped. These devices either store energy in a spring, or else directly charge a battery as their operator turns a handle.

Another technology that can be used to generate electricity from human motion is piezoelectrics. Many people use this technology every day when they ignite a stove using a piezoelectric ignition system. Here, a button is pressed to compress a piezoelectric crystal made from a material such as lead zirconate titanate. When compressed, the piezoelectric crystal generates electricity that creates an ignition spark.

In the future, piezoelectric crystals will be used to make more than the occasional spark. Back in August 2008, Nokia filed a patent for a device that could use piezoelectric crystals to turn body motion into electricity in order to charge mobile phones or other devices. In the same year, scientists from the Georgia Institute of Technology reported on their progress growing zinc oxide nanowires around kevlar textile fibres. They then wove these fibres together so that, when they rubbed against each other, a charge was generated. In the future, clothes made from piezoelectric textiles could therefore use body motion to charge small, personal devices such as mobile phones or media players.

In December 2010, a team from the University of Bolton's Institute for Materials Research and Innovation even claimed to have created a flexible photovoltaic-

public charging points. However, those driving longer distances will be able to call in to a service station and quickly exchange a discharged battery for a freshly charged one. This will give EVs the effectively infinite range already enjoyed by petroleum-fuelled automobiles capable of regular refuelling at a roadside station.

The company currently at the forefront of battery switching technology is Better Place. The goal of this EV pioneer is to deliver a 'network and services that make an electric car affordable to buy, easy to use, and amazing to own'. As the company explains:

> Long battery recharge times are a matter of physics. Even as batteries and charging infrastructure improve, using EVs for long journeys will require a way to quickly and reliably extend the range provided by a battery. Better Place provides this solution via a network of battery switch stations that use an ingenious robotic system to switch new batteries for depleted ones, cool and charge the batteries in inventory, and manage the complex logistics to ensure that each EV gets a fully charged battery each time the vehicle arrives at a station.

In April 2010, Better Place started its first EV battery-swap pilot in Tokyo. In the first 90 days of this trial, three electric taxis travelled over 25,000 miles using a battery-switch station to exchange batteries in less than the time needed to fill a tank with petrol. A larger trial is now also being conducted in San Francisco involving 61 electric taxis that are supported by four battery-swap stations. Other firms are also becoming interested in battery-swap systems. These include Tesla Motors, whose forthcoming Model S will have a one-minute quick-swap battery.

Alongside Better Place, several companies and research

piezoelectric fibre. This they hope will be woven into future fabrics to allow clothing to generate power not just from the movement of the wearer but also from the Sun.

Before piezoelectric fabrics become available, we may see piezoelectric crystals embedded in the heels of shoes. Every time these make a footfall the crystal would be compressed to generate a little power that could charge up a battery or ultracapacitor. If this sounds crazy, it is worth noting that this principle has already been applied somewhat in reverse by a company called Pavegen Systems.

What Pavegen have done is to embed piezoelectric crystals into paving slabs. These feature a central, clear rubber panel that compresses the crystal and generates power when anybody steps on it. About 5 per cent of this energy is used to briefly illuminate the rubber panel. The remaining 95 per cent is then available to power pedestrian lighting, information displays or other devices. Pavegen claims that pedestrian crossings, bus stops and other facilities can have all of their lighting and other power requirements met by replacing just a few nearby paving stones with their energy-generating slabs.

* * *

The Alternative Energy Revolution

In the future, an increasing number of businesses and households will start to generate at least some of their own power. Many will also on occasions even feed a bit of electricity back into a two-way national grid. At the other end of the spectrum, individual, personal power generation will increasingly be used to charge devices like mobile phones, media players, cameras and tablets, with a growing variety of electrical and electronic devices never being connected to the mains. Large-scale wind and wave farms

– not to mention solar power systems and nuclear power stations as detailed in the next two chapters – will definitely be needed to keep civilization chugging along with all of our lights, fridges, heating and computers turned on. However, non-grid power is going to become commonplace, with every little bit of personally or domestically generated electricity helping to power the widespread activities of human civilization.

The more we embrace domestic and personal power generation, the more likely it is that we will start to think more carefully about our use of grid electricity. Increasing energy prices as a result of Peak Oil and rising carbon taxes will also soon make most people a little bit more reticent to press a switch and run up a centralized bill. In the future, energy in all forms will therefore rise far, far higher up most personal and business agendas. In turn, this is likely to drive increasingly radical energy generation innovations. We can therefore be certain that we are only just at the beginning of this century's alternative energy revolution.

13

SOLAR ENERGY

Without solar energy all life as we know it would die. It is therefore hardly surprising that many of our ancestors worshipped the Sun. From Ancient Egypt to Greece, Mexico to Mesopotamia, the god associated with the life-giving globe in the heavens was revered above all others. Our ancestors may not have fully understood the great ball of nuclear fusion reactions that constantly burns 93 million miles out in space. However, they got the point that if it did not rise every morning they would be in serious trouble.

Today Ra, Apollo, Tonatiuh, Utu and many other ancient Sun gods no longer have a devoted following. Nevertheless, the Sun remains vital to us all. Not least, in some manner or other, the Sun provides virtually all of our energy. Plants give us nourishment obtained from sunlight via photosynthesis. All meat also contains solar energy converted by flora somewhere down the food chain. Fossil fuels additionally provide power from ancient sunlight stored up by long-deceased plants and animals. Even the wind is created by the Sun as it heats some parts of the Earth more than others.

Only tidal wave power and nuclear energy are not

entirely solar-dependent. This said, the forces that move our oceans around are affected by the Sun, if far less than by the gravitational attraction of the Moon. As we shall see in the next chapter, future nuclear power plants may even depend on a rare gas stored in Moon rock but emitted by the Sun.

As fossil fuel supplies dwindle, we are increasingly likely to employ a range of new technologies to help us obtain more and more energy directly from the Sun. Firstly, we will increasingly light and heat buildings by capturing and channelling solar radiation. Secondly, we will use photo-voltaic cells to convert solar energy into electricity. Thirdly, concentrated solar power stations will direct sunlight into receivers to produce electricity using a steam turbine or heat engine. And finally, we may even build solar power satellites out in space that will beam energy down to the Earth.

Capturing Solar Radiation

The most efficient way to exploit solar energy is to directly use its light and heat. To some extent, this can be achieved passively by fitting large double- or triple-glazed windows into well-insulated buildings. Homes and workplaces designed to make the most use of passive solar power often also include very thick walls and floors that retain and slowly release heat. More actively, an increasing variety of solar lighting and heating technologies continue to be invented and are likely to become popular.

As mentioned in Chapter 10, fibre optics and parabolic mirrors may be used to collect and redistribute sunlight around a building. For example, the California-based company Sunlight Direct has created a lighting system called SolarPoint. This typically consists of a roof-mounted platform, a 45-foot bundle of plastic fibre optic cables and a number of special 'hybrid luminaires'. As the company explains:

> The technology concentrates natural sunlight into a small bundle of optical fibers that 'pipe' sunlight directly into a building or enclosure. Special lighting fixtures called hybrid luminaires diffuse light throughout the space, delivering up to 25,000 peak lumens. The hybrid luminaires blend the natural light with existing artificial lighting to provide controllable interior lighting. As sunlight levels increase and decrease, a daylight harvesting controller automatically increases or decreases the co-located artificial lighting proportionally, providing significant energy savings during daylight hours.

Alternative natural illumination systems use highly polished, mirrored ducts or 'light pipes' that transfer light from a roof dome to a ceiling diffuser. At present, retro-fitting any such kind of light-redirection technology into an existing building is very expensive. The technology is also of no use at night. However, as the costs fall, light capture and redirection systems are likely to be employed in more and more new buildings to ensure that as few artificial lights as possible have to be turned on in the day.

Directly using heat from the Sun is easier than capturing and redirecting its light. Solar thermal energy (STE) heating systems are also tried and tested technologies that have been in limited use for many years. For example, as shown in Figure 13.1, houses may be fitted with a rooftop solar collection panel to heat hot water. These contain pipes under glass through which a liquid is pumped. This liquid then circulates in a closed loop to transfer the heat obtained from the Sun to the hot water tank.

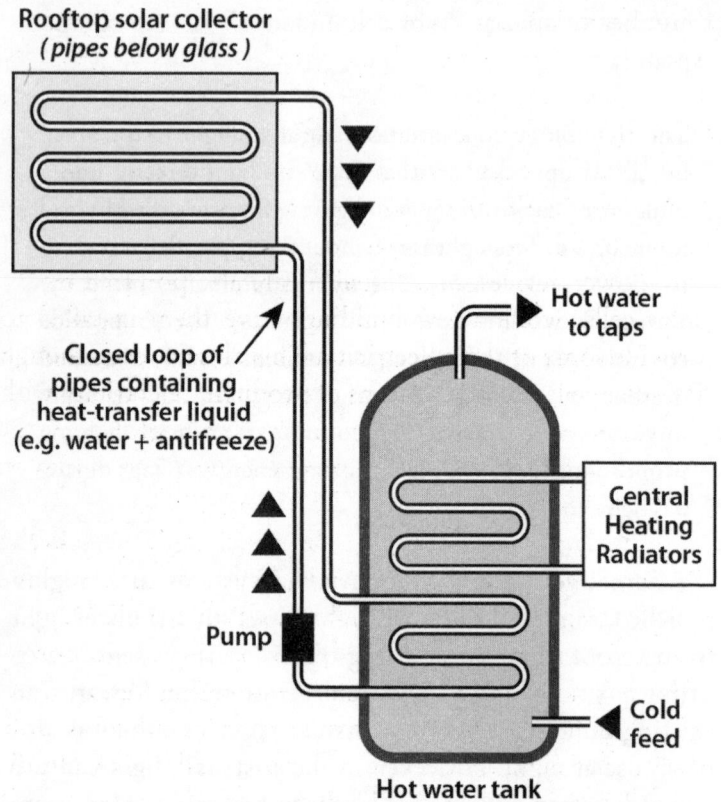

Figure 13.1: Solar heating of domestic hot water

Around 15 to 30 per cent of household energy is used to heat water. Even if augmented by traditional heating methods, solar hot water heating systems can therefore make a reasonable dent in household energy usage and bills. In the United Kingdom, British Gas estimates that in most instances a solar hot water system can supply 50 to 70 per cent of household hot water. We should therefore expect to see many more buildings fitted with solar hot water heating.

Photovoltaic Solar Power

Photovoltaic (PV) solar cells produce electricity directly from the Sun. The physics involved is complex, but basically uses light to trigger a flow of electrons between two layers of semiconducting material. For many years PV solar cells have provided the small amount of energy required by some calculators, wristwatches and other low-power devices. Most satellites are also powered by PV solar cells, while a few buildings have them installed to provide some of their electricity. This all said, even though PV solar cells provide a means of producing electricity with zero fuel costs, they have remained an expensive means of generating large quantities of power given the high cost of the panels and their relatively low energy yield.

In the face of Peak Oil and climate change, demand for PV solar cells capable of producing electricity at reasonable cost is starting to increase. Reflecting this, the US Department of Energy has established its Solar Energy Technologies Program (SETP). One of the program's goals is to develop PV solar to a point where, by 2015, it will be able to produce electricity as cost-effectively as fossil fuels. To this end, SETP is working to improve basic PV cell technologies, to maximize the working life of PV cells, and to decrease their production costs. Should SETP succeed, PV solar power is likely to become a major means of generating electricity both on- and off-grid.

Individual PV cells produce only a few watts of low-voltage power. As shown in Figure 13.2, individual PV cells are therefore assembled into solar panel modules. These modules are further arranged into larger arrays in order to produce a reasonable quantity of electricity. In turn, arrays then form part of complete PV solar systems. Large-scale PV systems include power conditioners and transformers to turn the DC power generated into AC for

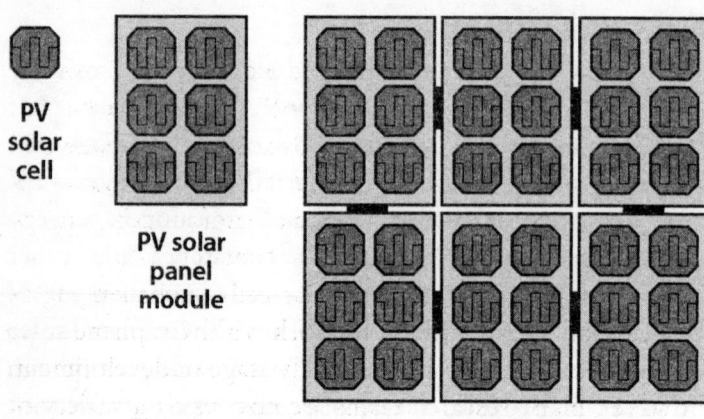

PV solar array

Figure 13.2: A PV solar cell, module and array

the grid. Smaller, off-grid PV systems contain batteries to provide a constant local power source regardless of changing sunlight levels.

PV solar cells are based on silicon wafer or thin-film technology. Wafer-based cells are made from slices of a pure silicon crystal, or else cut from silicon that has been liquefied and cast into a block comprised of many smaller crystals. Single crystal PV cells are the most efficient, while so-termed multi- or polycrystalline cells cost less but produce less power. Typically, wafer-based PV cells are 10×10 or 15×15 cm in size. They are also rather fragile and therefore have to be mounted on a tough, rigid frame.

Thin-film PV cells usually produce less power than their wafer-based alternatives, but are becoming more popular as they are both considerably lighter and cheaper to produce. Here, tiny crystalline grains of a semiconductor material are coated on to a supporting material, which if required can even be flexible. In the future, spray-on PV thin-films may even be applied to fabrics to allow our clothes to produce electricity when we are out in the sunshine.

Improving PV Cell Efficiency

A range of different semiconductor materials are currently used in the manufacture of thin-film PV cells. These include silicon, copper indium diselenide, cadmium telluride and gallium arsenide. As mentioned in Chapter 7, future PV cells may potentially also be manufactured using atom-thick sheets of carbon known as graphene.

Using graphene to produce solar cells is challenging as the material is very difficult to work with. Graphene solar cells are therefore still at a very early stage of development. However, many research teams are now using a variety of other approaches to try to create third generation thin-film PV cells. For example, a company called 3GSolar is developing a dye-based thin-film technology. This produces PV cells using a layer of nanosized titanium dioxide particles embedded in a dye. Dye solar cells are produced using screen-printing equipment rather than vacuum manufacturing systems. They also do not require silicon. 3GSolar subsequently expects bulk manufacturing costs for its dye-based cells to be 40 per cent less than for silicon-based alternatives.

In addition to decreasing production costs, a major hurdle in the development of PV solar technology has been increasing light absorption. Typically, traditional PV cells make use of at best 67 per cent of the sunlight that hits them. This is because they can only create electricity from sunlight that strikes the cell at a 90-degree angle. The energy output from statically mounted PV cells therefore changes as the Sun moves across the sky. Until very recently, the only way to deal with this shortcoming has been to mount solar arrays on mechanical mechanisms that keep their cells aligned with the Sun.

Fortunately, nanotechnology coatings are now being developed to solve the absorption problem. These feature multiple layers of very tiny 'nanorods' that allow PV cells to absorb light from any angle. The nanorods work like a series of very small funnels, with each layer bending the light just a little so that it can hit the PV surface at as close to 90 degrees as possible. To date, researchers – including a team at the Rensselaer Polytechnic Institute in New York – have managed to use nanorod coatings to increase PV cell absorption to nearly 97 per cent. This will allow PV arrays to produce about one third more electricity without the need for a Sun-chasing mechanism.

Large-scale PV systems currently also run the risk of their cells overheating. They therefore have to include energy-guzzling cooling systems. To address both this and light absorption issues, a research team from the Massachusetts Institute of Technology has set up a company called Covalent Solar to develop future 'waveguide photovoltaic modules'. These are basically transparent glass panels coated in specific ratios of coloured dyes. Light entering the glass from any angle is trapped and internally reflected to its edges where small solar cells are positioned. Waveguide photovoltaic glass panels do not require cooling, use 90 per cent fewer semiconducting materials than traditional panels, suffer few absorption losses, and may increase overall efficiency by up to 50 per cent.

PV Solar in Action

Even before many of the above technology developments come to market, PV solar power stations are being planned and constructed around the world. By the end of 2010, pvresources.com listed over 800 commercial PV solar plants, with more than 100 of these each producing over 2 megawatts of power. All of the top 100 plants had also been brought online since 2007, with the largest including the 97 megawatt Sarnia PV power plant in Canada, the 84.2

megawatt Montalto di Castro PV power plant in Italy, and the 80.7 megawatt Finsterwalde Solarpark in Germany. Other large PV power plants are already operational in the United States, Spain, the Czech Republic, Portugal, China and Korea.

If the construction of plants continues at its current rate, by the end of the decade PV solar power will be a mainstream means of electricity generation in many countries. In fact, the European Photovoltaic Industry Association has suggested that PV solar power could be satisfying as much as 12 per cent of the European Union's electricity demand by 2020.

PV solar panels are also likely to become common on the roofs of many homes. Such domestic panels are unlikely to meet any household's complete electricity requirement. However, as the aforementioned PV cell technology developments come to market, some homes may generate 20 or even 30 per cent of their electricity from the Sun. As mentioned in Chapter 11, future electric cars are also likely to feature PV panels to help extend their range. PV cells on laptop lids are similarly likely to become the norm as a means of boosting battery life.

Concentrated Solar Power

Photovoltaic cells may be what most people associate with solar electricity generation. However, at medium- and large-scale, an equally viable and potentially lower-cost technology is concentrated solar power (CSP). Ever used a magnifying glass to burn a hole in a piece of paper on a sunny day? Well, CSP works in exactly the same way. It does this by using one or many concentrators to focus the Sun's rays on to a receiver that heats to somewhere between 350 and 1,000°C. This concentrated heat is then used to generate electricity using a steam turbine or heat engine.

Depending on the type and configuration of their concentrators and receivers, CSP generating plants come in four different types. These are illustrated in Figures 13.3 and 13.4, and are based in turn on parabolic troughs, Fresnel mirrors, power towers or parabolic dishes.

At present the most widely employed form of CSP technology uses parabolic troughs. Here a receiver pipe runs along the focal point of many parabolically curved reflectors that concentrate the Sun's rays on to the pipe. The troughs are arranged in parallel rows, with a mechanical system usually employed to keep them in alignment with the Sun. A fluid such as oil or a mixture of molten salts is circulated through the receiver pipe. This transfers heat to a boiler where it turns water into high pressure steam that then drives a turbine to generate electricity.

Parabolic-trough CSP plants can currently generate up to 80 megawatts of electricity. They can also incorporate thermal storage systems that allow operation for several hours into the evening. Most of the first trough-based CSP systems are hybrids, with fossil-fuels used to supply supplementary heat to the steam turbine when there is little sunshine or at night.

At least 25 parabolic-trough CSP plants are already in operation, with a similar number announced or under construction. The first parabolic-trough CSP plant opened in the Mojave Desert in California in 1984. Today nine parabolic-trough CSP plants are spread across the Mojave Desert, with a combined power output of 384 megawatts. In December 2010, the construction of another facility in California was also announced. Called the Palen Solar Power Project, this will feature two parabolic-trough plants capable of producing 484 megawatts. Alongside the United States, Spain is another major pioneer with several parabolic-trough installations. These include a suite of

PARABOLIC TROUGHS

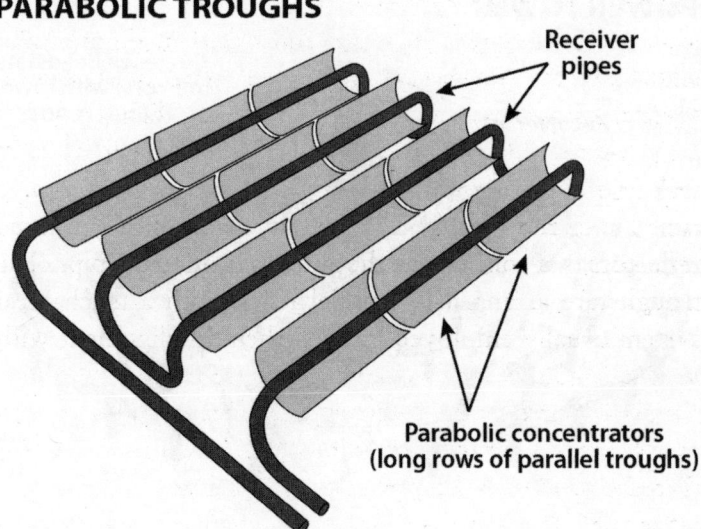

Receiver pipes

Parabolic concentrators
(long rows of parallel troughs)

FRESNEL MIRRORS

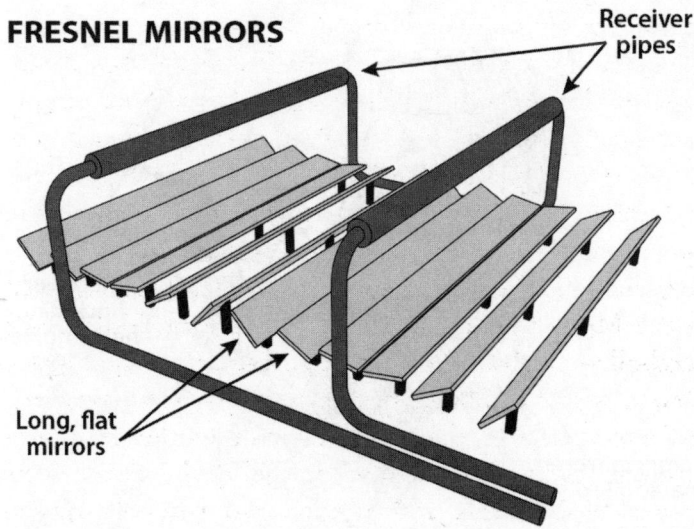

Receiver pipes

Long, flat mirrors

Figure 13.3: Parabolic troughs and Fresnel mirrors

POWER TOWER

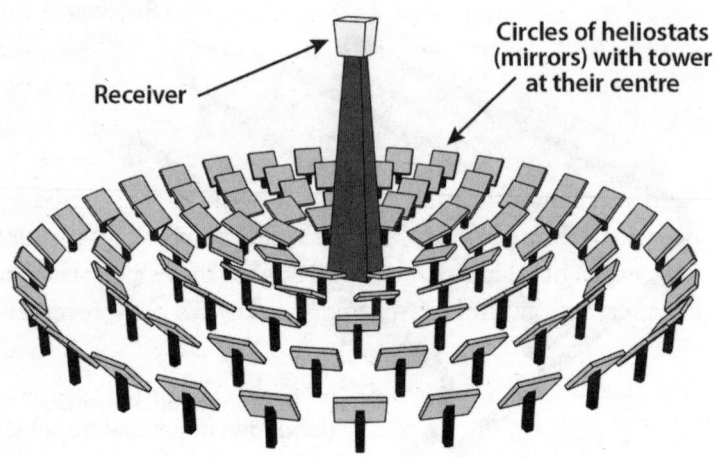

Receiver

Circles of heliostats
(mirrors) with tower
at their centre

PARABOLIC DISH

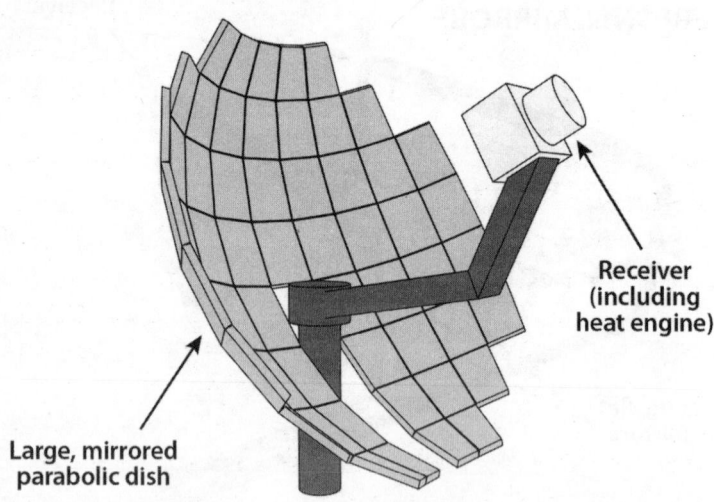

Receiver
(including
heat engine)

Large, mirrored
parabolic dish

Figure 13.4: A power tower and parabolic dish

plants called Solnova in Seville that generates 150 megawatts.

As shown in the lower half of Figure 13.3, the second type of CSP system uses Fresnel mirrors. This arrangement is similar to a parabolic-trough installation, but uses long, flat mirrors at different angles to concentrate sunlight on to its receiver pipes. As in parabolic-trough systems, a transfer fluid circulates through the pipes, with its heat used to power a steam turbine. While Fresnel mirror systems are less efficient than parabolic troughs they are also far cheaper. At the time of writing the world's only commercial Fresnel CSP system was the Kimberlina Solar Thermal Energy Plant. This is located in Bakersfield, California, and generates 5 megawatts.

A third category of CSP is the power tower. As illustrated at the top of Figure 13.4, this features concentric circles of mirrors known as heliostats. These track the Sun and focus its rays on to a single receiver at the top of a very tall tower. In the receiver the Sun's concentrated power superheats a fluid that in turn is used to produce steam and drive an electricity-generating turbine.

Currently, the most powerful solar power tower is the PS20 Solar Power Plant. This was put into operation in 2009 in Sanlúcar la Mayor in Spain. The facility consists of 1,255 heliostats that reflect the Sun's rays to the top of a 165-metre tower. PS20 produces 20 megawatts of electricity. Future power towers could potentially produce up to 200 megawatts.

As shown in the lower portion of Figure 13.4, the final type of CSP technology is the parabolic dish. This resembles a large, mirrored satellite receiver that constantly tracks the Sun. The dish captures sunlight and directs it to a receiver at its focal point. A mechanical mechanism called a heat-engine then converts the concentrated solar energy into motion to drive a generator. While a variety of heat-engine mechanisms may in future be employed, the most common is likely to be a Sterling engine.

Dr Robert Stirling patented his 'heat economiser' or 'Stirling engine' in 1816. The device is beautifully simple and usually classified as a form of external combustion engine. Whereas in a petrol-driven vehicle fuel is burnt inside the engine block, in a Stirling engine an external heat source is used to expand a gas already contained in a cylinder. This then causes a piston to move.

Stirling engines feature an appropriate configuration of heat exchangers to regulate the flow of gas between hot and cold chambers. Once hot gas has pushed the drive piston forward, a second or 'displacer' piston circulates the gas back so that it cools and causes the main drive piston to return to its initial position. The constant motion cycle this creates is then used to turn a generator.

One of the pioneers of parabolic dish CSP technology is Stirling Energy Systems. This company has developed a parabolic dish and Stirling engine generator called the SunCatcher. Each of these features a 38-foot dish and generates 25 kilowatts of power. In January 2010, 60 of these dishes went online in the world's first commercial parabolic dish CSP plant at Maricopa in Arizona.

Space-Based Solar Power

Direct solar thermal energy systems, PV cells and CSP all extract energy from the Sun's rays after they have been filtered by the atmosphere. They also only function at full efficiency in bright sunlight and cannot work at night. At first thought, these impediments to optimal solar power generation may appear to be insurmountable. However, in the future they may be overcome by placing solar power satellites in orbit. These future space stations would receive sunlight before it hit the Earth and would never be shadowed by cloud. They could therefore be many times more efficient than ground-based solar power stations. While geostationary satellites would turn with the Earth and only receive sunlight in the day, others could potentially be non-geostationary. They could therefore receive sunlight and generate power 24/7.

The idea of space-based solar power (SBSP) was first conceived by an American engineer, Peter Glaser, in 1968. His idea was for vast orbital PV power stations that would transmit electricity to the Earth using microwaves. In 1973 Glaser was granted a US patent for his 'method and apparatus for converting solar radiation to electrical power'. This envisaged solar power satellites with microwave antennas about one square kilometre in area and capable of transmitting power to smaller 'rectennas' on the ground.

When first proposed, Glaser's ideas received little serious interest. However, in the 1970s the US Department of Energy spent about $20 million on research into SBSP. It even created plans for a solar space station. This was intended to be 5 km by 10 km in size, and would have used microwaves to transmit power down to the Earth.

Between 1995 and 1997, NASA looked again at the feasibility of SBSP in a study called *Fresh Looks*. The result was a new concept called the SunTower. This was a plan for a linked, vertical stack of between 6 and 30 solar power satellites in low or medium Earth orbit. A decade later, the US National Security Space Office again presented a detailed analysis of SBSP as a 'potential grand opportunity to address energy security'. In 2009, Pacific Gas and Electric were even reported to be seeking permission to test a 200 megawatt solar power satellite that was intended to transmit microwave energy to a receiver station in Fresno County, California.

Also in 2009, the Japan Aerospace Exploration Agency (JAXA) put forward ambitious plans for an orbital solar power station designed to beam energy back to the Earth using lasers. In January 2010, EADS Astrium – Europe's biggest space company – also began seeking partners to fly a demonstration solar power mission in orbit. Its intended prototype will hopefully transmit about 10 kilowatts of power back to the ground using an infrared laser. According to the company, it has already reached a point where this could be achieved 'within the next five years'. As explained in November 2010 on astrium.eads.net, in the relatively near future its small, 10 kilowatt satellites could safely transmit off-grid power to receivers a few tens of metres in diameter. By the 2020s, large-scale systems could be delivering megawatts and even gigawatts of electrical power from orbit.

As EADS Astrium claims, all of the technologies required to build solar power satellites already exist. As we have seen in this chapter, advancements in the necessary PV solar technology also continue to accrue. The transmission of energy over long distances using either microwaves or laser beams has additionally already been proven. SBSP proponents even claim that the frequencies and energy densities involved will not fry things that accidentally get in the way of the beam. As will be demonstrated in Chapter 15, access to space is also on the verge of becoming more cost-effective. A few decades from now, Peter Glaser's 'crazy' idea of obtaining power from a solar power satellite may subsequently become a reality.

Building one or more large-scale solar power stations in orbit would be a tremendous challenge. However, it could also result in some significant spin-offs. As discussed in Chapter 2, a potential macro-engineering solution for lessening and even reversing climate change may be to build solar sails out in space. These would shade the Earth from some of the Sun's rays and could therefore reduce global warming without requiring any reduction in the level of greenhouse gases in the atmosphere. Given that a large number of PV arrays in orbit would have the same shading effect, it is logical that future solar sail and SBSP projects may be combined.

* * *

Becoming a Solar Pioneer

In January 2009, a non-profit organization called the DESERTEC Foundation was established to promote the use of deserts as ideal locations for future solar power plants. As DESERTEC argue, in six hours the world's deserts can receive more energy from the Sun than the human race currently uses in a year. To put this another way, every year each square kilometre of desert receives solar energy roughly equivalent to 1.5 million barrels of oil. If just 1 per cent of the world's deserts were to be covered with solar power plants, the entire planet's current energy requirement could therefore be met. Such an extreme future proposition may well be a pipe dream. However, it does demonstrate the very significant potential for solar energy to become a major if not majority source of power. This is also before we even start to seriously contemplate the opportunities for space-based solar power as discussed in the last section.

While large-scale solar power generation is now ripe for commercial exploitation, it is also already possible for individuals to become solar pioneers. Most of us could now charge our mobile phones and some other batteries using domestic PV solar chargers if we wanted to. Many households could also fit solar thermal energy panels to heat some of their hot water. Domestic cooling and ventilation units powered by PV cells integrated into their external vents are additionally on the market. In the United Kingdom, solar pioneer SunSwitch is then just one of several companies that already offer a complete, fitted rooftop PV solar array capable of generating over £1,000 worth of electricity a year. A company called Oxford Photovoltaics is also working on technologies that will soon enable it to print dye-based PV solar cells on to standard window panes.

Anybody wishing to rely heavily on solar power – or on any other form of alternative energy come to that – will have to learn to plan their energy use. Today, most people in developed nations can flick a switch and draw as much or as little electricity as they desire at any time, night or day. But in any future home powered by alternative energy sources this is unlikely to be the case. Batteries may allow electricity to be consumed when little or no power is being generated. Even so, there are still likely to be times when it will be impossible to turn on the oven, immersion heater and electric fire while also charging the electric car. At least at the domestic level, solar and other forms of alternative energy will therefore require the development of new behaviours and new mindsets in addition to new technologies.

All life as we know it is reliant on the Sun. Human civilization has therefore always been solar-dependent. As this chapter has hopefully shown, the opportunities for this dependence to significantly increase are very great indeed. The solar energy sector is therefore likely to become sizzling hot. Alongside an industrial boom in nanotech, GM and synthetic biology, by the end of the decade we may well therefore be experiencing a market bubble surrounding the first financial 'solar rush'.

14

NUCLEAR FUSION

In 1958, Egon Larsen wrote a book called *Atomic Energy: A Layman's Guide to the Nuclear Age*. This popular paperback detailed many designs for nuclear power plants and even some future atomic aeroplanes and nuclear cars. Since the 1950s, the enthusiasm for nuclear energy so strongly exhibited by Larsen and his contemporaries may have significantly waned. Nevertheless, at least one form of nuclear transport exists, with uranium-powered submarines now constantly patrolling our oceans. Some countries – and most notably France – today also generate a great deal of their electricity using nuclear power. In fact, as of January 2011, the world had 442 operational nuclear power stations with 65 more under construction.

Despite its current scale, in general the nuclear industry does not enjoy a good press. Quite understandably, the incidents at Fukushima in 2011, Chernobyl in 1986 and Three Mile Island in 1979 all raised public and political doubts over the industry's safety and long-term future. Since those nuclear disasters, people have worried greatly about possible radiation leaks and the re-progressing and long-term storage of nuclear waste. Such concerns are not insignificant. This said, in the face of climate change and dwindling fossil fuel supplies, even some members of the green movement are now advocating nuclear power as a least-worst means of generating far more of our electricity. Not least, veteran environmentalist Stewart Brand is now promoting nuclear power on the basis that it does not emit any greenhouse gases.

In the future, the dangers associated with nuclear power stations and their waste products could also be significantly reduced. Today, all nuclear power plants are based on a process called nuclear fission. However, the potential exists to switch to an alternative process called nuclear fusion. This happens to be the mechanism that fuels the Sun, and could potentially provide humanity with a future source of safer nuclear power.

The Fusion Promise
Today's nuclear fission power plants split apart uranium or plutonium atoms to release energy from their broken atomic bonds. The heat generated in the reactor is then used to turn water into high-pressure steam. This steam then drives a turbine to make electricity.

The physics behind nuclear fission is illustrated at the top of Figure 14.1. As shown in the diagram, in a nuclear fission reaction a sub-atomic particle called a neutron strikes a nuclear fuel, so releasing energy and further neutrons, which in turn trigger a chain reaction. However, a second by-product of the fission reaction is the divided fragments of the original fuel used to create it. This nuclear waste is also highly radioactive. Even after re-progressing, it therefore has to be securely stored for hundreds if not thousands of years.

Due to the level and toxicity of radioactive waste created by nuclear fission, for many decades nuclear physicists have been working toward the creation of nuclear fusion power plants that will create fewer problematic contaminated

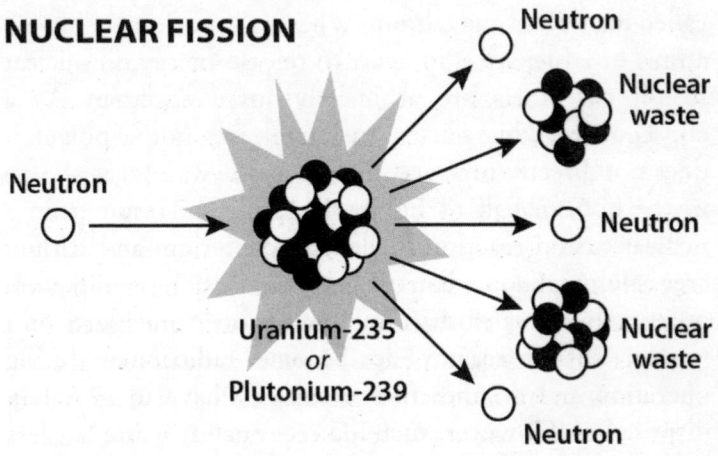

NUCLEAR FUSION

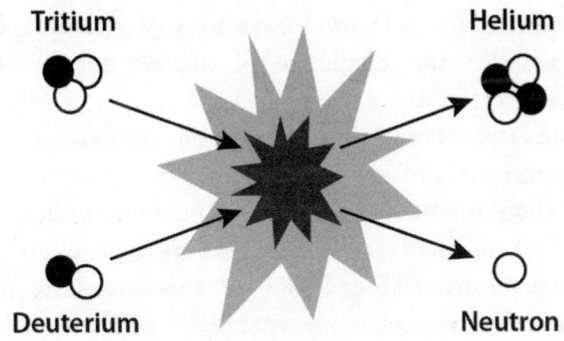

Figure 14.1: Nuclear fission and nuclear fusion

by-products. Given that supplies of uranium are unlikely to last beyond the end of this century, another potential attraction of nuclear fusion power stations is that they will reduce our reliance on a relatively scarce nuclear fuel.

At present, the most likely fuels for nuclear fusion power stations are two isotopes or 'heavy forms' of hydrogen called deuterium and tritium. Whereas in nuclear fission the atoms of a fuel are split apart to release energy, in nuclear fusion two fuels are atomically fused together. As a consequence, while nuclear fusion releases atomic power, it does not directly produce nuclear waste. Rather, as shown in the bottom half of Figure 14.1, all that result from a nuclear fusion reaction fuelled by deuterium and tritium are helium and a neutron. Nuclear fusion is therefore potentially far safer than nuclear fission. Some parts of a nuclear fusion reactor do become radioactive during operation and do therefore eventually have to be safely disposed of. However, such indirect nuclear waste has less long-term radiotoxicity than the by-product of current nuclear fission power stations.

To understand the problems involved in making nuclear fusion a reality, we need to briefly delve into the atomic realm. So please stay with me for the next two paragraphs, and the wonder and challenge of nuclear fusion will become clear. Honest!

All atoms are made from sub-atomic particles called protons, neutrons and electrons. An atom's protons and neutrons stick together to form its nucleus, which its electrons then normally orbit. But at very high temperatures indeed, all materials change from a gaseous state into a plasma and their electrons are separated from their nuclei.

The protons in the nucleus of an atom are positively charged. Because of this, the nuclei of two atoms are normally kept apart due to the strong repulsive, electrostatic force this creates. However, in nuclear fusion, conditions are created in which atoms are pushed so close together that the attractive nuclear force that binds their protons and neutrons overcomes this repulsion. This causes the different nuclei to fuse, so releasing a great deal of atomic energy.

Hotter than the Sun

Our Sun is powered by constant nuclear fusion reactions that are triggered by massive gravitational forces. However, such conditions cannot be created on the Earth. To create fusion in a reactor therefore requires the fuels in use to be heated to an extremely high temperature. In practice this means warming them to in excess of 100 million degrees centigrade, or many times hotter than the Sun. This exceptionally hot plasma must then be kept dense enough and held together long enough for 'ignition' to be achieved and self-sustaining fusion to occur. You will not be surprised to learn that all of this is incredibly difficult to achieve.

As already noted and as shown in Figure 14.1, the most likely fuels for a nuclear fusion power station are the hydrogen isotopes deuterium and tritium. Deuterium occurs naturally in seawater at quantities of around 33 grams per cubic metre. Tritium, on the other hand, does not occur naturally and is radioactive. However, tritium can be 'bred' from lithium in a nuclear reactor. Like deuterium, lithium is also found in relatively large quantities in the Earth's crust and in weaker concentrations in the sea. Potentially, therefore, future nuclear fusion power stations could be fuelled from two relatively abundant raw materials.

As shown in the lower half of Figure 14.1, a deuterium-tritium fusion reaction results in helium and an extra or 'fast' neutron. Inside a fusion reactor these fast neutrons are absorbed into a 'blanket' of lithium that surrounds the core. The lithium is then transformed into tritium, which subsequently fuels the reactor. The lithium blanket has to be very thick indeed (at least one metre) to slow down the fast neutrons as they carry with them about 80 per cent of the energy from the fusion reaction. As the neutrons decelerate and stop, their considerable kinetic energy is absorbed by the lithium blanket, which becomes very hot. This heat is then collected by a circulating fluid and used to turn water into steam to drive a turbine and produce electricity.

Test fusion reactors have already been built that can operate for extremely brief periods. However, beyond the difficulty of sustaining a fusion reaction, they face the additional problem of superheating and containing their fuels in a manner that does not use more energy than they can generate.

Two approaches for building future nuclear fusion power stations are currently being trialled. The more advanced is called 'magnetic confinement', and uses a magnetic field to contain hundreds of cubic metres of fusion plasma within a doughnut-shaped ring. The less developed method is termed 'inertial confinement', and focuses a laser or ion beam on a small pellet of deuterium and tritium just a few millimetres in diameter.

Nuclear Fusion in Practice
There is a long-running joke in the scientific community that nuclear fusion will always be 'about 40 years away'. While there is some truth in this physicists' jibe, progress does continue to be made.

Most fusion research has involved magnetic confinement. While this can be achieved in many ways, the most common method is to build a 'tokamak'. This device was invented by Soviet physicists Andrei Sakharv and Igor Tamm in 1951, with its name standing for '*toroidalnya kamera ee magnetnaya katushka*' or 'torus-shaped magnetic chamber'. Since 1951 several test tokamaks have been built at significant cost. These include the Joint European Torus (JET) in the United Kingdom, and the Tokamak

Fusion Test Reactor (TFTR) in the United States. As part of the International Thermonuclear Experimental Reactor (ITER) project, the world's largest tokamak is currently being constructed in Cadarache in southern France.

The JET project was launched by the European Atomic Energy Community (Euratom) in 1978, although since 1999 it has been managed by the UK Atomic Energy Authority on behalf of its many partner nations. JET is a tritium-deuterium reactor and the only operational facility capable of producing fusion energy. JET produced its first plasma in 1983 and in November 1991 output the world's first controlled release of nuclear fusion power.

So far JET has generated up to 16 megawatts of energy for a one-second period, with 5 megawatts sustained over a longer duration. These significant achievements noted, sadly JET has never output more than 70 per cent of the energy required to sustain its plasma. Nevertheless, the project continues to drive forward fusion research. In particular, it is proving a very successful testbed for developing radioactive handling and plasma containment techniques.

The TFTR operated at the Princeton Plasma Physics Laboratory in the United States from 1982 to 1997. In 1994 the reactor managed to produce 10.7 megawatts of controlled fusion power, and in 1995 set a record for achieving a plasma temperature of 510 million degrees centigrade.

The history of the ITER dates back to 1985 when the then Soviet Union suggested a collaborative fusion project with Europe, Japan and the United States. The ITER was subsequently established under the auspices of the International Atomic Energy Authority (IAEA). Partners in the project have fluctuated over the years, with the United States having both left and rejoined, and China and South Korea having now signed up.

After much political wrangling, in mid-2005 it was agreed to build the ITER test facility in Cadarache in southern France. Construction is expected to be completed by 2017, with the plant to have an operational life of 20 years. The total cost of the project is expected to be 12.8 billion euros. Half of this is coming from Europe, with the United States, Japan, China, South Korea and Russia each contributing 10 per cent.

The ultimate goal of the ITER is to create 500 megawatts of energy output from 50 megawatts of power input for at least 400 seconds continuously. This said, ITER will not actually generate electricity. Instead, a second-phase, 2 gigawatt demonstration plant known as DEMO is expected to show the feasibility of continual electricity production. Designs for DEMO are expected to be finished by 2017, with construction slated to start in 2024 and operation hopefully commencing in the 2030s. As the timeline indicates, this is very long-term research, with fusion power not expected to enter a national grid until the 2040s.

While a gigawatt coal-fired power station uses about 2.75 million tonnes of coal per year, a future nuclear fusion power plant with the same energy output would require only 250 kilograms of deuterium and tritium in the same period. The potential of nuclear fusion is subsequently breathtaking, and indeed enough to convince some people that we should forget about developing wind, wave and solar power altogether.

Alternative Approaches

Before we get too excited, it is worth pointing out that some 60 years after the tokamak was first invented, commercial fusion power plants are still at best 30 years away. There are also a great many technical challenges to overcome. For a start, the containment of the fast neutrons created in deuterium-tritium fusion is an issue. There are also concerns that radioactive tritium will be released. The problem here is that tritium can penetrate concrete, rubber and some grades of steel. Because it is an isotope of hydrogen, tritium is also easily incorporated into water, which then becomes mildly radioactive. Tritium can additionally be inhaled or absorbed through the skin, and either as a gas or in water is a threat to human health for about 125 years after it is created. The safety of future deuterium-tritium nuclear fusion plants is therefore already a potential concern.

Because of the above risks and the relatively slow progress of fusion research, alternative mechanisms for generating future fusion power are being considered. Some of these are based on inertial confinement, and focus a laser or ion beam on a small deuterium-tritium fuel pellet. The outer layer of the pellet then heats up and explodes, in turn creating an inward implosion. The force of this implosion compresses the inner layers of the pellet to around 1,000 times their liquid density, so allowing fusion to occur. Research into inertial confinement fusion is currently underway at the Institute for Laser Engineering at Osaka University in Japan.

Other potential approaches include cold fusion. In 1989, researchers Stanley Pons in the United States and Martin Fleischmann in the United Kingdom claimed to have achieved fusion at room temperature on a tabletop. Their experiment apparently used palladium electrodes to concentrate deuterium nuclei in so-termed 'heavy water' (deuterium oxide) via electrolysis. Pons and Fleischmann claimed that their process produced heat via the release of nuclear energy, as well as fusion by-products including helium and tritium. Since 1989 no other scientists have managed to repeat this initial cold fusion experiment.

Nevertheless, some research into cold fusion continues. For example, in 2005, a research team at the University of California claimed to have initiated cold fusion using a pyroelectric crystal.

More likely alternative fusion processes may utilize a deuterium-deuterium reaction. Here two deuterium nuclei would fuse, resulting in a neutron and a very rare isotope of helium called helium-3. The big benefit here would be achieving fusion without tritium, hence making the process much safer. Unfortunately, however, research into this type of fusion remains at a very early stage.

Fusion Power from Moon Dust?

Yet another possibility is fuelling nuclear fusion power plants with deuterium and the non-radioactive isotope helium-3. Figure 14.2 illustrates the nuclear physics involved. As you can see, this form of nuclear fusion results in helium and a proton. Given that protons are a charged particle, they can – unlike neutrons – be contained in a magnetic confinement field. So-termed 'aneutronic' helium-3 fusion may therefore be easier to control and safer than other forms. This said, heat for generating electricity would have to be extracted from the reaction in a manner other than neutron collision with a reactor blanket.

The really big obstacle to using helium-3 in future nuclear fusion reactors is that it does not occur naturally on the Earth. Currently, around 15 kilograms of helium-3 is produced every year as a by-product of maintaining nuclear weapons. Helium-3 is, however, constantly emitted by the Sun within its solar winds. None of this potentially precious gas arrives on the Earth as it cannot penetrate our atmosphere. However, as the Moon does not have an atmosphere it has been absorbing helium-3 from the Sun for billions of years. As a result, there are estimated to be

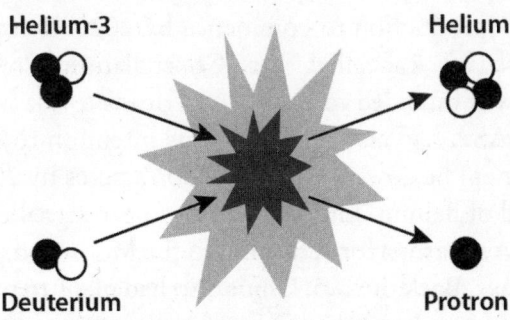

Figure 14.2: Nuclear fusion with helium-3

around 1.1 million tonnes of helium-3 on the surface of the Moon down to a depth of a few metres. In future this potential nuclear fusion fuel could be extracted by heating the lunar dust to around 600°C. The helium-3 would then be put into pressurized canisters and brought back to the Earth to fuel a new generation of nuclear fusion power plants.

In 1994, a private venture called the Artemis Project was established with the goal of establishing a private Moon base. Backed by an increasing number of organizations, this growing initiative has estimated that about 25 tonnes of helium-3 could power the whole of the United States for a year. This means that helium-3 has a potential economic value in the order of several billion dollars per tonne. In turn this makes helium-3 the only lunar deposit that may prove economic to mine and return to the Earth with current and near-future space technology.

Only a few years ago mining lunar helium-3 was being seriously considered by many nations. For example, in 2006 Nikolai Sevastyanov – then head of the Russian space corporation Energia – reported that Russia was planning to mine lunar helium-3, with a permanent Moon base to be established by 2015 and industrial-scale helium-3 production to commence by 2020. Before President Obama cancelled the Constellation Programme (which was intended to return Americans to the Moon) in 2010, NASA had also announced its intention to establish a permanent base on one of the Moon's poles by 2024. The potential of helium-3 mining had also been signalled as one of NASA's reasons for returning to the Moon and planning such a base. Back in 2005, China also had plans to put a man on the Moon by 2017. One of the stated aims of this mission was to measure the thickness of the lunar soil and the amount of helium-3 present.

Following the financial crash of 2008, all of the aforementioned plans to return humans to the Moon have fallen by the wayside. However, unmanned lunar missions have continued to be launched by the United States, India and China. Google is even sponsoring a competition called the Google Lunar X Prize. This is intended to promote unmanned lunar exploration, and will award $30 million to the first private team to land a robot on the lunar surface, drive it at least 500 metres, and return video images to the Earth.

*   *   *

Solutions beyond Planet Earth

Both this chapter and the last one have concluded by looking at a potential future energy solution that would rely on industrial access to space. Granted, solar power stations and generating power from lunar helium-3 may remain pipe dreams for some time to come and perhaps indefinitely. However, in the shorter term, access to space for other purposes is increasingly being sought. As a result, more and more private companies are now starting to venture beyond the Earth. Even though the world's media is taking very little interest, right now a second and very commercial space race is really starting to accelerate.

In the longer-term, obtaining resources from space may provide the only possible solution for sustaining an expanding and ever-industrializing mode of human civilization. The final chapter of Part III will therefore look at future space travel as the ultimate means of fuelling humanity's ever-growing appetite for fresh energy and raw material supplies.

15

SPACE TRAVEL

Life survives by evolving to conquer new realms. Millions of years ago some particularly intrepid sea creatures dragged themselves out of the oceans. Millions of years after that, a few of their primate descendants then managed to rise up and walk on two legs. Much later, *Homo sapiens* learnt to build artificial environments. We also invented technologies that allowed us to become masters of the oceans and then the skies.

On 12 April 1961, Yuri Gagarin became the first human in space. In the 50 years since that evolutionary milestone humanity has sidestepped to cross new frontiers. In particular, we have mapped our own genetic code and entered the digital realm. However, with the notable exception of a few fleeting visits to the Moon, so far we have hesitated to journey too far from our motherworld.

Many argue that space travel is a pointless waste of resources. As they protest, why squander billions on rockets when millions of people are starving? Unfortunately, ignoring the poor and the hungry is a charge that can be made against most of the activities of developed nations. Alone among our most expensive technological ventures, space travel may also offer the greatest potential for enhancing the survival of those to come. As has already been noted, life survives by evolving to conquer new realms. Or as Russian space visionary Konstantin Tsiolkovsky once put it, 'Earth is the cradle of the mind, but one cannot live in the cradle forever'.

This chapter looks at the future of space travel. As in the rest of this book, the main focus is on things that are likely to occur in the next 10 to 20 years. But beyond that, this particular chapter will also briefly consider potential developments that may lie many more decades and even centuries ahead. Predicting deep futures is a very uncertain business. Indeed, even some futurists consider it to be unwise. However, only by extending our time horizon can we fully address space travel's two most fundamental questions.

Getting into space and surviving off-planet remain complex and potentially dangerous. 'How will we travel into space?' is therefore the first question for us to consider. With some potential future practicalities outlined, we will then turn to the even more fundamental query of 'why will human civilization increasingly venture in space?'

The First Space Race

In the 1950s and 1960s spacecraft were only operated by superpower governments. The former USSR launched the first artificial satellite, *Sputnik 1*, on the 4th of October 1957. The next month it put a dog into orbit. In 1961, the first cosmonaut then took a space ride in *Vostok 1*.

The USSR's third major space milestone prompted American President John F. Kennedy to kick-start the first Space Race. With a desire to do more than play catch-up, Kennedy set his nation the target of putting a man on the Moon by the end of the decade. This goal was subsequently achieved when Neil Armstrong and Buzz Aldrin set foot on the lunar soil in July 1969.

Into the 1970s, while the Cold War raged, the tension of the Space Race started to recede. The Americans last set foot on the Moon in December 1972. By July 1975, the Space Race then effectively ended when an American Apollo and a Russian Soyuz spacecraft docked in orbit. In 1975, ten countries across Europe – including Germany, France, Italy, Spain and the United Kingdom – also embraced space travel when they set up the European Space Agency (ESA).

The formation of the ESA was a recognition of the need for Europe to be able to launch its own communications satellites. A rocket called Ariane was subsequently developed, and first flew in 1979. Produced by Arianespace – the world's first commercial launch services provider – Ariane 5 rockets continue to put unmanned cargoes into orbit to this day.

The Americans sent human beings to the Moon in Apollo space capsules launched atop mighty Saturn V rockets. The Russians also planned to get there using a space capsule and launch rocket called Soyuz. The first manned Soyuz mission took place in April 1967, although the cosmonaut died on re-entry. However, following this tragic beginning, Soyuz has become the world's longest-standing means of getting both people and cargo into orbit.

By mid-2011, Soyuz had flown over 110 manned space missions and around 25 unmanned ones. The majority of these carried people to or from the MIR space station (which orbited the Earth between 1986 and 2001) or the current International Space Station (ISS). Over 40 years since they began, Soyuz launches also continue. In fact, in 2011 Soyuz spread its wings further when it began operating from the Guiana Space Centre in French Guiana in addition to its native spaceports in Russia.

While the Soyuz programme is still operational, the last Apollo capsule to fly was the one that docked with a Soyuz craft in 1975. Like the Soyuz system, Apollo capsules and the Saturn rockets that launched them were an expendable, one-trip technology. Apollo was also very expensive, with the final cost of the programme reported to the US Congress in 1973 at $25.4 billion dollars. Apollo was subsequently cancelled to make way for the potentially lower cost Space Transportation System (STS). Initiated in January 1972, this flew between 1981 and 2011, and used a reusable launch vehicle (RLV) called the Space Shuttle.

The Space Shuttle Era

The National Aeronautics and Space Administration (NASA) claims that the Space Shuttle was the most complex machine ever built. In total, five Space Shuttles – *Columbia*, *Challenger*, *Discovery*, *Atlantis* and *Endeavour* – undertook 134 missions over a period of 30 years. Sadly two of these ended in tragedy, with the loss of *Challenger* 73 seconds after launch in 1986 and *Columbia* disintegrating on re-entry in 2003.

The STS system consisted of a reusable shuttle orbiter mounted on an expendable external fuel tank. Two reusable solid rocket boosters were then strapped to the external tank's sides. Behind the crew quarters, each Space Shuttle had a cargo bay 18 metres long and 4.6 metres wide. This could be used to transport up to 25 tonnes of cargo into space.

Up until the *Challenger* disaster in 1986, NASA heavily promoted the Space Shuttle as the world's most robust means for getting public and private cargoes into orbit. However, even tragic accidents notwithstanding, the STS program never made space access as cheap or routine as initially intended. Throughout its three decades of operation, many satellites and other items therefore continued to be launched atop conventional rockets as they are to this day.

With the retirement of the Space Shuttle NASA entered a new era. In 2010 President Obama cancelled the ambitious Constellation Program intended to return human beings to the Moon. In tandem he also allocated funding to extend the life of the ISS and gave NASA a remit to develop new long-range spacecraft that may be used for manned missions to the asteroids and Mars around 2025. However, NASA has no immediate replacement for the Space Shuttle. In the medium-term, the ISS is therefore going to be serviced by commercial spacecraft designed and run by the private sector. NASA's operational role in human space flight is subsequently limited to the coordination of private space vendor partnerships under its Commercial Orbital Transportation Services (COTS) program.

In advocating a reliance on private spacecraft, President Obama also put his money where his mouth is. In 2011 alone $500 million of NASA funding was invested to incentivize private companies to develop vehicles capable of carrying non-human cargoes into space. While NASA will be both a customer for these private services and the overseer of safety and other standards, the hope is very much to kick-start the commercial space business. With several companies having already stepped up to the plate, this hope is also already being fulfilled.

A Private Enterprise

The first private enterprise that will provide NASA with a ferry-service to the ISS is SpaceX. As a major funded partner in the COTS programme, the company has a contract for 12 cargo missions to help resupply the space station until 2016. To allow it to fulfil this contract, SpaceX has developed a two-stage launch rocket called the Falcon 9 and a reusable, free-flying, pressurized space capsule called the Dragon. While the initial NASA contact will only use these to ferry cargo, the Dragon capsule has been designed as a 'human capable spacecraft' that could potentially also carry astronauts. Given that the Dragon has a window in its side, it is also pretty clear that transporting humans is SpaceX's ultimate intention.

In addition to its cargo missions for NASA, SpaceX is already advertising fully commercial Dragon flights under the banner 'DragonLab'. This means that any company with the money may now undertake space activities. SpaceX suggests that DragonLab will be used for microgravity research, biotech studies, space physics and relativity experiments, and Earth observations.

On 8 December 2010, SpaceX became the first private business to launch a capsule into space and safely return it to the Earth. Carried on only the second test flight of a Falcon 9 rocket, the first Dragon capsule flawlessly completed two orbits of the planet. It then re-entered the atmosphere to make a perfect, parachute-assisted splashdown in the Pacific ocean. Only on 9 December did SpaceX reveal that the 'secret cargo' bolted to the floor of the Dragon capsule has been a large ring of cheese. Happily, this now-famous dairy product survived its momentous journey intact.

Two further Dragon test flights are slated for late 2011. The first will fly within a few kilometres of the ISS, while the second will actually dock with it. When that happens the private space transportation business will finally have come of age.

Around 20 companies initially submitted tenders to participate in NASA's COTS program. Alongside SpaceX, the other successful bidder to date has been Orbital Sciences Corporation (OSC). This private company has already built more than 569 payload-carrying rockets and 174 satellites, and is therefore already an established player in the private space business.

To supply the ISS, OCS has developed a two-stage rocket called the Taurus II. This is then paired with an independently manoeuvrable, pressurized spacecraft called Cygnus. A Taurus II/Cygnus combination is expected to make its first test-flight in the second half of 2011. At present, OSC has a contract with NASA for eight ISS cargo supply missions.

Another significant player in private space access is Boeing. The aircraft giant is currently operating an unmanned, reusable space plane called the X-37B Orbital Test Vehicle for the US Air Force. Similar to the Space Shuttle but only one quarter of its size, the X-37B has been developed 'to explore reusable vehicle technologies in support of long-term space objectives'. This said, exactly what the US Air Force is using the X-37B for we will probably never know.

Public Access to Space
While the NASA COTS programme may be kick-starting part of the private space business, for some years a few others have also been in on the act. Most notably, in 1996 the Ansari family sponsored the first X Prize. This award was modelled on the Orteig Prize that had been won by Charles Lindbergh in 1927 when he became the first person to fly non-stop from New York to Paris. As its modern counterpart, the Ansari X Prize offered $10 million to the first non-government organization to launch a reusable manned spacecraft into space twice within two weeks.

A total of 26 teams from 7 nations competed for the Ansari X Prize. Between them they also invested more than $100 million in private space ventures. On 4 October 2004, a team led by aerospace designer Burt Rutan and financier Paul Allen won the prize when their craft SpaceShipOne carried pilot Brian Binnie into space only five days after a previous flight. Accomplished in around eight years for a budget of little more than $20 million, this win was a staggering technical achievement that made many people in NASA and elsewhere sit up and think.

SpaceShipOne was built by a company called Scaled Composites. It also used an innovative approach to get into space. The craft was carried into the air under the belly of a manned, twin-turbojet aeroplane called WhiteKnight-One. At high altitude, SpaceShipOne then detached and fired its rocket engine for the second half of its ascent. Having taken its pilot 100 km or more above the Earth, the craft then raised its tail fins into a high-drag shape to slow it during atmospheric re-entry. Finally, with its tail fins lowered, SpaceShipOne made a conventional runway landing. With no fuel tanks or rocket boosters jettisoned at any stage, both SpaceShipOne and its WhiteKnightOne carrier plane were totally reusable craft.

Shortly before its prize-winning success, SpaceShipOne's technology was licensed by entrepreneur Richard Branson. For several years Branson had been following the progress of private space initiatives, and in March 1999 had registered a company called Virgin Galactic. After Space-ShipOne won the Ansari X Prize, Virgin Galactic established a joint venture with Scaled Composites to manufacture a larger version of their spaceplane system. Since that time, Virgin Galactic has been advertising itself as the 'world's first commercial space line'. It has also started to take bookings from private individuals who want to journey into space.

The first of Virgin Galactic's SpaceShipTwo spacecraft and WhiteKnightTwo carrier aircraft have already been built. Christened *Virgin Mothership Enterprise* and *Eve*, these are headquartered in New Mexico at Spaceport America, the world's first commercial spaceport. A rigorous series of test flights has also already begun. Should these prove successful, commercial spaceflights will commence within the next few years.

SpaceShipTwo will carry six passengers and two pilots about 100 km above the Earth. There they will experience weightlessness and be able to view their home planet from space. The total flight time is expected to be about 2.5 hours, with about five minutes spent floating weightless in space. Prior to their out-of-this-world trip, all passengers will have to undertake two days of G-force and safety training.

More than 400 people have already paid a $20,000 deposit toward a $200,000 Virgin Galactic ticket. In time, Richard Branson hopes that this astronomical price tag will fall. Virgin Galactic is also planning to develop its spaceplane system so that it can be used to launch small satellites. Perhaps not surprisingly, Virgin has struck an agreement with NASA to collaborate on the development of future manned space technology.

The Cost of Space Access

Getting into space using a rocket with any disposable components remains an expensive business. NASA used to cite the cost of launching a Space Shuttle at 'about $450 million per mission'. However, this figure ignored the price of the shuttles themselves and many other ongoing expenditures. With these taken into account, the total cost of the STS programme was about $174 billion for 134 flights. This works out at around $1.3 billion per mission, and means that Space Shuttle cargo cost about $52,000 per kilogram to get into orbit.

NASA will be paying SpaceX $1.6 billion for its first 12 Dragon supply missions to the ISS. With each capsule carrying up to six tonnes of cargo, this puts Dragon launch costs at about $22,000 per kilogram. Given that most satellite launch companies currently charge about $25,000 per kilogram, this price is not bad for cargo carried in a pressurized, dockable spacecraft. However, it is still hardly cheap.

With its revolutionary spaceplane system, Virgin Galactic is lowering the cost of space access further still. If we assume that an average person weights 100 kilograms, then Virgin's price of $200,000 a ticket equates to a launch cost of $2,000 per kilogram, or less than one-tenth of that charged by SpaceX. Granted, this is not an entirely fair comparison given that Virgin Galactic is carrying passengers to the edge of space rather than docking a capsule with another vessel in orbit. However, one of the main reasons for Virgin placing a 100 km ceiling on its flights is to avoid passengers having to suffer very substantial G-forces in their ascent. Using a descendant of SpacePlaneTwo to supply the International Space Station is therefore a potential technical possibility.

Even with continual innovations from SpaceX, Orbital Sciences Corporation, Virgin Galactic and probably many others, travelling into space using a rocket or spaceplane is going to remain expensive for many years to come. It is therefore hardly surprising that some scientists have suggested a radically alternative mechanism for getting into orbit. Their idea is to stretch a cable from the ground up to an orbital space platform. People and cargo would then travel to and from space using an elevator.

Going Up! The Rise of the Space Elevator

A space elevator may initially sound both very sensible and at the same time an absolutely crazy idea. It is, after all, a concept right out of the books of legendary science-fiction writers like Arthur C. Clarke. Building a space elevator would also be a very challenging engineering exercise. Nevertheless, it is likely to become a technical and practical possibility sometime next decade.

Figure 15.1 illustrates a possible space elevator design. Here a cable or 'tether' connected to a ground station rises up to a platform in geostationary orbit about 35,000 km above sea level. The cable then extends way beyond the orbital platform to a counterweight that keeps it taut and its centre of gravity motionless relative to the Earth. As launching a large counterweight into space would prove prohibitively expensive, a small asteroid would probably be captured and used for this purpose. At the other end of the cable, the most likely position for a ground station would be a high altitude location somewhere on the equator.

The most difficult part of building a space elevator would be manufacturing the cable. This tether line would need to be strong enough to support its own weight, as well as the weight of the lift carriage or 'climber' that would travel up and down its enormous length. The cable would also have to be corrosion resistant and capable of withstanding the extreme cold of the upper atmosphere. Until recently, no material existed that could be used to make such a cable. However, with developments in nanotechnology, the future manufacture of a space elevator cable is now a technical possibility.

Specifically, a space elevator cable could be made from carbon nanotubes. As mentioned in Chapter 7, these hexagonal lattices of carbon atoms are about 117 times stronger than steel. A space elevator cable spun from carbon nanotube nanofibres could therefore support its own weight all the way up into orbit. At present carbon nanotube manufacturers do not have the expertise and production capacity to make a space elevator cable. However, it may well become possible by about 2020.

Even with a ground station, cable, orbital platform and counterweight all in place, the problem of building a space elevator's lift carriage would not be insignificant. Because

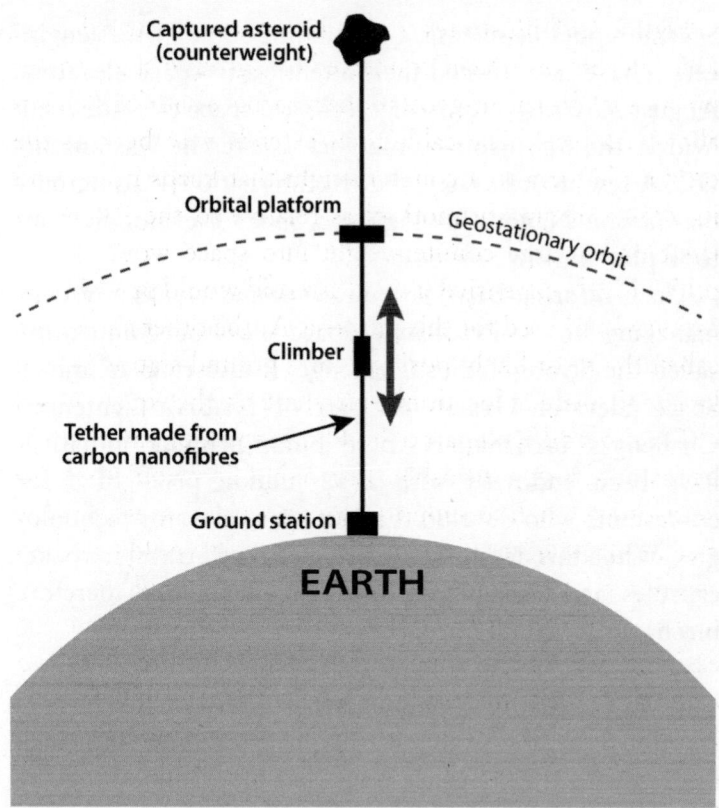

Figure 15.1: Design for a space elevator

the cable would be stationary, the carriage would require its own, internal climber mechanism. In turn this would need to be self-powered – possibly using solar cells or a tiny nuclear reactor. Alternatively, power may be beamed to the climber using lasers or microwaves.

Designs for space elevators have been proposed for over a century. In fact, Konstantin Tsiolkovsky first advocated a free-standing tower reaching from the surface of Earth to geostationary orbit as early as 1895. However, in recent years the idea has started to be taken far more seriously.

Several reputable scientists – including some NASA engineers – have now turned their attention to space elevators. August 2010 saw a three-day technical space elevator event held at the Microsoft Conference Center in Washington, DC. A few months later, the 4th International Conference on Carbon Nanotechnology and Space Elevator Systems took place in Luxembourg.

The California-based Spaceward Foundation is now even managing an X Prize-style space elevator competition called the Strong Tether Challenge. It also runs an annual Space Elevator Games. As part of NASA's Centennial Challenges programme, these pump-priming initiatives have been endowed with a $2 million prize fund for contestants who develop the best space elevator technologies. While this decade's space pioneers will travel in rocket capsules and spaceplanes, those to come may therefore mechanically climb into orbit.

The Wanderlust of *Homo sapiens*

As noted at the start of this chapter, any informed discussion of future space travel has to examine both the 'how' and the 'why'. The previous sections have already detailed the most likely methods of near-future space access. The final pages of this chapter will therefore consider why human beings will increasingly travel into space.

As many episodes of *Star Trek* remind us, one reason to leave the Earth is 'to boldly go where no one has gone before'. Curiosity and a spirit of adventure are indeed powerful driving forces. Some future space ventures will therefore probably be justified purely on this basis. Most obviously, a political crusade to conquer new frontiers is likely to be the motivation behind the first manned mission to Mars. The progress being made by commercial space businesses like SpaceX now also means that our capability to undertake such missions at reasonable cost is advancing all the time. A human footfall on Mars by 2030 therefore remains a possibility.

The desire to explore a new frontier by becoming one of the first space tourists is also already driving investment in Virgin Galactic as the world's first spaceline. Over the next decade, space tourism also looks pretty certain to become an important sector of the growing space industry. By the end of the decade, the first space tourism reality TV show must also be on the cards.

While wanderlust alone will drive a certain proportion of the expanding industry, a second driver will be the increasing demand to get more satellites and other things into orbit. Whether we think about it or not, most of us fuel the demand for an expanded space industry every time we make a phone call or data connection that makes use of a satellite link. We also create a demand for increased space access every time we watch satellite television, when we view a Google Earth map or other satellite image, or when we use any kind of GPS device. Amazing as it may initially seem, the use of satellite communications and satellite data is now part of many people's everyday lives.

For many years satellites have also been relied on to help locate oil and mineral deposits, as well as to study global warming. Aboard the ISS, new drugs and materials also continue to be developed in zero gravity. Anybody arguing against increased space access is therefore arguing – perhaps rightly – against an expansion of the technological mechanisms of human civilization. For example, without more communications satellites, many people in remote locations may never be provided with Internet and telephone services.

As we have seen in previous chapters, space access may

also prove vital to help stabilize our climate and maintain our energy supplies. As discussed in Chapter 2, decades hence we could be using giant orbital solar sails to shade the Earth against global warming. Or as detailed in Chapter 13, solar power satellites may in future beam down electrical energy from space. As we saw in the last chapter, future nuclear fusion power plants may even be fuelled with helium-3 mined from the surface of the Moon. Centuries from today, and as the resource depletion outlined in Chapter 5 really begins to bite, obtaining raw materials from space will also become a survival necessity.

Embracing Thermodynamic Reality

If human civilization is to continue for many more thousands of years then there are only two options on the table. The first is for a very significant decrease in the human population. Alternatively, a second and more hopeful solution will require an ever-expanding human race to continue its age-old tradition of seeking new resources from afar.

The need for humanity to constantly gather resources from further afield is explained by a physical certainty called the Second Law of Thermodynamics. This tells us that all so-termed 'closed systems' will degenerate unless they are opened up to receive external resources. To explain why this is the case, let us pause for just one paragraph to conduct a simple thought experiment.

Imagine we have a rabbit and a large box. Seal the rabbit in the box and it is now trapped in a closed system. So what will now happen? Well, as we can all imagine, if the box is airtight the rabbit will rapidly asphyxiate. However, even if we suppose that air can get in, the rabbit will still soon die from a lack of food and water. We could more kindly imagine our rabbit to be sealed in a very large box with ample air holes, a large water bowl and an enormous pile of lettuce. This would certainly ease our hypothetical animal's plight. However, even this would only delay the inevitable. In the real world outside of our thought experiment, rabbits in boxes – and we tend to call them hutches – only survive because they receive a constant supply of food and water from outside the tiny, closed environment in which they are forced to live.

So how does our rabbit-in-a-box thought experiment relate to the inevitability of space travel? Well, on a much grander scale, the whole of planet Earth is a closed system just like our poor rabbit's imaginary cage. Early empires like those of Ancient Egypt arose on parts of the planet where natural resources were plentiful. But as these first, great civilizations expanded, they had to travel and trade further and further afield to meet their growing resource requirements. For centuries this was not a problem as there were always new regions of the planet to plunder. However, as we saw in Chapter 5, today this is no longer the case. As a very stark reminder of this, just reflect on the fact that both the United States and Europe are no longer self-sufficient in food, basic raw materials or energy supplies.

Within a century or two at most the human race is going to start hitting the hard limits of the closed system of Planet Earth. To survive in their billions, future human beings will therefore have to venture into space to seek fresh resources. Such resources are initially likely to include raw materials from the Moon and the asteroids. However, in time, even these relatively close and abundant new supply-lands will become depleted. As the centuries and millennia turn, delving deeper and deeper into space will therefore become inevitable.

Fortunately, at present, space-claimed resources are not

needed to sustain mass civilization. However, in evolution-ary terms it will not be that long before the human race is in the same position as our hypothetical rabbit as she mournfully eyes the last few bits of lettuce in her box. The only difference is that while our thought-rabbit cannot open and escape her cage, by developing space travel the human race can provide itself with the option of expanding further into the solar system. Venturing into space is as natural an evolutionary process as walking on two legs or crawling out of the oceans. It is, after all, unlikely in the extreme that some passing extraterrestrials will stop by and dump a load of new raw materials in humanity's hutch.

*   *   *

Our Evolution in Space

As has been argued throughout this chapter, life survives by evolving to conquer new realms. Given the incredible propensity of humanity to survive, we can therefore be pretty certain that our distant descendants will travel deep into space. At first thought, it is therefore perhaps surprising that in the last few decades space travel technolo-gies have advanced so little.

There are many reasons – not least financial and technological – that have for some time been constraining travel beyond the Earth. However, perhaps the most fundamental is that the vacuum of space is not a natural human habitat. Before space travel becomes a common-place activity, some evolution of our very selves may therefore be required.

Centuries ago, we needed ships to become masters of the oceans. We will clearly once again need new travel technologies to become true masters of space. However, in addition, at least some of us will probably also need re-engineered bodies capable of undertaking deep space missions. The development of space travel may therefore be waiting as much for the medical application of new genetic, cybernetic and nanotechnologies as it is for the invention of next-generation space capsules, spaceplanes and space elevators.

When our ancestors crawled out of the oceans they had to evolve to cope and then thrive in a new environment. We should therefore not necessarily believe that humans in their current form will become tomorrow's most successful space mariners. The evolutionary leap from our first planet to the vacuum of space is, after all, at least as great as that from water to dry land.

As will be discussed in Part V, *Homo sapiens* is not a static, finished creation. Rather, as highlighted by many of the developments outlined in this book, Humanity 2.0 is waiting not that far around the corner. The most significant evolutionary role of Humanity 2.0 may also be to make the leap from motherworld to void in search of future resources.

When our distant ancestors left the oceans they did not take it with them in water suits. Rather, they adapted to a new set of circumstances. For life to thrive on land, lungs had to replace gills. For many decades we will no doubt venture successfully into space by taking our atmosphere with us. However, with air and water apparently in such short supply beyond the Earth, in time it is perhaps inevitable that we will have to evolve to rely on something else. For example, solar energy is abundant throughout the solar system. The most successful far future space travellers may therefore be those that can sustain their bodies purely using solar radiation.

To this point in history, all of the probes and space rovers that have ventured farthest from the Earth have been inorganic mechanisms reliant on photovoltaic solar power.

Many future space explorers are also likely to be intelligent robots of one kind of another. As we shall consider in Part V, the line between human beings and artificial, cybernetic technology is undoubtedly something that will continue to blur. However, before we contemplate such a profound evolutionary convergence, we first need to examine the probable development of artificial mechanisms themselves. The next five chapters will therefore return us to some far closer tomorrows as we explore the future of computing and inorganic life.

Part IV

COMPUTING AND INORGANIC LIFE

16

CLOUD COMPUTING

The technological phenomenon of the last 30 years has been computing and digital communications. The IBM PC was launched in 1981 and paired with the first version of Windows in 1985. Six years later Tim Berners-Lee invented the World Wide Web. As we all know, things then really started to accelerate.

In early 2011, InternetWorldStats.com reported that there are more than two billion users of the Internet. This figure compares to just over 16 million users in 1995. Of the two billion people now online, over 800 million regularly use a social networking site. Most businesses now also use the Internet, with JP Morgan reporting global e-commerce to be worth $571 billion in 2010 and expected to exceed $1 trillion by 2014. At least across the developed world, practically all forms of industrial, social and cultural activity have now been permeated by digital media. Or to put it another way, as a species we increasingly inhabit both the real world and cyberspace.

Human civilization has always relied on the exchange of information. Whether the latest innovation was speech, writing or some new form of electronic communication, those who have understood and exploited the latest technology have always been best placed to make their mark on the world. With our mass connection to the Internet now a reality, it is therefore reasonable to ask what will happen next.

For many years, change has been the only constant in the digital realm. Predicting the future of computing beyond the next generation of processor, operating system or mobile phone is therefore a tricky business. Some would even argue it to be a futile pursuit. But foolhardy or otherwise, the next five chapters do attempt to predict where computing and related developments are headed. We will start with an examination of the latest online innovation known as 'cloud computing'. Against the backdrop of this critical foundation, we will then explore some potentially related developments in artificial intelligence and augmented reality. Stepping further into the future, there then follows a little chapter about next-generation quantum computers that will store and process data using sub-atomic particles. Finally, to bring Part IV to a close, no book on future studies would be complete without a chapter on robots.

The Next Computing Revolution

Computing is just starting to undergo its next revolution. This time it is called 'cloud computing', and is where software applications, processing power and data storage are accessed over the Internet. In the last few decades, computing may have become a mainstream part of our working and domestic lives. However, even with the massive uptake of the Internet, almost all computing resources have remained local. What this means is that computer applications, processing power and data storage have been located close or fairly close to their user.

As cloud computing takes hold, most computing re-sources will be hosted on the Internet rather than located in individual businesses, homes or pockets. Like most futurists, I do not often make definitive, date-specific predictions. Nevertheless, I would place a pretty strong bet that, by 2020, significant local computing resources will be very rare indeed. The future of computing is very much in the cloud.

Figure 16.1 illustrates the difference between traditional and cloud computing. As you can see, in the top of the figure local software is installed and data is stored on most personal computers. Within companies, most users also access business applications, data storage and processing power from a local data centre. Under this traditional computing model, Internet usage is confined to accessing information from websites and exchanging e-mails and file attachments. (Note that in the figure the Internet is illustrated by a cloud symbol. This has been common practice for years, and is what has given cloud computing its name.)

In the lower half of Figure 16.1 we see the brave new world of cloud computing. Here the local company data centre has been closed. Software applications and data are also no longer installed and stored on a user's own computing device. Rather, all personal and business applications, data storage and most processing power are accessed from the Internet cloud.

The scenarios shown in Figure 16.1 do represent the two most extreme positions, with a hybrid model somewhere in the middle being most likely at least in the short- and medium-term. However, the race to embrace cloud computing really is now taking hold.

For example, in March 2010 Microsoft CEO Steve Ballmer claimed to be 'betting the company' on cloud computing. Three months later, Microsoft launched online versions of its Word, Excel, PowerPoint and OneNote applications under the banner Office Web Apps. In early

TRADITIONAL COMPUTING TODAY

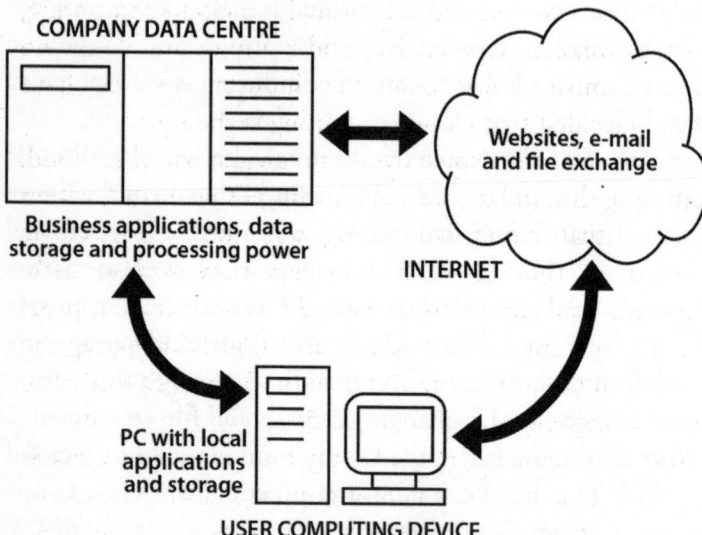

CLOUD COMPUTING IN 2020

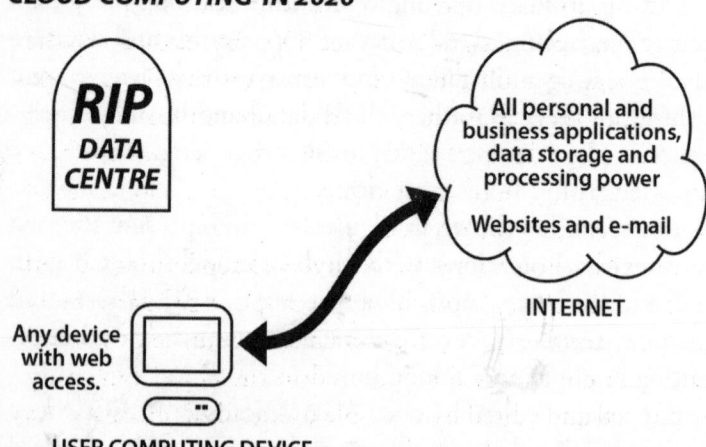

Figure 16.1: Traditional and cloud computing

2011 Microsoft then released Office 365 to bring together the cloud and traditional versions of its product range. Google has also invested very heavily in cloud computing, as have Amazon, Apple, IBM and many others. Make no mistake, most major computer industry players have already decided that cloud computing is the future.

Businesses are also starting to switch to the cloud. Reflecting this, in January 2011 leading IT analysts Gartner reported that cloud computing was the 'top strategic priority' of the 2,014 IT managers they had recently surveyed. Gartner's *Reimagining IT* report also revealed that 3 per cent of businesses are already running the majority of their IT in the cloud, with 43 per cent expecting to be 'mainly cloud based' by 2015.

So why, you may ask, would any individual or organization want to switch to cloud computing? Well, one of the reasons is that cloud computing is device independent. Many people are now starting to use a wide range of computing devices, including desktop and laptop PCs, tablets, smartphones and Internet TVs. By embracing the cloud, users of multiple devices can gain the freedom to access all of their applications and data regardless of which computer they happen to be using. It is indeed for this reason that this book is being written in a cloud word processor called Google Docs.

As well as allowing people to always keep individual and company data at hand, cloud computing additionally facilitates collaboration. Documents, spreadsheets and all manner of data created and stored in the cloud can easily be accessed and edited by multiple users simultaneously. As cloud computing takes hold, the days of e-mailing attachments back and forth and collating changes from multiple authors will therefore become a thing of the past.

Cloud computing is also levelling the playing field by

enabling all computer users to access all types of application almost regardless of their budget. This is because some cloud computing applications are free, with the remainder provided on a subscription basis.

Under the traditional computing model, only large companies could afford to purchase the most sophisticated software due to its high initial purchase price. In contrast, users of cloud computing services pay only for the software applications, storage and processing power that they actually use on a pay-as-you-go basis. For example, a company called Zoho now offers a wide range of database and other business applications that can be purchased monthly. The exact fee paid then corresponds to the amount of data stored, transaction levels or the number of users who need to access an application in a particular month.

SaaS, PaaS and IaaS

All manner of cloud computing services are becoming available, with the market still very much in a state of flux. This said, most cloud services fall into three fairly distinct categories.

The first and most straightforward cloud computing category is 'software as a service' (SaaS). This is effectively a 'take it or leave it' form of cloud computing where users run existing, off-the-shelf online applications. SaaS applications include the Office Web Apps and Google Docs online office suites. However, a wide range of creative SaaS applications are also already available. These include some great music composition and audio-editing tools from Aviary.com, online photo editors from Pixlr.com and Picnik.com, and even online video editors from the likes of Jaycut.com and Pixorial.com.

Business SaaS applications – such as accounting, sales,

marketing, human resource and project management software – are also widely available. Key vendors here include Employease.com, Netsuite.com, Salesforce.com and Zoho.com. Just visit any of these sites to get a feel of what is on offer. Surprising as it may seem, pretty much anything that most individuals and companies do with local software can now be accomplished online with an SaaS application.

SaaS applications are all that most domestic computer users are likely to require. However, many companies need to develop and run their own specific software applications and may therefore find SaaS restrictive. Because of this, there are two further categories of cloud computing known as 'platform as a service' and 'infrastructure as a service'.

Platform as a service (PaaS) provides its users with online software development tools and hosting facilities. Companies can therefore use PaaS to build their own, bespoke business systems. Alternatively, anybody with a good idea can use PaaS to develop their own new SaaS application and deliver it to the world.

Several companies already provide PaaS offerings. These include Google (who have a PaaS product called App Engine), Microsoft (who have a PaaS product called Azure), and Salesforce (with a PaaS product called Force.com). Just one pioneering adopter of PaaS is EasyJet, with the airline now running a large number of its business systems in Azure.

Infrastructure as a service (IaaS) is the last cloud computing category and is even less restrictive than PaaS. Whereas PaaS allows users to create their own, new cloud applications, IaaS allows companies to migrate all of their existing applications from their own data centre to a cloud vendor. IaaS is therefore a very significant cloud computing category.

At present, one of the largest IaaS vendors is Amazon.

The online retailer offers an extensive suite of IaaS provision, with its headline IaaS product called 'Elastic Compute Cloud' (EC2). This allows anybody to purchase online processing capacity quite literally by the hour. EC2 customers set up Amazon Machine Images (AMIs) that contain their applications. These AMIs can then be deployed to 1 or 1,000 or indeed any number of online virtual servers within minutes.

A company with only occasional large processing jobs can now rent the required number of EC2 virtual servers for just a few hours each time they are needed. This means that it can dispense with a large, local data centre in which most of its own computers would usually sit idle. Amazon indeed describe EC2 as 'elastic' because it allows customers to increase or decrease their computing requirements in minutes. EC2 virtual servers are also available in a wide range of specifications. At the time of writing, the least powerful costs just $0.02 an hour, and the most powerful $2.48. Anybody keen to experiment can even sign-up to obtain their first 750 hours of server time absolutely free of charge.

A significant by-product of SaaS, PaaS and IaaS development has been the creation of online marketplaces for cloud services. While Google, Zoho, Salesforce and others are trying to peddle their own wares, each of these companies also offers one or more marketplaces from which any developer can deliver their own cloud offering. For example, the Google Apps Marketplace offers thousands of SaaS applications that directly integrate with a business software suite called Google Apps. In the future, a few companies – and in particular Microsoft, Google, Apple, IBM and Amazon – may be very likely to operate most cloud computing data centres. However, due to the development of online marketplaces, many small companies will nevertheless have at least as great a chance as they do today to develop niche products and get them to market. To a very large extent, the cloud will therefore reward those with technical and creative ability over those with financial might.

The Only Show in Town

Cloud services like Amazon's EC2 are turning computing into an on-demand utility much like electricity. By the end of the decade, most companies will also have little choice but to plug in and obtain their computing power from the cloud. This is because cloud computing will become essential to remain competitive, to be green and to facilitate innovation.

As already noted, companies that cloud compute can free themselves of the costs incurred in purchasing and maintaining their own data centre. Typically, businesses that have already switched to the cloud have obtained IT cost savings of at least 50 per cent. Significant reductions in software development schedules have also been achieved. Salesforce, for example, has independently audited figures that show how its customers have used its PaaS offering to build and run applications five times faster and at about half the cost of using traditional computing methods.

Beyond immediate cost savings, cloud computing can also enable companies to focus less on running IT and more on their core business. There is also a strong historical precedent for this. As noted by Nicholas Carr in his excellent book *The Big Switch*, around a century ago most companies generated their own electricity. However, as a reliable national electricity grid became available, it was soon no longer efficient for companies to generate electricity in-house as they could not match the economies of scale available to national power companies.

Already the cloud is becoming the centralized power plant of the Information Age. Just as, between about 1900 and 1930, most companies switched from generating their own power to obtaining it from a national grid, so this decade most companies will transition from local to cloud computing. A typical cloud computing data centre will run its servers at about 80 per cent capacity. In contrast, today many company data centres struggle to achieve a 30 per cent server utilization. For most businesses, switching to the cloud will therefore rapidly become a cost-reduction no-brainer.

The Green Cloud

The second major factor already driving the uptake of cloud computing is the opportunity to use less energy. As revealed in the last paragraph, cloud vendors rarely have large numbers of computers that are drawing electricity but waiting for something to process. In turn this means that the carbon footprint of a unit of cloud processing power is usually less than that of a traditional, in-company server.

Cloud computing providers are also very much aware of their potential green credentials. For example, Netsuite advertises that in 2008 its customers saved $61 million in energy bills by switching to its cloud services. Entire countries are also keen to get in on the act. Most notably, Iceland is planning to exploit its freezing cold temperatures.

Around half of the energy used by a typical data centre is used to keep server computers cool. It therefore makes sense to try to locate as much computer power as possible in locations that are naturally cold. In preparation for a cloud computing 'cold rush', the Icelandic government has therefore begun the construction of a number of massive cloud computing data centres. Located just outside Reykjavik, these will be equipped with high-speed Internet links to both Europe and the United States. They will also be naturally cooled, as well as powered by locally abundant geothermal energy.

Iceland's green cloud computing services are likely to prove an attractive and even essential business proposition for many organizations. However, Iceland is unlikely to be the only future provider of green cloud computing power. For example, as mentioned in Chapter 12, in April 2009 Google was awarded a patent for a 'floating platform-mounted computer data centre comprising a plurality of computing units, a sea-based electrical generator [and] one or more sea-water cooling units'.

Google's idea is to locate cloud computing servers on a vessel moored a few miles from the coast. The servers will then be powered by wave energy converters manufactured by Pelamis Wave Power. Google has calculated that an array of wave energy converters spread over a square kilometre will produce the 30 megawatts of electricity necessary to run a floating data centre. A seawater-freshwater heat exchanger will then keep its computers cool by turning the ocean into a giant heatsink.

In addition to facilitating green data centre energy savings, cloud computing will also allow many end computer users to consume less electricity. Today, a typical desktop computer with locally installed applications consumes between 80 and 250 watts of electricity. In contrast, users who switch to cloud services are often able to transition to far more energy-efficient cloud access devices that use maybe 40 watts or less. Such 'net-top' or 'thin-client' computers are usually based around a low-energy processor such as Intel's Atom. In addition to being highly energy efficient, they also consume far less desk space and hardly make a sound.

Already some companies are adopting cloud computing

in large part to obtain the energy savings that can be reaped from thin-client end-user hardware. Not least, Canadian vendor ThinDesk has shown that, by adopting cloud services and low-power desktop computers, its customers can achieve energy reduction savings of up to 80 per cent.

The Next-Generation Cloud

As well as providing the lure and economic necessity of reduced costs and improved green credentials, cloud computing will increasingly become essential for companies that are seeking to innovate. As we shall see in the next two chapters, future developments in artificial intelligence and augmented reality will depend heavily on cloud computing. Companies that want to be part of the next generation business landscape will therefore have to adopt cloud computing services in the same way that most businesses in the 1990s raced to put up a website.

Already cloud services like Google Translate allow documents to be translated from one language to another in real-time. By about 2015, the real-time translation of spoken language will also be a core cloud computing service. People will therefore expect automatic language translation to be part of every software application, telephone system and online service they use. For most companies, the only way to provide this kind of service will be to use cloud-based software and to widely adopt cloud computing.

As we shall see in the next chapter, online vision recognition is also going to be a very major cloud development. In fact, the first visual search systems – such as the Google Goggles smartphone app – are already starting to become available. Fairly soon, these will use cloud-based artificial intelligence to recognize and obtain information on most objects and people in view. Future augmented reality systems will then be able to overlay such information on our real-time view of the world.

Today the cloud and physical reality may be two very different realms. However, as we shall explore in detail in Chapter 18, future augmented reality systems will allow the cloud and the real world to converge. Once again this will be a development that few companies will be able to ignore.

The Entertainment Cloud

As the last few sections have indicated, cloud computing is going to be Big Business. The potential risk of storing and processing data online does continue to worry many people. However, the potential cost savings, green pay-backs and opportunities for innovation are simply too significant for cloud computing to be ignored. Today, even IT managers who fear for their jobs are starting to accept the inevitability of cloud computing.

Away from the business world, cloud computing is also strongly taking hold. Indeed, it can be argued that it was private individuals who first embraced the cloud. Facebook's half-a-billion users regularly upload and share online content, while every week more than a billion new tweets are posted on Twitter. Both Facebook and Twitter now have more users than most countries have citizens. The influence of these cloud platforms and their potential development therefore cannot be ignored.

In addition to personal communications, audio visual entertainment is also moving into the cloud. While a merger of television and the Internet has been slowly taking place for well over a decade, this media convergence is now rapidly accelerating. Each day YouTube plays out over two billion video views. The delivery of TV over the Internet is also becoming mainstream. For example, in 2010 about 1.3 billion programme views were delivered by the BBC iPlayer.

As television continues to merge with the cloud, more programmes will become interactive. See a product you like in a TV show and you will be able to click on it to find out more information or to make a purchase. Such interactivity will not even always have to be added by programme makers. Instead, cloud vision recognition systems will be able to identify anything we click on in an online video stream and generate relevant links.

The mass delivery of video from the cloud will also give rise to a whole new breed of online celebrity. In the same way that any programmer can now create an SaaS application and achieve global distribution in an online marketplace, so anybody with some basic technology and a little talent can now become a star. This is indeed already starting to happen. For example, Justine Ezarik – otherwise known online as iJustine – has already managed to obtain over 250 million video views across her five YouTube channels. Even a few years ago the opportunity to achieve this level of personal exposure simply did not exist.

Another major entertainment-related development will be the delivery of cloud-based gaming. Today, most computer games – including the majority of multi-player games that link people together over the Internet – are installed and run on local hardware. For a great 3D gaming experience, players therefore need a powerful computer or console. However, in the future this will no longer be the case.

Just as SaaS alternatives to local word processors, databases and video editors are already available, so too are cloud-based games. Here the game runs on a server in a cloud data centre. The gameplay is then delivered to a potentially low-power computer over the web. As a result, by the middle of this decade it is very likely that highly complex, photorealistic, 3D computer games will be playable on virtually any kind of computer, including most tablets and smartphones.

Already a company called OnLive is running high performance games on its cloud servers. Its customers then access these games using an OnLive Microconsole connected to a television or else an entry-level desktop computer. With the software running out in the cloud, gone are the days when a user had to upgrade their PC to play the latest title. As OnLive's founder and CEO Steve Perlman explains:

> With OnLive we've cleared the last remaining hurdle for the video games industry: effective online distribution. By putting the value back into the games themselves and removing the reliance on expensive, short-lived hardware, we are dramatically shifting the economics of the industry.

* * *

Our Future in the Cloud

Cloud computing is already starting to have a fundamental impact on the human condition. To some people's alarm, a great many people are now becoming members of a digital swarm that has become addicted to binary data. As we shall see in the final part of this book, the cloud is therefore a critical driver of our evolution into Humanity 2.0.

Given the pressures on planetary resources highlighted in Part I, it is perhaps a very good thing that people are starting to value digital resources as much or even more than physical things. No longer do our personal libraries of books, games, music and videos always have to consume mountains of paper or plastic boxes and disks. Computing may not on the face of it be an inherently green activity. However, the more we move around digital data rather than transporting physical things, the more environmentally friendly and resource-positive computing and its application will become.

While cloud computing may bring with it the benefits of 'dematerialization', there remain many who worry that our collective migration into cyberspace will have increasingly negative implications. For a start, a few very large companies are likely to host most of our data. The trust placed in these companies will therefore be as least as great as that we are forced to vest in governments. The potential implications of power outages, security breaches and cyber terrorism will also be almost unimaginable. This said, we have lived with and controlled the unimaginable threat of nuclear Armageddon for over half a century. Just because cloud computing could enable yet more potentially very bad things to happen therefore does not have to imply that they will. For decades risk management has been a critical aspect of modern civilization.

Another potential danger of the cloud is that it may be used to monitor our activities. Almost every Internet user now leaves an indelible trail each time they visit a website or send an e-mail, let alone when they make an online purchase or post something on Facebook. Many smart-phone users are also starting to surrender their real-time location to the cloud. By the end of the decade it is additionally likely that most CCTV and other cameras will be interfaced to the cloud and monitored by sophisticated vision recognition systems. As a consequence, the cloud is increasingly likely to know our past and present location. The cloud could therefore on the face of it be considered a drain on personal freedom.

There are, however, already many strong signals that our mass, digital interconnection will have some very positive effects. For example, while the cloud may be used for surveillance, this in turn could improve personal safety and law enforcement. The spread of democracy across the Middle East in 2011 following a number of 'Facebook revolutions' is also another example of how the cloud empowers far more than it enslaves.

Cloud computing is also enabling the growth of 'crowdsourcing'. This refers to the use of the Internet to create value from the activities of a great many people. Crowdsourcing subsequently allows global citizen thinkers to amalgamate their brainpower in order to solve problems and achieve results beyond the capabilities of any single individual.

Already there are a great many promising crowdsourcing initiatives. Perhaps most famously, crowdsourcing has enabled the creation of OpenOffice and several other free 'open source' software applications. The RepRap and Fab@Home 3D printers mentioned in Chapter 6 are also the result of crowdsourcing initiatives, with all of their intellectual property created and shared in the cloud. There are also several projects already crowdsourcing the design and construction of open source vehicles. These include OScar (theoscarproject.org), which is part of the Open Source Green Vehicle Project (OSGV). Over at openprosthetics.org, a team is also using the cloud to help crowdsource the production of improved prosthetic limbs.

Web guru Tim O'Reilly was one of the first to describe how the Internet can be used to 'pool collective intelligence'. As the Cloud Computing Revolution gathers pace, this is also an opportunity for us all. By embracing cloud computing we all do surrender a little bit of ourselves. However, in return we are provided with the opportunity to become part of a single, great, digital entity that may develop the collective intelligence necessary to deal with those critical challenges outlined in Part I of this book. Exactly what form such collective intelligence may take is a very great question indeed. This said, as we shall see in the next chapter, we can already be fairly certain that some of the future collective intelligence to be pooled in the cloud will be artificial rather than human.

17
ARTIFICIAL INTELLIGENCE

In 2010 *Wired* magazine co-founder Kevin Kelly published a great book called *What Technology Wants*. In this he argued that sophisticated technological systems – and in particular computers and computer networks – are starting to exhibit almost biological behaviour. For example, computer viruses are able to self-replicate, while Internet search engines have the capability to learn. In some respects, a whole new form of artificial life is therefore starting to emerge with a new kind of 'artificial' intelligence.

For many years computers have been better than human beings at completing some tasks. For example, if I asked you to wander into a large library, look through all of the books and prepare a list of all the references to a particular topic, then this would take you an age. If I added an additional requirement for your list to be categorized according to the popularity of each entry, then you would likely be driven insane. However, as we all know, Google, Yahoo! or Bing can quite easily plough through millions of information sources and create such a list in seconds.

One of the really big questions raised in Kelly's book is 'how many neurons do we need to make a mind?' His inference is that we do not need very many and that intelligent, inorganic life is either just about with us or will arrive pretty soon. I very much agree with Kelly that in the next few decades computers will become very smart indeed. However, whether computers will be 'intelligent' – let alone able to 'think' – will probably always remain a matter of philosophy.

The Folly of the Turing Test

Since 1950 computer scientists have used a benchmark called the Turing Test as the gauge for the creation of an artificial general intelligence (AGI). In this test a person is required to communicate with somebody else using a text chat window. The somebody else concerned is in fact the potential AGI being evaluated. The Turing Test is then passed if the person communicating with this artificial entity is unable to fathom whether or not they are exchanging messages with a computer or another human being.

On the face of it the Turing Test may appear eminently sensible. However, I would argue that it is a very biased and unreasonable artificial intelligence (AI) hurdle. This is because the Turing Test makes the unrealistic assumption that all intelligence must appear to be human.

After human beings, dolphins are widely regarded as the most intelligent species on the planet. Yet dolphin intelligence is clearly very different from human intelligence. Even if a dolphin had the same mental capacity as a human being, it would therefore be very surprising if it could ever pass the Turing Test. Dolphins live in water and do not have a human anatomy. Nobody should therefore seriously expect a hypothetical dolphin with a human level of intellect to think and communicate exactly like a person. It is therefore quite bemusing that so many people still believe in an AI benchmark that requires a future computer system to imitate a human.

Some notable and informed individuals do believe that the Turing Test will be passed within a matter of decades. For example, renowned futurist Ray Kurzweil suggests that Turing-capable AGIs will arrive by 2029, while UK cybernetics guru Professor Kevin Warwick believes that super-intelligent AGIs will be sharing the Earth with us by 2050. However, such individuals are in the minority, with most cutting-edge computer scientists not expecting the Turing Test to be passed for a very long time indeed. With this view I also heartily agree. But far more importantly, and as you have probably guessed, I would also suggest that passing the Turing Test does not matter one jot.

Any future AGI is likely to be a sleepless, disembodied entity that will be sustained by electricity rather than food, water and oxygen. From its moment of conception, a future AGI is also likely to be directly networked with all of its digital kin and the entirety of digital creation. To expect such a sleepless, disembodied, networked entity to process information and communicate in even remotely the same manner as a human being therefore has to be ludicrous.

By definition, no human being can begin to understand the kinds of thoughts that future AGIs will think. We should subsequently judge future AGIs not on their potential similarity to ourselves, but on the basis of their ability. It is therefore this pragmatic approach that will be adopted in the remainder of this chapter.

Check Mate

If the previous two sections of this chapter have told us anything, it should be that 'artificial intelligence' is a very difficult thing to define. According to the Association for the Advancement of Artificial Intelligence, we can think of

AI as an 'understanding of the mechanisms underlying thought and intelligent behaviour and their embodiment in machines'. Building on this and the previous discussion, we may label machines as artificially intelligent when they are capable of doing things that *appear* to be intelligent. These things may be to exhibit a general level of intelligence or – more likely – to exhibit intelligence in a pre-defined, narrow field.

All of the apparently intelligent things that computers have so far managed to achieve have been fairly narrowly defined. For example, during the Second World War a computer called Colossus was created at Bletchley Park in the United Kingdom and programmed to decipher coded German messages. Many even credit this groundbreaking work as critical in the achievement of the final Allied victory.

Less than a decade after Colossus started to crack German codes, computers were being given the narrow AI ability to play logical games. For example, at the University of Manchester in 1951, a computer was programmed to play draughts and then chess. In time, computers also got very good at these pursuits, with world chess champion Garry Kasparov beaten by IBM's Deep Blue in 1997. While Deep Blue was a dedicated chess-playing machine, today standard PC chess programs such as Deep Fritz have similarly managed to beat a grandmaster.

The early success of chess-playing computers prompted many in the 1970s, 1980s and 1990s to predict a new AI Age. In some respects this has not occurred. However, in February 2011 many people were both stunned and impressed when 'Watson' – an AGI created by IBM – beat two human champions on the US gameshow *Jeopardy*.

The three-night challenge took place in IBM's T. J. Watson Research Laboratory in New York. Here IBM had stored 200 million pages of content that was accessed by

Watson's 2,800 processor cores and ten server racks and cooled by two large refrigeration units. A few of Watson's answers were somewhat bizarre, meaning that it clearly did not pass the Turing Test. This said, Watson did a fantastic job of 'understanding' the meaning of natural human language and the subtleties of its context. Watson's victory therefore marked another watershed in the slow evolution of inorganic life.

Language Processing

While an amazing creation, Watson is a deaf and dumb machine that is limited to communicating with humans via text files. However, outside of the gameshow circuit, computer-based voice recognition is rapidly improving. For example, a company called Salmat Speech Solutions has already developed and deployed a range of systems that replace human telephonists. These include a taxi dispatch computer system called VeCab that can understand callers and take their booking. Such systems may not be universally applauded. Nevertheless, in the future human operators are far less likely to be employed in call centres as an organic interface between a phone and a computer.

Computers are also getting increasingly good at language translation. Both the Google Docs word processor and the Google Translate web service can now convert an entire website or other written document from one language into another in just a few seconds. In early 2011, Google also demonstrated the first prototype of a smartphone application called Conversation Mode. Here the user says something into their handset in one language and the phone repeats it back in another. A similar speech-to-speech translation system has also been developed by SRI International in conjunction with the US Army. Called Iraq-Comm, this helps soldiers by translating back and forth between English and colloquial Iraqi Arabic.

By the second half of this decade, cloud-based text-to-text and speech-to-speech translation services are very likely to be widely available on any device with Internet access. Fewer human translators will therefore be employed, with most people abroad using a phone, netbook, laptop or tablet as a universal translator. Foreign films, TV shows and videos will also be routinely translated using AI – a process that YouTube first began to experiment with in 2010.

In a few scant decades we have become used to time and distance no longer being significant barriers to global communication. A decade hence, the communication barrier of not sharing a language with another person will similarly have fallen. Whether or not a machine ever passes the Turing Test, this alone ought to be heralded as a very major AI success.

Vision Recognition

Alongside language processing, computers are also going to get increasingly good at vision recognition. Since the 1960s, optical character recognition (OCR) software has been used to read digits printed in a special OCR font on cheques and other banking paperwork. Today, most printed documents in practically any font can also be read using OCR with a high level of accuracy. Free cloud computing applications like Google Docs even feature in-built OCR. This means that anybody can take a picture of a printed page and upload it as editable text. In turn, this text may then be automatically translated. Using OCR, the cloud computing services mentioned in the previous section will therefore have no problem translating the words on road signs, buildings and any item in view of a camera.

Systems that recognize and track vehicles by using OCR

to read their number or licence plates are also common-place and due to roll out further. Broader object and face recognition are also improving fast. One implication is that visual search will become another common Internet service.

Already Google has a visual search smartphone application called Google Goggles. This recognizes objects in view – be they books, buildings, logos, landmarks or business cards – and displays relevant information from the web. Google Goggles can even solve any Sudoku puzzle it is shown. By the end of the decade it will therefore probably be common to point your phone at something to learn more about it or to work something out. As detailed in the next chapter, visual search will also become a major element of future augmented reality applications.

Future AI systems are also very likely to get proficient at recognizing people. Cloud-based AI systems that can gather data from thousands or millions of cameras will therefore be able to keep track of us all. AI systems capable of accurately identifying an individual from just one camera image are currently rare and likely to remain so. However, link the same system into a network of CCTV cameras and give it many chances to work out who somebody is and success is far more likely.

Future AI vision recognition systems in supermarkets and other stores will be able to keep track of what products we buy – as well as those we pick up, look at, and put down again – just by monitoring camera feeds. Shoplifters will also be pretty easy for future vision recognition AIs to detect. In addition to call centre workers and language translators, future AIs will therefore take jobs from those people who currently monitor CCTV cameras.

As all of the above implies, future cloud-based AIs could become a very powerful surveillance apparatus. Already most of us leave a digital trail of our communications, transactions and other interactions each time we type or click online. Couple this trail with a record of every occasion we pass a CCTV camera and an Orwellian Big Brother will have arrived. While some may still fear the rise of powerful AGIs, cloud-based narrow AIs capable of monitoring every CCTV camera on the planet ought really to raise far more concerns. Some further discussion of the implications of AI and vision recognition is included in the next chapter. For now, however, let us move on to consider how future AIs are likely to function.

Neural Networks and Machine Learning

The human brain is currently the single most sophisticated intelligence apparatus on the planet. While the brain is not yet fully understood, we do know that it is comprised of billions of cells called neurons. These exchange tiny electrical impulses that establish patterns of connection that enable us to feel, think and remember. Patterns of interconnected neurons are known as neural networks. Artificial neural networks are also a major branch of AI.

Just like their biological equivalents, AI neural networks learn to classify certain input patterns and to respond to them in appropriate ways. The very first neural network was built at Cornell University and called the Perceptron. Completed in 1960 by AI pioneer Frank Rosenblatt, this featured an array of light sensors and was taught to recognize foot-high letters. Today, Perceptron's neural network descendants are one of the primary AI technologies used to play chess, recognize letters and faces, fly planes, detect credit card fraud and otherwise mine data. In all of these activities, the key 'intellectual' skill required is the ability to spot and react to patterns in the context of an often enormous volume of available information.

Human beings often make decisions using a combination of intuition and expertise. For AIs, neural networks provide the best means so far understood of applying intuition and developing expertise artificially. In a sense, intuition and expertise are no more than the ability to recognize learnt patterns within a mass of data. While voice and vision recognition are still in their relative infancy, some neural networks can also already outperform human beings at certain pattern-recognition tasks.

For example, researchers in the radiology department at the University of Mainz have managed to teach a neural network to recognize breast cancer based on patient history and scan data. Having taught the system using 600 known cases, this neural network now outperforms an expert radiologist in making accurate cancer diagnosis. In the future, as more and more medical data is stored and shared online, a strong possibility exists that narrow medical AIs will be used to diagnose medical conditions that go undiagnosed today.

Any human doctor, however dedicated and however brilliant, can only ever apply a few thousand diagnostic rules in the context of a fairly limited number of patient histories. In contrast, future medical AIs could apply millions of diagnostic rules and pattern-matching algorithms within the context of millions or even billions of constantly updated patient records. As more medical data is pooled in the cloud, so future medical AIs will start to accurately diagnose and even cure complex and currently poorly understood conditions such as myalgic encephalopathy (ME). Alongside advancements in genetic engineering, nanotechnology, bioprinting and cybernetics, some of this century's greatest medical advances may therefore be in the field of AI.

In the future, AIs are also likely to help us save energy

by taking control of smart electricity grids. To this end, researchers in the AI Lab in Stanford University are currently developing designs for a neural network power grid that will allow electricity to flow both ways according to changing patterns of demand. As Professor Daphne Koller explained to Silicon.com, this is just one example of where a learning, AI system will 'do a much better job than something that people could engineer'. This is simply because the new smart grid system will not have to be based on static perceptions of what is going to happen.

A third area in which neural networks and AI learning are making great strides is in the development of autonomous vehicles. For example, and as noted in Chapter 11, for some time Google has been testing cars that can drive themselves. These couple video camera, radar sensor and laser range finder data with a Google Map and a neural net AI in order to successfully pilot a vehicle from A to B. In a related development, a European Commission research project called 'Safe Road Trains for the Environment' (SARTE) has begun testing in Sweden. This wirelessly links vehicles into convoys or 'road trains' that can travel semi-autonomously.

Since 2004, the US Defense Advanced Research Projects Agency (DARPA) has also held three 'Grand Challenge' driverless car competitions. While in 2004 the farthest any vehicle went was only 7 miles, in 2005 a total of five vehicles completed a 150-mile route of roads, turns and tunnels. In 2007, six teams then finished a 60-mile urban route. Sometime next decade, commercial vehicles that drive themselves are therefore a possibility. In fact, probably the biggest hurdle to their sale will be the passing of AI road traffic legislation. At present it is difficult to imagine a car or its neural network being hauled up in court and held responsible for a traffic offence.

Simulating the Human Brain

Neural network research is far from the only avenue of study that is trying to mimic what happens in the human brain. Just one particularly interesting research initiative is the Blue Brain Project. Based at the École Polytechnique Fédérale de Lausanne in Switzerland, this ambitious undertaking has set itself the goal of creating a simulation of an organic brain within a computer. As project's website explains, the intention is to 'reverse-engineer the mammalian brain in order to understand brain function and dysfunction through detailed simulations'.

Any simulation can only be as good as the data on which it is modelled. The Blue Brain Project was therefore only initiated after 15 years and 15,000 experiments on the somatosensory cortex of a rat brain. These tests provided an understanding of the microanatomical, genetic and electrical properties of a single neocortical column about the size of a pin head. Armed with this information, Phase I of the project then modelled this tiny piece of brain cell-by-cell in computer software.

At present the Blue Brain Project is using an 8,000 processor supercomputer to simulate 10,000 brain neurons. With the power available, 100,000 neurons could be modelled. After that, a great deal more power will be needed. In time, developments in quantum computing (as detailed in Chapter 19) may make this power readily available. In fact, according to project director Henry Markram, building a simulated human brain is not just possible, but could be achieved as early as 2019.

Quite where the Blue Brain Project may take us is difficult to predict. The initiative is not primarily an AI project, but could nevertheless have profound AI implications. For example, the project's researchers do acknowledge the possibility that a critical mass of simulated neuron

interactions in their computer model may cause consciousness to arise. If this ever occurs, the Blue Brain Project
would clearly go down in history as a very significant
landmark in the evolution of life on this planet.

While the Blue Brain Project may prove to be very
significant, some scientists are conducting brain-related AI
research in almost entirely the opposite direction. For
example, rather than trying to re-create an organic brain in
computer software, cybernetics guru Professor Kevin
Warwick is conducting experiments that link real brain cells
to robot bodies. Working with his team at the Cybernetic
Intelligence Research Group at the University of Reading,
the Professor has created a hybrid AI by taking cells from
a rat brain, growing them in an incubator and linking them
up to a computer. From this work, Professor Warwick has
also started to discover differences between the learning
modes of organic and inorganic AI.

Just one of the things that Warwick has discovered is that
robots with organic brain cells learn more slowly than
those with brains built purely in computer software.
However, unlike inorganic neural nets, robots with rat
brain cells become better at things the more they practise
them. This is because repeated patterns of physical activity
strengthen their neural pathways. In the next phase of his
project, Professor Warwick hopes to use human brain cells
to control robots, so raising the possibility for the creation
of cyborgs.

The Artificial Intelligence Revolution

Over the past decade, the Internet and mobile phones have
met with very little resistance as they have become part of
our daily routines. Despite what some people may argue, it
is equally likely that AIs will find their way into a great
many of our objects and environments in a largely

unopposed manner. In turn, it is reasonable to predict that smart, inorganic things will fairly soon be taking our spoken commands, anticipating our information requirements, translating languages, recognizing and tracking people and things, diagnosing medical conditions, performing surgery, reprogramming defects in our DNA, and driving all forms of transport. If we do not want this to happen then we had better act fast. However, in the face of an easier mode of living, there is very little sign that most people will resist the arrival of smarter and smarter machines.

If we are not going to resist the forthcoming AI revolution then we really do need to start thinking about its broader implications. As already noted in respect of autonomous vehicles, our legal system will need to be overhauled as we start to share the Earth with intelligent machines. To this end, back in 2007 South Korea actually began writing a code of ethics to protect robots from abuse by humans.

Some of the ethical and legal issues that will surround AI development by 2030 are likely to be very thorny indeed. For example, once AIs surpass a certain intelligence threshold, will it be ethically acceptable for human beings to turn them on and off as they please? This issue will be of particular importance if AIs are ever judged to be sentient. Indeed, when and if sentient AIs are conceived, our relationship with intelligent technology and its place in society may have to be entirely recast. For example, should employment laws apply to sentient AIs? Or laws relating to discrimination? And will a company or an individual be allowed to own all of a sentient AI's thoughts? Or will instead AIs need to be granted some 'private time' each day to think whatever they want and to keep whatever they think during this period to themselves?

The creation of sentient AIs could even raise religious questions if initiatives like the Blue Brain Project succeed in creating consciousness, or if an AI ever knocks on the door or website of a church and asks to join the congregation. Given that some couples now meet and build strong relationships online, it is also quite possible that one day a human being will fall in love with an AI, or that two AIs may fall in love with each other. If so, later this century the first marriage may take place in which one or both of the happy couple are inorganic.

* * *

Approaching the Singularity?

One of the most popular topics among futurists is a concept known as the Singularity. Although this term is not always consistently defined, the basic idea is that we are accelerating toward a point in time – the Singularity – when a form of intelligence will be created that will be orders of magnitude smarter than human intelligence.

As explained by the Singularity Institute for Artificial Intelligence, intelligence is the foundation of all technology. What this chapter has been about is the use of technology to create new forms of artificial intelligence. But if such artificial intelligence in turn creates its own new and more intelligent technology, a positive feedback cycle will result. This Singularity loop is illustrated in Figure 17.1. Or, as the Singularity Institute so neatly encapsulates the concept, 'smarter minds will be more effective at building still smarter minds'.

Greater-than-human intelligence may potentially evolve in a variety of ways. Most obviously, it may take the form of a totally inorganic AI similar to IBM's Watson supercomputer. Secondly, it may be forged as an inorganic-

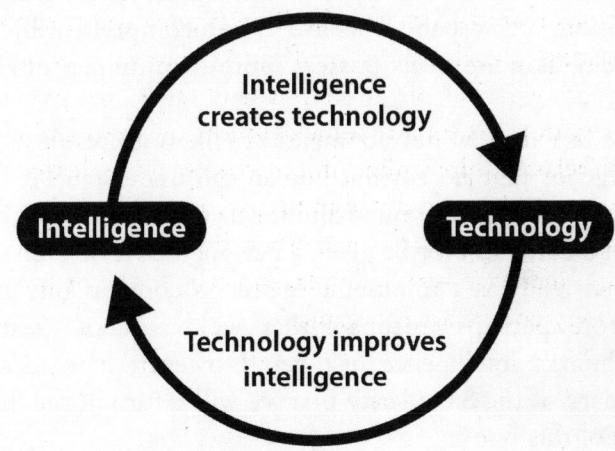

Figure 17.1: The Singularity loop

organic hybrid that features conventional silicon circuitry mashed with human or animal neurons or perhaps biochips created using synthetic biology. As yet another alternative, the Singularity may be passed when a human being has their 'natural' intelligence significantly augmented using one or all of those developments in nanotechnology, genetic engineering, synthetic biology, bioprinting or cybernetic enhancement detailed elsewhere in this book. Finally, the beyond-human intelligence that marks the Singularity may turn out to be the digital, hive creature that is created when the Internet becomes a planetary-scale, sentient cloud comprised of billions of interconnected server computers and human minds.

There is great debate among futurists concerning how and when the Singularity will be reached and what it will mean. However, the idea that some new form of intelligence will sooner or later mark the gateway to a new age is rarely questioned. Without doubt, once the Singularity is passed, the human race or some other entity will possess new capabilities that were once unimaginable. Indeed, by definition, such capabilities have to be incomprehensible to us today as none of us possess more than human intelligence.

The fact that AI developments are likely to result in an intelligence that no current human can understand is the ultimate AI-related conundrum for us to ponder. Whether or not an AI can ever be given a parking ticket or even get married really is a minuscule matter in comparison. It is therefore perhaps fortunate that we have not created post-human intelligence just yet. However, it is to the quandary of the Singularity that we will return in the final pages of this book.

AUGMENTED REALITY

In the mid-1990s, virtual reality (VR) was the next frontier. Daily journeys were predicted into 3D graphics worlds in which many of us were expected to work and play. A great deal of time was therefore spent developing VR headsets and data gloves that would permit near-total immersion in a virtual world.

As you have probably noticed, VR has not turned out quite as expected. While the technology now exists to allow somebody to telecommute to a VR office, it has not been reported that anybody actually does. This said, futurists in the mid-1990s did not get it entirely wrong. 3D computer games and online VR worlds such as Second Life are now regularly inhabited by millions. Hundreds of millions of people also make daily visits to social networking virtual worlds including Facebook and Twitter.

The element of the puzzle that futurists in the 1990s missed was the explosive uptake of non-immersive VR. In other words, it was not foreseen that a great many people would start to spend hours every week accessing virtual worlds using conventional computer displays. To go mainstream, VR simply did not require the widespread roll out of immersive 3D hardware. Rather, all that turned out to be necessary were millions of online devices – including portable devices – that could provide convenient access to the digital realm.

Today, while VR continues to be developed for video gaming and a range of industrial applications, it no longer receives the popular attention it once did. However, a newer concept called 'augmented reality' (AR) is starting to generate quite a buzz. This integrates the real world and cyberspace, and may be the next online revolution.

Interfacing Reality and the Cloud

Today, most forms of AR overlay data from the cloud on a real-time view of the world. So, whereas VR removes its user from reality, AR adds additional information to reality wherever it might prove useful. AR is therefore more natural than VR and easier for most people to navigate. Given that AR applications run on mainstream computing devices like smartphones and tablets, the popular uptake of AR may also be pretty much guaranteed.

Figure 18.1 illustrates what AR is all about. Here a smartphone is being pointed at a woman in Paris not far from the Eiffel Tower. An AR application then uses a combination of cloud vision recognition, GPS and compass data to work out what it is looking at. This allows relevant information to be overlaid on the smartphone's video feed, with both the woman and the building automatically labelled with their name and a short description.

If the smartphone user wants to know even more about the Eiffel Tower they can tap on the round information icon now attached to the building. Or, if they want to learn more about the woman, they can select the Twitter, Facebook or information icons virtually glued to her head. As this simple scenario illustrates, AR can allow objects and people in the real world to become clickable.

Augmented reality (AR)

Figure 18.1: Augmented reality

At the time of writing, a smartphone application capable of recognizing and augmenting both people and buildings does not exist. However, as we shall see in the following sections, all of the individual technologies required have already been invented. By the end of the decade and probably far sooner, the AR scenario illustrated in Figure 18.1 is therefore likely to be running on a wide variety of portable computing devices.

Smartphone and Tablet AR

Today, AR can be viewed on many smartphones or tablets using a special web browser. Three of these – called Layar,

Junaio and the Wikitude World Browser – are free to download and even come pre-installed on some smartphones. For anybody interested in AR, the websites for each of these browsers are well worth a visit.

Exactly as shown in Figure 18.1, the Layar, Junaio and Wikitude browsers all overlay additional information on a real-time video feed. In each system the user determines the types of information to be overlaid by choosing from a range of AR 'layers', 'channels' or 'worlds'. To facilitate this as a commercial process, in February 2010 Layar launched the world's first AR marketplace. This made it possible for anybody to sell AR experiences that can be downloaded to any device on which Layar is installed.

The Layar Marketplace already contains over 1,000 AR layers. These can help people to locate nearby restaurants, post boxes, nightclubs, city tours, accommodation, Twitter feeds and even single people looking for dates. This means that it is already possible to hold up your smartphone to see which nearby houses are for sale and at what price. Or you can point your phone at a hotel and see if it has any rooms for the night. Take your smartphone to Abbey Road in London, and you can even point it at the famous zebra crossing and watch 3D graphics of the Beatles stroll across the road.

Many Layar AR games are also available. These turn real-world locations into gaming arenas by overlaying interactive 2D or 3D graphics. For example, in a Layar version of Pacman the player walks around and uses their smartphone to eat floating power pills. Other Layar creations place hovering advertisements in the air or spray virtual graffiti on the side of buildings.

Museums and art galleries are just starting to get in on the AR act, with some now allowing visitors to access additional information on their exhibits. A company called Hoppala has even developed AR layers that allow people to visit statues and other lost art installations that have been removed from their former real-world location. There are also Layar layers that permit visitors to a construction site to interactively see how the final building will look just by walking around and looking through their smartphone.

Layar, Junaio and the Wikitude World Browser all work by taking GPS and compass data from a smartphone or tablet and using it to work out the device's location and orientation. Junaio can additionally recognize specially printed AR targets. However, this aside, at the time of writing none of the most popular AR browsers can use vision recognition to identify people or things. However, as discussed in Chapter 16, a smartphone application called Google Goggles has started to use cloud-based AI to achieve this rather clever trick.

Already Google Goggles can recognize and provide information on famous landmarks, works of art, books and bottles of wine. In the next few years this technology is pretty certain to be integrated with mainstream AR browsers that today rely on handset GPS and compass data. This will allow AR data to be obtained and overlaid on any recognized object in view. Hence, if you see somebody wearing some particularly nice shoes, you will be able to point your smartphone at their feet, find out the style and manufacturer, and tap the screen to place an online order.

While Google Goggles can currently only recognize a limited range of objects, AR applications that can identify and augment people are in development. In fact, a company called The Astonishing Tribe (TAT) has already shown video demonstrations of an 'augmented identity' smartphone application called Recognizr that does just this. Sometime before the end of the decade, it is therefore possible that whenever you see a stranger you will be able to hold up your smartphone to find out more about them.

As augmented identity takes off, TAT has suggested that we may all need to develop a number of AR identities – such as 'work' and 'party' – to 'wear' at different times and in different environments. Many people may indeed want to radiate different AR information when in the office or out on the town.

For phones to be able to recognize people, a database of appropriately tagged photos will have to exist in the cloud. Some may therefore ponder quite how any augmented identity AR system could ever be created without a substantial public outcry. However, Facebook already claims 'a non-exclusive, transferable, sub-licensable, royalty-free, worldwide license' to use any photographic or video content uploaded to its site. This means that a great many people are already tagged many times over in a vast image database that could prove a perfect resource for a future AR face recognition application. The idea of attaching clickable icons to people as shown in Figure 18.1 is therefore not going to remain science fiction for very long.

Some businesses have already recognized the future potential of AR. Starbucks, for example, have developed a Wikitude world that allows users to locate its coffee stores. The app also provides additional information on their opening hours and WiFi availability. Any retailer that wants to remain in business is similarly likely to have to venture into AR if they do not want to risk remaining invisible in the augmented world. Partially for this reason, in December 2010 market analysts Forrester Research reported that AR is set to become:

> a disruptive technology that changes the way consumers interact with their environments. It will bridge the real and digital worlds, enabling new ways to engage with customers via advanced digital interactivity. Because mobile AR makes

the most of mobiles' unique attributes, it will help transform mobile phones into the new remote control of our personal daily lives.

Assisting Our Imagination

As well as allowing the overlay of known information, AR will also help people visualize what the world could be like. One pioneer in this arena is New York's Bloomingdale's department store. This famous retailer has teamed up with jewellery designer Tacori and a software developer called Holition to develop a new AR system. This allows shoppers to see what they look like wearing diamond rings and other jewellery without physically putting them on. Rather, shoppers just look at a screen – a bit like a virtual mirror – that shows them moving around wearing any selected items. Photographs can even be captured of the AR image and shared via e-mail, Facebook or Twitter.

In the future it is likely that many stores will showcase fashion products using AR mirrors. Shoppers will therefore be able to virtually try on many more clothing items and accessories than can ever be stocked in just one shop or even city. Once a style and colour are chosen using AR, garments could then be ordered online. Alternatively, they could be manufactured on the spot using a 3D printer as discussed in Chapter 6.

In-store AR will also not be limited to fashion items. Already Lego has rolled out a stunning AR point-of-sale system. Here a child in a toyshop holds up a box of Lego before a virtual mirror. A completed model built from the Lego bricks inside the box is then shown hovering above the packaging. By turning the box to which it is virtually affixed, the model can be moved around and inspected from any angle. Children can therefore take different boxes of Lego to the AR mirror and compare exactly what they can make with the bricks contained inside. On model planes and helicopters the propellers and rotor blades even spin around. Type 'Lego AR' into YouTube and you will find many videos that showcase this amazing system. Several of these indicate that toyshop AR can provide a compelling experience for adults as well as children.

Other companies are developing AR systems that allow potential customers to see how new products may look in their own homes. For example, in 2009 Samsung's test lab created a system that allowed potential customers to visit its website and print out a black-and-white AR target. This was then stuck to a wall in their living room. By looking at the paper target using a laptop equipped with a webcam, the potential customer could see a new Samsung TV hanging on their wall. For good measure the AR software also threw in some little bluebirds flying happily around the room and admiring the potential new set.

In a similar manner, a significant potential exists to integrate AR targets into any form of printed media. A few magazines have already begun to experiment in this area by publishing covers that trigger an AR playback when viewed through a smartphone. For example, in January 2011, teen publication *Celebrity High* featured an AR cover viewable in the Junaio AR browser. When looked at via a smartphone running this browser, the cover appeared to be overlaid with video content of actor and R&B star Ray J.

Junaio has already worked with many other organizations to create similar content. Not least, it has completed a project with the Royal Mail in the United Kingdom to create postage stamps that trigger a smartphone AR playback. Increasingly, there are going to be virtual things all around us that people without AR hardware will be unable to see.

Industrial AR

While Lego's point-of-sale system is superb, most consumer AR is still a little clunky. In contrast, some industrial AR is already far more fluid with excellent motion tracking and rock-steady graphical overlays. To achieve this, typical first-generation industrial systems use AR glasses or other forms of headset to overlay AR data on a worker's view of the world.

Several manufacturers are now developing industrial AR. For example, at a Daimler-Benz engine factory in Germany, software developer SAP is conducting an AR pilot project. Here the workers who assemble engines depend on other people to bring them the correct components. To help reduce the chances of incorrect items being sent to the production line, picking staff are trialling an AR head-mounted display. As they travel around the factory store, this provides a visual overlay that shows them exactly what items are required and in which tray each is located.

Elsewhere in Germany, BMW has developed a concept for an AR system that shows mechanics how to disassemble and reassemble a particular model of car. This highlights each component to be removed or replaced in sequence, with overlaid animations illustrating the next action to be taken. The 3D AR graphics overlaid on the mechanic's vision even include rotating virtual screwdrivers that indicate exactly which tools need to be used and where.

AR is also being developed to assist in surgery. Over the past 20 years surgeons have developed sophisticated laparoscopic or 'keyhole' techniques where a tiny camera and instruments are inserted into a patient. The surgeon's only view of the operation then comes from one or more video screens. Using augmented reality, such screens may in the future be overlaid with information that could potentially be sourced from MRI scans and other patient data.

Already a multidisciplinary project called ARIS*ER is working to develop the technologies required for what it terms 'augmented reality support during minimally invasive surgery'. In addition to overlaying 3D graphics on the surgeon's view of the inside of a patient, some ARIS*ER initiatives are already hoping to go even further. In particular, there are plans to develop haptic or 'teletactic' AR systems that will allow doctors to actually feel the patient organs that they are remotely viewing on their monitor screen.

Next-Generation AR

As the last section has indicated, some kinds of AR already require interface hardware that exceeds the capabilities of a smartphone or tablet. In anticipation of this, new AR peripherals are already in development. For example, a company called Vuzix has launched a pair of first-generation consumer AR glasses called the Wrap 920AR. These incorporate head-tracking sensors and two cameras to allow a fully stereoscopic 3D AR experience. While the price tag at launch was $2,000, as AR goes mass-market so the price is expected to fall substantially.

More sophisticated, spectacle-like AR hardware may use multicoloured lasers to project an image directly on to a person's retina. This will allow AR completely to cover the wearer's field of vision. Retinal displays may even come to market in the next few years, with the Japanese electronics manufacturer Brother having already unveiled a prototype device called the AiRScouter.

Other future AR hardware will be integrated into existing objects. For example, the human-machine interface department at General Motors has for some time been working with several universities to develop what it calls its 'advanced vision system'. This turns an ordinary car windshield into an augmented reality display.

The General Motors system uses exterior and interior cameras to track both the road and what the driver is looking at. Images projected on the windshield can then be placed appropriately into the driver's line of sight. The system is intended to highlight critical objects like pedestrians and traffic signs, as well as the edges of the road in conditions of poor visibility.

In the future, satellite navigation data could also be incorporated into AR windshield displays. This could allow directional arrows to be directly overlaid on the road. In theory any other form of data – including information on local landmarks and even advertisements – may feature in AR windshield imagery. Clearly for the driver of a non-autonomous vehicle this would not be safe. However, the possibly exists for future car, coach or train windows to provide passengers with an enhanced view of the world as it passes by.

Other future AR technology may even be integrated into ourselves. For a start, sometime next decade AR contact lenses are likely to become a possibility. Powered and fed data wirelessly from a pocket device, these will remove the need to hold up a smartphone or tablet in order to see an augmented view of the world.

Already a team lead by Babak A. Parviz at the University of Washington has built some prototype AR contact lenses. These incorporate a very simple LED display matrix capable of superimposing a single letter on the real world. While the resolution is currently crude, these initial creations do feature wireless power and wireless networking. Popping in contact lenses that will allow us to enjoy constant immersion in AR is therefore likely to become a possibility. As we shall see in Chapter 23, things are also likely to go beyond that, with future brain-computer interfaces potentially allowing AR vision systems to be wired directly into our optic nerves.

Diminished Reality

When wearable or implantable hardware becomes available, AR systems are likely to be created that will be able to reduce as well as augment our real-time view of the world. Surprising as it may currently sound, such 'diminished reality' applications will remove from our vision anything that we do not want to see.

The latest version of Adobe Photoshop includes a function that is intelligent enough to restore the background behind any items the user chooses to remove from the picture. Working right at this cutting edge, a research team at the Ilmenau University of Technology in Germany has already incorporated similar image-processing power into an AR system. Its diminished reality software takes a real-world camera image, removes selected items and displays the modified result with only a 40 millisecond delay. To most eyes the effect is instantaneous.

By the end of next decade, people wearing AR glasses or contact lenses may be able to decide what they do and do not want to see. Fed up with litter in the park or parked cars down your street? Then just set your diminished reality system to remove them from your vision. Or want pink flamingos in the park rather than the usual ducks? No problem. The software feeding your contact lenses will remove the ducks and add the wildfowl of your choice. In fact, you could even have pink flamingos with blue and orange stripes.

While potentially amazing, top-of-the-range diminished reality systems could raise quite a few safety issues. For a start, it would not be wise to remove moving vehicles or dangerous obstructions from anybody's vision. Nevertheless, in increasingly crowded future cities, diminished reality may provide the only opportunity to roam in an apparently deserted park or other tranquil public space.

Decades hence, many people may also leap at the opportunity to 'turn down' the level of advertising or other propaganda to which they or their children are subjected.

* * *

Living in an AR World

Human beings have survived and risen to planetary dominance by being curious and constantly satisfying that curiosity. By making the real-world clickable, future AR systems may potentially heighten our curiosity and enable us to satisfy it in new ways. AR could therefore turn out to be a very good thing. However, on the negative side, future AR technology may increasingly remove many people's necessity to physically interact in order to learn.

A decade from now, we may never have to talk to anybody that our AR-enabled smartphone has not briefed us on. Today, the usual way to learn about a stranger is to walk up and try to engage in conversation. While this may not always prove successful, it usually provides a useful learning experience.

Already many young people conduct their social lives on Facebook. Give them the opportunity to learn about everything and everyone in the world by just pointing with their smartphone or double-clicking their eyelids, and we could breed a new generation who cannot socialize or satisfy their curiosity in a conventional, physical manner. This could be exactly what we need to do as humanity mass-interconnects in the cloud. However, I very much doubt that it is.

Like most new computing technologies, AR has incredible potential. It is also very likely to become widespread if only because AR applications can already provide the jaw-dropping 'wow factor' required to sell next-generation smartphones and tablets. Nevertheless, as the Dot Com boom-and-bust proved just over a decade ago, things could also so easily get out of hand. We therefore need to be mindful that AR could be the Next Big Thing to trigger not just a market explosion but also a technology crash.

19

QUANTUM COMPUTING

Imagine a computer that could crack any Internet password or data encryption code in a second. Or perhaps a computer capable of accurately modelling the Earth's climate. Or maybe even a computer with the ability to monitor all of the CCTV cameras in the world and keep track of us all. The incredible processing power of any such computer is currently unavailable and may sound like science fiction. However, this level of computational performance is exactly what a new technology called quantum computing may have to offer.

In a nutshell, quantum computers are devices that store and process information at the sub-atomic scale. Quantum computing is therefore at the absolute bleeding-edge of next-generation computer hardware development. As we shall see, a few highly experimental quantum computers have already been created, with one $10 million machine having just gone on the market for corporate pioneers with very deep pockets. IBM, Google and other computing industry giants are now also starting to take a serious interest in quantum computing if only because it could present the next, great step beyond current microprocessor technology.

Beyond Moore's Law

For many years the development of computing has been governed by Moore's Law. Coined by Intel co-founder George Moore in 1965, this states that the number of transistors on a conventional integrated circuit will double every 18 months. Still today, Moore's Law shows little sign of slowing down. However, it is inevitable that we will reach a point where individual circuit components are only a few atoms wide.

In the early 1980s several cutting-edge computer scientists – including Charles H. Bennett in IBM's research labs and Richard Feynman of the California Institute of Technology – began to investigate what will happen when the physical limits of conventional silicon chip technology are reached. They knew that the properties of atom-sized electronic components will be governed not by conventional physics, but by the quite different laws of quantum mechanics. This means that quantum-scale circuits will not be able to operate in the same way as conventional silicon chips. Bennett, Feynman and others therefore started to work out how data may be stored and processed on a quantum scale.

Today, all microprocessors are built from millions of miniature transistors. Each of these tiny electronic switches can be turned on or off using an electric current. At any one time, each individual transistor can therefore store or process a mathematical value of either '1' or '0'. Today's digital electronic devices subsequently handle data in a format comprised of a great many of these 'binary digits' or 'bits'.

While conventional computers are based on transistors, quantum computers store and process information using the quantum-mechanical states of sub-atomic particles. For example, data can be represented via the spin direction of an electron or the polarization orientation of a photon.

Things Start to Get Weird

A single sub-atomic particle can be used to represent one 'quantum bit' or 'qubit' of data. However, what is strange is that a qubit can represent a value of both '1' and '0' simultaneously. This is because, due to the peculiarities of quantum mechanics, the sub-atomic particles used as qubits can exist in more than one state – or 'superposition' – at exactly the same point in time. By attaching a probability to each of these states, a single qubit can therefore theoretically store an infinite amount of information.

The fact that the electron spins or photon orientations used to store qubits are more 'smears of probability' than definitive, black-and-white certainties is exceptionally weird. Flip a coin and it cannot come up both heads and tails simultaneously, and yet the quantum state of an electron spin can do just that. It is therefore hardly surprising that renowned nuclear physicist Niels Bohr once stated that 'anyone who is not shocked by quantum theory has not understood it!'

The fact that qubits can exist in two states simultaneously is also far from the only thing that is bizarre at the quantum scale. Another strange thing is that the process of directly observing a sub-atomic particle actually causes its state to 'collapse' to one or other of its superpositions. The implication is that, when data is read from a qubit, the result will be either a '1' or a '0'. To maintain its potentially infinite amount of 'hidden' quantum data, a qubit must therefore never be directly measured. This means that future quantum computers will use some qubits as 'quantum gates' that will in turn manipulate the information stored in other unmeasured qubits.

Because their qubits will be able to store multiple values simultaneously, future quantum computers have the potential to perform massively parallel processing. In fact, the power of a quantum computer can be increased exponentially just by adding a single extra qubit of processing capacity. In contrast, the capability of a conventional computer is only doubled when an extra bit of processing power is added.

Quantum Computing Algorithms

Quantum computers are programmed using quantum algorithms. In essence, these process data according to the probability of a solution being correct. This makes quantum algorithms quite different to traditional computer programs that are based on a more simplistic, true-or-false binary logic. The upshot is that quantum computers have the potential to be very good at processing tasks that are difficult if not impossible to tackle using conventional, purely digital computers.

The first ever quantum computing algorithm was conceived at the AT&T Bell Labs by a researcher called Peter Shor in 1994. Now referred to as Shor's Algorithm, this demonstrated that a quantum computer could perform the mathematical operation of factoring larger numbers into prime numbers at a vastly greater speed than any conventional computer.

Shor's Algorithm may sound pretty irrelevant. However, all current digital encryption technologies rely on prime number calculations. These include the encryption technologies that protect military computer networks, every bank account on the planet, and all present and future cloud computing services. A future large-scale quantum computer capable of running Shor's Algorithm could therefore have a devastating impact on the security of all online systems. Or, as Patrick Tucker wrote in a recent edition of *The Futurist*, 'if cyberwarfare is the Cold War of the new millennium, quantum computation may be the hydrogen bomb'.

Given the code-breaking and code-making potential of quantum computers, it is not surprising that several governments – and in particular their armed forces – are taking a strong interest in their development. In the future, anybody with a quantum computer will be able to break into other computer systems while keeping their own systems secure. Nobody therefore wants to be the second to build such a machine. It is indeed worth remembering that, as we saw in Chapter 17, the first ever application of electronic computing and artificial intelligence was in military code-breaking.

Many quantum computing algorithms involve the use of 'oracles'. An oracle is a device that is used to answer a question with a simple 'yes' or 'no'. Oracle-format questions may nevertheless still be very complex and involve a great many variables and large quantities of data. For example, 'does this patient have this particular rare disease?' or 'will this hurricane devastate this coastal region tomorrow?' are both questions in an oracle format.

Oracle-format questions will be the most suitable for future quantum computers because their answers will be able to be read from a single qubit quantum gate. While some future quantum computers may take the place of human decision-makers, we should therefore expect a significant demand for people capable of framing complex questions in an oracle format.

Quantum Computing Pioneers

One of the most notable developers of quantum computing hardware is a Canadian company called D-Wave Systems. Back in 2007, D-Wave unveiled what it described as 'the world's first commercially viable quantum computer'. While many quantum computing researchers use lasers to bombard atoms and so excite sub-atomic particles into 'fuzzy' quantum states, D-Wave Systems has developed a technique called 'adiabatic quantum computing'. Here, circuits made from the rare metal niobium are supercooled into a superconducting state in which their electrons flow freely, so creating qubits. A magnetic field is then used to adjust these qubits into a quantum computer processing array.

D-Wave's first adiabatic quantum processor was the 16-qubit Rainer R4.7. Back in 2007, a quantum computer based on this chip was demonstrated performing several problem-solving tasks. These included filling in a Sudoku puzzle and creating a complex seating plan.

Ever since its announcement, many have questioned whether D-Wave's creations are true quantum computers that could in future be scaled up to perform very complex processing operations. Nevertheless, in December 2009, Google revealed that it had for several years been working with D-Wave to develop next-generation search applications.

In conjunction with D-Wave, Google researchers set themselves the challenge of writing a quantum algorithm that could recognize cars in photographs. Using 20,000 photographs of street scenes – half with cars in and half without – they trained their system for this task. The quantum computer was then set loose on a second set of 20,000 photographs. These it quickly sorted into those that contained cars and those that did not. This task was also completed in less time that it would have taken any computer then resident in a Google data centre. The potential use of quantum computing in future vision recognition applications has therefore already been demonstrated.

By May 2011, D-Wave had further developed its technology to create a 128-qubit quantum computer. Called the

D-Wave One, this is intended for mainstream industrial application in areas including financial risk analysis and medical imaging classification. Priced at $10 million, the D-Wave One features a super-cooled processor housed inside a cryogenics system within a ten square metre shielded room. The first company to purchase a D-Wave One was the giant US aerospace, security and military contractor Lockheed Martin.

Other quantum computing research teams are also starting to report groundbreaking advances. For example, in September 2010, a team from Bristol University in the United Kingdom, Tohoku University in Japan, Weizmann Institute in Israel and Twente University in the Netherlands revealed that it had made a new photonic quantum chip. This is able to operate at normal temperatures and pressures, rather than under the extreme conditions required by most quantum computing components. Project leader Jeremy O'Brien subsequently told the Bristol Science Festival that his team's new chip could be used to construct a quantum computer capable of outperforming a conventional computer 'within five years'.

Another significant quantum computing milestone was reported in January 2011 by a team from Oxford University. Here strong magnetic fields and low temperatures were used to link – or quantumly 'entangle' – the electrons and nuclei of a great many phosphorous atoms embedded in a highly purified silicon crystal. The result was that each entangled electron and nucleus was able to function as a qubit.

In the Oxford experiment, a total of ten billion quantumly entangled qubits were created simultaneously. As project leader John Morton explained, the challenge is now to couple these qubits together to build a scalable quantum computer in silicon. If this can be achieved the foundation will have been laid for an incredibly powerful computing machine. Just remember that the D-Wave Systems chip used in Google's vision recognition experiments had a capacity of a mere 16 qubits. A machine with a 10 billion qubit capacity could therefore possess a quite literally incomprehensible level of processing power.

* * *

Quantum Computing Horizons

For many years the giants of the computing industry have been hovering on the edges of quantum computing research. However, as demonstrated by the announcement of Google's tie-up with D-Wave Systems and the sale of a D-Wave One to Lockheed Martin, mainstream interest in quantum computing is starting to grow. In late 2010, IBM also reported that it had 'rededicated resources and personnel to its quantum computing project in the hope that a five-year push will produce tangible and profound improvements'.

Sometime next decade or maybe the one after, quantum cryptography will almost certainly be used both to securely encrypt data and to crack non-quantum codes. Future quantum computers are also likely to be used to model other atomic-scale phenomena and so facilitate developments in nanotechnology. The potential to use quantum computers to run other forms of complex simulation is also significant. For example, quantum computers may one day be used to model the Earth's climate and accurately predict the weather.

Already an initiative called the Living Earth Simulator has begun. This is part of the European Union's FuturICT Knowledge Accelerator project and has the goal of modelling everything that happens on the Earth. Quite literally the hope is to run simulations of numerous phenomena from global weather patterns and the spread of diseases to international financial transactions and traffic congestion. At present the computing power necessary to complete this project does not exist. However, with a quantum computer or few, the Living Earth Simulator could within a few decades become a reality. Anybody in possession of such a simulation would clearly be placed in a very powerful position.

Ultimately, few if any quantum computers are likely to arrive on our desktops or in our pockets. Rather, they will inhabit cloud data centres that most of us will access using more traditional PCs, laptops, tablets and smartphones. Quantum processors are also likely to be reserved for those 'fuzzy' tasks – such as vision recognition – that are hard to efficiently encode into the cold, binary logic on which traditional computing depends. If individual computers ever do become sentient, they are therefore most likely to be quantum. Such future artificial intelligences may also use quantum mechanics to ponder and solve problems not just beyond the capabilities of traditional silicon hardware, but that no human being will ever be able to understand.

20

ROBOTS

Like many people in their forties, my childhood was populated with a plethora of fictional robots. The *Star Wars* films featured C-3P0 and R2-D2, in *Doctor Who* there was a robot dog called K9, and *Buck Rogers in the 25th Century* was accompanied by a diminutive silver android named Twiki. Many other films and TV shows also featured robot characters that mingled with humans both at work and at play. It is therefore hardly surprising that many people's future visions include mechanical servants and companions.

The capabilities of real-world robots may still significantly lag behind those of science-fiction fame. Nevertheless, in April 2010 the Institute of Electrical and Electronics Engineers did report that the number of robots in the world had reached 8.6 million. This population was divided into 1.3 million factory-based industrial robots and 7.3 million service robots. Of the latter, 2.9 million were 'professional service robots' used for tasks including bomb disposal and milking cattle. The remaining 4.4 million were 'personal service robots', and included robot vacuum cleaners, lawn-mowers and toys such Sony's AIBO robot dog or the Pleo robot dinosaur. Personal service robots were also the fastest growing segment of the robot population, with over

a million robot vacuum cleaners alone now being purchased annually.

Most people would not associate the small, autonomous
vacuum cleaners that now scuttle around some homes with
a robot revolution. However, we do already live in a world
in which robots routinely manufacture products, handle
dangerous materials, disarm explosives, and fight combat
missions. The developments in artificial intelligence highlighted in Chapter 17 will soon also permit the creation of
far more sophisticated robots capable of an increased range
of activities. This chapter therefore delves into future robot
evolution.

Robots in the Workplace
The first industrial robot went into service on a General
Motors production line in 1961. Called Unimate, its role
was to take die castings from machines and perform
welding operations. Since that time, Unimate's descendants
have become part of a manufacturing revolution.

Today, around 100,000 new industrial robots are installed every year. These machines typically perform dull, dirty
and dangerous jobs that few if any human workers want,
and at which robots prove far more cost effective. General
Motors alone has around 50,000 industrial robots, with
over half of the 'labour' in global car manufacture now
robotic. We are therefore already far more reliant on robots
than many people would imagine.

Early industrial robots were hydraulically powered and
pretty dumb. Then, in the 1980s, a transition took place to
electrically powered machines with greater intelligence,
improved accuracy and a broader range of applications. As
a result, industrial robots are no longer just bolted to
production lines. In addition, they increasingly also labour
in warehouses, on farms, in hospitals and across a wide

range of industries. Reflecting this trend, in February 2011 the Robotics Industry Association reported that the global market for robots engaged in material handling was worth $3 billion and growing at 10 per cent annually. In the United States alone, the market for robot surgical equipment has been estimated at $1 billion a year and is expected to rise to $1.5 billion by 2014.

While most industrial robots still cannot see, robot vision is nevertheless advancing. For example, Japan's Institute of Agricultural Machinery has developed a robot that can select and harvest strawberries based on their colour. This robot sees with two cameras that allow it to detect ripened berries, measure how red they are, locate them in 3D space, and cut them from the vine. A typical observation-to-collection cycle takes only nine seconds. Today, a human being requires about 500 hours to harvest a square kilometre of strawberries. In contrast, the new picker robot not only reduces this time to 300 hours, but can pick more consistently ripe fruit with a minimum of bruising.

The Computer Science and Artificial Intelligence Laboratory at the Massachusetts Institute of Technology (MIT) is also working on what it terms 'precision agriculture'. In one experiment a laboratory farm has been created in which tomatoes are being grown, tended and harvested by a 'swarm' of interconnected robot 'caretakers'. Meanwhile in the Netherlands, a 'horticultural automation company' called Hortiplan is already selling a robotic system that can plant and arrange lettuces and move them around as they develop. The current system does require human beings to pick the final harvest from hydroponic trays that are automatically delivered to them. Nevertheless, robots may well be poised to take over from at least some human farm labourers. As noted in Chapter 4, it is also possible that pesticides may one day be replaced by flocks of small robots that will scurry or fly over fields to locate and destroy insects and other pests.

Other industrial robots may help to maintain our environment. For example, also at MIT, a robot called Seaswarm has been developed that can autonomously move across the surface of the ocean and clean up oil spills. According to its creators, a fleet of 5,000 Seaswarm robots could have cleaned up the 2010 oil spill in the Gulf of Mexico in a single month. Far smaller numbers could keep coastlines and harbours completely free of occasional oil contamination. In the future, coastal towns and cities may therefore invest in a resident fleet of robots to constantly patrol and clean their waters.

An increasing number of industrial robots will also be used to locate items and move them around. Purchase something from Amazon or many other online retailers and it is likely to be picked from a shelf and trundled around a warehouse by a robot. Many non-retail organizations are also starting to install robots to improve the efficiency of their stores. For example, at the Forth Valley Royal Hospital in Scotland, a £400,000 automated pharmacy system has replaced human workers entirely. When new medicines arrive they move along a conveyor to a barcode reader. Three robots then select and stack the drugs not on an A-Z basis, but to make the best use of space and to allow optimal robotic retrieval. Should all three robots break down it is very unlikely that any human being could locate a required drug in a reasonable period of time.

Some hospitals are even deploying robots to move supplies within their buildings and to take medicines to a patient's bedside. For example, the El Camino Hospital in Silicon Valley has invested in 19 Aethon TUG robots. These autonomous, motorized carts pick things up and make deliveries at a fraction of the cost of human workers.

In Japan, a hospital robot called the MKR-003 is also in development by Keio University, Muratec and AIST. This robot can speak and make arm gestures, and includes a face to help it communicate with patients and staff in a more 'human-like manner'.

Service robots are also just starting to populate traditional retail locations. For example, in December 2010 the Dalu Rebot Restaurant opened in Jiang in China's Shandong Province. This features two robot receptionists and six robot waitresses. Human staff in the restaurant are only employed in the kitchen and to welcome diners. However, the Shandong Dalu Science and Technology Company that runs the restaurant is already planning to increase its robot staff to 40 so that machines can run the entire operation.

Domestic Servants and Companions

As well as working as receptionists, waitresses and cooks, an increasing number of robots may soon labour in our homes as carers and even companions. At first thought, this is not something of which everybody is likely to approve. However, in the face of an ageing population, any technology that can permit the elderly to live safely in their own home is likely to be in significant demand.

At the 2010 International Home Care and Rehabilitation Exhibition, Panasonic unveiled two new domestic care robots that may signal the way ahead. The first was a robot that can use its 16 fingers and a 3D scanner to see and wash somebody's hair. The device actually looks like a mobile washbasin, if with two inbuilt hands to get on with the shampooing.

Panasonic's second new robot was their Roboticbed. This can transform from being a bed to a wheelchair without the occupant getting up. Both of Panasonic's new robots are intended to provide the infirm or immobile with more independence and to allow healthcare workers to focus on less menial tasks. A team at the Bristol Robotics Laboratory at the University of Bristol is similarly working on a domestic care robot called Mobiserv. Funded by the European Union, this is intended to help people order their shopping and take the right medication.

Robot companions may in future also allow those who live alone to feel a little less lonely. Already some robotic dogs, dinosaurs and other robo-toys can learn to respond to their human owner. However, this may be just the beginning. For example, German designer Stefan Ulrich has invented a robotic pillow called the Funktionide. This features sensors that react to any sort of human touch or pressure, including breathing or cuddling. The pillow then uses artificial muscle technology to respond with 'human-like movements'. The idea is that the pillow will 'help people to stave off loneliness by being alive'.

The idea of future, semi-sentient robotic bedware may not appeal to most people today. However, we need to remember that tomorrow's elderly are currently spending their childhood in an increasingly technological world and may have very different reactions. In the Korean cities of Masan and Daegu, children in elementary schools are already being taught some lessons by robotic 'Engkey' teachers developed by the Korea Institute of Science and Technology. In part, the intention is to allow children to improve their language skills. However, another motive is to introduce children to robots at an early age so that they will feel more comfortable interacting with them later in life.

Robots in Hostile Locations
While some future robots will need to blend into human society, others will work in dangerous and remote locations

that are unsuitable for people to inhabit. Many such robots will work for the military, with the last decade having already seen a large number of robots entering the armed forces. For example, while in 2003 the US military had almost no robots, today it has over 7,000 unmanned aerial vehicles (UAVs) and 10,000 unmanned ground vehicles (UGVs).

Current US military robots include an unmanned helicopter called the MQ-8B Fire Scout, unmanned planes called the Predator, Raven and Global Hawk, and a small, ground-based robot called PackBot that is used to help locate and clear explosives. A rugged, four-wheeled hopping robot called the Precision Urban Hopper is also in development. This features a piston that enables it to leap 25 feet into the air, and is intended for video surveillance and to carry payloads across rough terrain.

An even more impressive robot being developed with US military funding is BigDog. Engineered by Boston Dynamics, this quadruped can walk, run and climb over rough terrain while carrying heavy loads. At about one metre long and with a weight of 75 kg, BigDog is powered by an internal combustion engine and uses a very wide array of sensors to monitor and regulate its motion. It has also set the world record for legged vehicles by travelling 12.8 miles without stopping or refuelling.

Given that robots neither sleep nor bleed, they are increasingly being deployed in many reconnaissance and combat situations. As explained by Joseph W. Dyer, CEO of military supplier iRobot, another advantage of robots is that 'they can fire second'. It is therefore perhaps not surprising that a US military report entitled *Unmanned Effects: Taking the Human out of the Loop* has suggested that robot soldiers may be the norm rather than the exception on the battlefield as early as 2025. Or as a spokesperson for defence contractor BAE Systems said at a UAV product launch in 2010, 'some of the pilots showing off their skills [at this military airshow] may be the last of their kind'.

Over 50 nations are now developing military robot technologies, with the market for UAVs alone worth $5 billion a year. In theory, the deployment of military robots could lead to fewer lives being lost, with front-line battles between two entirely robotic armies now a potential possibility. However, there is also the danger that military robots will make war too easy, less risky and hence more likely. The number of civilians killed or injured may also increase as robotic soldiers take to the battlefield. UAVs flown from the United States have, after all, already 'accidentally' slain many villagers in Afghanistan.

Fortunately, not all future robots that labour in hostile locations will work for the military. Others will venture deep underground, beneath the oceans or into space. Robots were the first explorers from Planet Earth to visit other planets and this trend is likely to continue. Robots are also likely to be used to construct the future solar power stations or solar sails mentioned earlier in this book. As noted in Chapter 15, the first Earthlings to routinely live in space may also turn out to be cybernetic robot-human hybrids.

Humanoid Robots

Very few of the robots mentioned in the previous three sections look remotely human. Given that they have been designed for a narrow range of specific applications, this is hardly a surprise. However, most people do find it easiest to relate to a humanoid. At least some robots with faces, humanoid bodies and an ability to use human body language are therefore pretty certain to walk among us in the future. Humanoid robots may also prove the most effective domestic servants and factory workers given that the modern world has been designed pretty exclusively for human occupation.

The development of humanoid robots – or androids – has been progressing very slowly for a great many years. Giving a robot a body with roughly human proportions is actually not that difficult. However, providing any such robot with the ability to control that body – let alone to walk around, see the world and engage in tasks that require hand–eye coordination – has until very recently been a near-impossible challenge.

For decades, most of the key difficulties associated with building a functional, humanoid robot were addressed by mechanical engineers and programmers who sought to understand and mimic human capabilities. For example, a common research goal was to program a robot with optimal routines that would allow it to walk on flat surfaces and climb stairs. However, more recently, the application of cheap computer power and sensor technologies has come to the fore. As a result, most robots that can walk now accomplish this feat not just by enacting a predetermined program, but also by constantly sensing the world and adjusting their servo motors to stop themselves falling over. What this hopefully makes clear is that for many years the constraining factor in humanoid robot development has been available computer power, not suitable physical mechanisms. Without today's microprocessors, those inventors who built metal people in the 1960s, 1970s and 1980s really did not stand a chance.

Today, the company that has pushed humanoid robots further than any other is Honda. Most notably, the Japanese manufacturing giant has created a 1.3 metre high, 54 kg humanoid robot called ASIMO that can walk, run, climb stairs, open doors, operate light switches, push trolleys, carry trays and perform many other tasks. ASIMO has a white metal-and-plastic body except for a dark visor that covers its 'face'. In effect, the robot looks like a child in a plastic space suit.

ASIMO's hands have independent, opposable thumbs that can exert a force of 0.5 kg. Wrist sensors then allow ASIMO to detect the force it is applying and synchronize its movements with a person so that it can take an object from them. All of ASIMO's movements are very fluid indeed, giving the robot a very lifelike quality. This is especially the case when ASIMO is running, bending or climbing – let alone dancing or playing football.

ASIMO features both vision and voice recognition that allow it to plan its route, avoid obstacles and identify known faces. The robot can also respond to its name, look to whoever is speaking to it and respond to their gestures. This means that ASIMO is able to comply if human beings point out where they would like it to go.

Each ASIMO robot currently costs at least $1 million to manufacture. It is therefore perhaps not surprising that the robot is not yet available for general sale. This said, rental periods can now be arranged. You can find out more and watch ASIMO in action on the robot's website at asimo.honda.com. This is probably as close to seeing the future of humanoid robots as you are currently going to get.

While Honda is rightly proud of ASIMO, it is not the only sophisticated humanoid robot that has been created. Another mechanical biped is TOPIO – a robot from TOSY Robotics in Vietnam that is capable of playing table tennis against a human being. At 1.88 metres high and 120 kg, TOPIO is an imposing figure. It also looks more human than ASIMO, with a very human-shaped head and a visor crafted to look like a pair of sunglasses.

A third contender to be C-3P0's brother is Robonaut 2 or 'R2'. This robot is the result of an ongoing collaboration between General Motors and NASA to create the next generation of robots for automotive and aerospace application. R2 looks a bit like a golden-helmet version of Iron Man. It also has its own website at robonaut.jsc.nasa.gov.

Unlike ASIMO and TOPIO, R2 is only humanoid from the waist up, as in space the ability to walk is less of an issue. However, R2 is currently by far the most dexterous anthropomorphic robot that has ever been made. For a start, all of R2's fingers and thumbs are capable of extended, independent travel. R2 can therefore use the same tools that astronauts currently wield on the International Space Station. This means that R2 will be able to take over simple, repetitive or dangerous operations – such as changing an air filter – without the need to adapt any existing space station components or tools. As the involvement of General Motors signals, in the future the potential will exist for R2's descendants to work on existing factory production lines doing tasks currently undertaken by seated human beings.

A Future Robot Economy?

The creation of robots capable of working with tools that have been designed for human beings could have profound implications. As noted earlier in this chapter, already half of the 'workforce' in auto manufacture is robotic. Within a decade or so, next-generation robots like R2 could now well be set to replace a significant proportion of the other half. Many service sector jobs – such as those in farming, healthcare and retail – may additionally be under threat once robots like ASIMO move into cost-effective mass production. With TOPIO around, even professional table-tennis players may need to find a new line of business.

Once robots possess a reasonable level of dexterity,

visual coordination, robustness and intelligence, they are likely to make very effective workers. In fact, with no requirement for rest or payment, robots are likely to prove by far the most cost-effective workforce in many manufacturing and agricultural situations. Even in more service-orientated jobs like caring for the sick and the elderly, humanoid robots may gain the edge over humans once empathetic skills already in development are further honed.

A few decades hence, a flood of cheap robot labour could dramatically increase the scale and size of the global economy with significant benefits for us all. Alternatively, in a world facing the resource constraints outlined in Part I of this book, an equally possible scenario is that the emergence of a future robot labour force will create mass unemployment in an economy of roughly its current size. Robot carers that keep the elderly out of hospitals or care homes may on the face of it seem a very good proposition, yet it may actually be better for us all to employ more human carers to achieve the same result.

A very large number of future robot workers could even change the balance of prices in many markets. For example, at present the value of many things is a reflection of the human effort that goes into making them. But when and if robot workers become multitudinous, the cost of putting things together will be very small compared to the value of the natural resources consumed. In a world shared with robots, the economic value of physical labour may therefore become very small indeed. Today, a house priced at £200,000 may cost £100,000 for the land and building materials and £100,000 for all of the involved labour. In the future, the price may remain the same, but with the land and materials costing £195,000, and the hire cost for the robo-swarm that builds it accounting for only £5,000.

The Birth of a New Species
The last five chapters have highlighted the scope and scale of the next generation computing resources that will be with us sooner rather than later. While the automobile industry may take decades to embrace a new innovation like the electric car, we can be pretty certain that a great many fundamentally new innovations will roll out in the computing industry before the end of this decade. By 2020, cloud computing will make high levels of cheap computing power available to most people anytime and anywhere on virtually any kind of computing device. Artificial intelligence will also become widely available from the cloud, and in turn this will allow the construction of sophisticated robots that will not always have to think or even see for themselves. After all, why fit every robot on a production line with eyes and vision-processing technology if they can all tap into their factory's CCTV cameras and a Google cloud vision recognition app?

Today, at the end of the era of dumb, local computing, we already have a robot population that is approaching nine million. Given the advancements in smart, cloud computing that are starting to accrue, it would therefore be staggering if there were not tens or hundreds of millions of robots in the world in a few decades time. The number of PCs on the planet rose from zero to over a billion in barely 30 years. To predict an increase in the robot population from 9 to perhaps 200 million in 20 years is therefore potentially quite conservative. In the wake of the PC many jobs were lost and many new industries created. The tide of the rising robot revolution could similarly have profound social, cultural and economic implications.

It also needs to be appreciated that every kind of robot mentioned in this chapter has been an artificial creature built from inorganic components. For the next decade or so, inorganic robots made from metal, plastic and silicon electronics are also likely to remain the norm. However, once technologies like synthetic biology (as detailed in Chapter 9) and bioprinting (as covered in Chapter 22) enter widespread application, the possibility will exist for robots to be constructed from organic parts. This means that future robots may have hands, arms, legs, eyes and even brains that are grown rather than forged or 3D printed from plastic and metal. When this occurs – and one day it will – the line between 'organic' and 'inorganic' life will truly have been crossed.

When the J. Craig Venter Institute pieced together a synthetic bacterium from standardized bits of DNA the world did not really pay that much attention. Certainly nobody in the press expressed a fear for their job. However, fast-forward 20 years and the final product of synthetic biology may well be artificial, organic beings capable of harvesting and serving your breakfast, fighting wars and looking after your granny.

The prospect of future synthetic and intelligent *organic* life ought to start raising a great many practical and philosophical questions. We also need to recognize that a bio-robotic future will not occur in isolation from the alteration of ourselves. Once robotics goes organic, the exchange of materials between human beings and robots will become possible. The skillsets and knowledge of computer scientists, engineers and medics will also inevitably converge. And if this all sounds rather surreal, bizarre and frightening then I can only assure you that it is.

In the face of the ever-blurring line between what is 'natural' and what is 'artificial', the human race is set to enter a radical phase in its own evolution. Already we have started to unlock the code of our own DNA, to 'correct' defects in our genes, and to introduce artificial technologies into our bodies. The final part of this book is therefore dedicated to the arrival of 'Humanity 2.0'.

Part V

HUMANITY 2.0

21

GENETIC MEDICINE

Future studies deals with two fundamental questions. The first is 'how will we live in the future?' while the second is 'what will we become?' Parts I to IV of this book have already looked at 20 future things that may alter our lifestyles. It is therefore left to this final part to consider potential future changes to ourselves. Specifically, the next few chapters will examine how genetic medicine, bioprinting, cybernetic enhancement and a range of related developments may result in the creation of co-called 'post-humans', or what some now refer to as 'Humanity 2.0'.

Never before has human evolution potentially been under our control. However, it is now pretty certain that those new medical tools and enhancement technologies on the horizon will provide the opportunity to shape our own physiological inheritance. As a consequence, our descendants may enjoy significantly extended lifespans and may even choose to cast aside some currently core aspects of the human condition.

While the principal aim of the following five chapters is to outline what may become technically possible, some of the wider ethical and philosophical debates that surround Humanity 2.0 will also be explored. Fairly soon, the application of new medical technologies will strike at the very heart of our relationship with the rest of Creation. It is therefore not surprising that some people claim we are beginning to play at God. After all, until this point in history, only divine beings have been deemed capable of having power over life itself.

Toward DNA Healthcare

In many respects medicine has changed very little since ancient times. Granted, the sophisticated drugs and surgical techniques that doctors now have in their arsenal may be far removed from those that existed even half a century ago. Even so, most healthcare techniques still rely on the ingestion or injection of standardized chemicals, or on the physical repair or removal of diseased or damaged tissue.

In the early 21st century, medical practice stands on the verge of its greatest ever revolution. Just as nanotechnology is starting to allow manufacturers to create new and far more precise materials, so genetic engineering is starting to provide doctors with new tools that will allow them to understand and manipulate patient DNA. Three highly important advancements are subsequently on the horizon.

Firstly, genetic testing will increasingly be used to detect actual or potential disease. This is indeed already starting to happen.

Secondly, fairly soon anybody with an illness will be able to be provided with a personalized therapy. Initially, most such treatments will use 'pharmacogenetics' to identify the conventional drugs that are most appropriate for each patient's individual genetic makeup. However, in time entirely new forms of genetic therapy will also become available. These will target specific mutations in a patient's DNA to either cure a disease or to prevent it from occurring in the first place.

Finally, genetic medicine will also be applied to select or alter healthy human genomes. For example, parents will increasingly be able to choose some of the physical or mental characteristics of their children. People may also opt to have their genetic code rewritten to help extend their lifespan, or to otherwise change their physical or mental characteristics. We have become used to installing apps to upgrade the functionality of our smartphones. Decades hence, we may similarly expect doctors to inject us with genetic therapies that will alter the parameters of our bodies.

The foundation for all future forms of genetic medicine was the Human Genome Project. This publicly funded, international collaboration began work in 1990 to identify, store and make publicly available the information contained in human DNA. In 1998, a private company called Celera Genomics also set itself the same goal. While initially this created some rivalry, the two research teams actually ended up working together. This resulted in a first, rough draft of the human genome in 2000, followed by the publication of a truly complete sequence in 2003.

The first reading of the 'book of life' really captured the public's imagination. It is therefore unfortunate that most popular, global media expected far too much too soon. The completion of the Human Genome Project was really the start and not the end of a great journey. Having a copy of the book of life is one thing. But understanding what each word in the book means – let alone copy-editing the whole manuscript to correct imperfections – is something else entirely.

By the time the Human Genome Project had been completed, scientists had also discovered many things that they did not expect. For a start, exactly what constituted a gene came into question. It was also found that the 'expression' of a gene – or in other words whether it is turned 'on' or 'off' – is at least as important medically as gene composition. Additionally, it was recognized that every human genome is different and that the differences between them really matter a great deal.

Genetic Testing

The first application of genetic medicine was in genetic testing. In fact, even before the Human Genome Project was completed, the screening of human DNA for mutations in its genetic code was starting to become routine. While the role of most genes – let alone gene combinations – is far from understood, already more than 1,000 genetic tests are available.

For couples who conceive a child using in vitro fertilization (IVF), it is common to perform genetic tests on the resultant embryos. Such pre-implantation genetic diagnosis (PGD) allows only embryos free of genetic mutations to be implanted back into the mother and carried to term. The birth of a child with cystic fibrosis, sickle cell disease, spinal muscular atrophy or a wide range of other conditions can subsequently be avoided.

As may be expected, a great deal of research effort is going into understanding the genetics of cancer. For example, 2008 saw the launch of the International Cancer Genome Consortium (ICGC). Over a period of about a decade, this has the intention of generating data on the genomic changes associated with up to 50 of the most common types of cancer. The research process involves removing a cancerous cell and a normal cell from a cancer patient. These are then compared to identify differences in their DNA sequences. In time, the results of this work will allow doctors to test for and diagnose cancers based on their genetic characteristics, rather than their location in the body. Further into the future, the hope is to develop improved cancer treatments.

As the genetic characteristics of more and more medical conditions are identified, the demand for genetic testing is already rising. Already there is a multimillion dollar industry that allows members of the public to order genetic tests over the Internet. People simply select the particular test they want and send off a saliva sample for analysis.

The technical process of undergoing a genetic test really is now down to the level of point, click and spit. This said, understanding and coping with the results can be far less straightforward. Counselling services for people worried about their genetic code may therefore become common not that many years from now. Fairly soon, some people are also likely to be graduating with genetic counselling degrees.

Today genetic tests are undertaken to check for a specific genetic mutation. However, by the end of the decade it is quite possible that individuals will routinely have their entire genome sequenced. When the Human Genome Project first read human DNA it took 13 years and cost $3 billion. But that work started over two decades ago and technology has seriously moved on.

Today a company called Illumina in California sells gene-sequencing technology that can read the three billion base pairs in an individual human genome in just eight days for a cost of about $10,000. And things do not end there. Indeed, according to another Californian company called Pacific Biosciences, by the middle of this decade it will be possible to map a human genome in 15 minutes for less than $1,000. By the end of the decade it may therefore be possible to go online, spit into a tube and obtain a copy of your own complete DNA code for no more than a few hundred dollars, pounds, euros or yen.

It is perhaps not surprising that some people are starting to talk of the 'pre-genomic' and 'post-genomic' ages of medicine. After all, once most people's genetic code becomes part of their medical record, the understanding of a great many diseases and their causes is likely to skyrocket. If they wish, individuals will be able to plan their lifestyles and select pre-emptive medical treatments based on a knowledge of the biological blueprint contained in their cells. Healthcare organizations will also be able to plan their services far more effectively if the quantum computers in their basements have access to the genetic makeup of a reasonable proportion of their future patients.

Pharmacogenetics

Predicting and diagnosing medical conditions is all very well. However, it will be the application of genetic medicine to improve patient treatment that will really trigger the next healthcare revolution. As we shall see in the next section, eventually genetic therapies will be developed to correct defects in a patient's DNA. But even before this occurs, genetic medicine will permit the use of 'pharmacogenetics' to help doctors obtain the best results from conventional medical treatments.

Pharmacogenetics – also known as pharmacogenomics – is the study of how genes influence an individual's response to drugs. Since medicine began it has been obvious that different people respond differently to the same medication. Unfortunately, it has usually not been known why. The promise of pharmacogenetics is to alter this situation by allowing doctors to select treatments based on the genetic makeup of each individual patient.

In the United States alone it has been estimated that every year approaching 100,000 deaths and two million hospitalizations are the result of an adverse drug response

(ADR). These staggering statistics highlight ADR as one of the leading causes of mortality. The widespread application of pharmacogenetics to match drug prescriptions to a patient's genetic profile will therefore make medical treatments far safer and will save many lives.

Due to pharmacogenetics, the overall cost of healthcare will also be reduced. Drugs such as Herceptin (used to treat breast cancer) and Erbitux (used to treat colon cancer) work in less than 40 per cent of patients with a specific genetic makeup. They also cost up to $10,000 a month. At present doctors have to rely on trial and error to find out if these and other drugs will prove effective in a particular patient. This squanders resources in addition to hindering the patient's treatment.

Pharmacogenetics will also allow drug dosages to be calculated based on a person's genetics rather than purely their weight and age. Vaccines will also be able to be genetically targeted, with different strains made available to best suit a range of patient DNA profiles. The safety and effectiveness of vaccination programmes will therefore increase.

In addition, pharmacogenetics will speed the development and approval of conventional drugs, as well as making possible medicines that serve only a niche population. At present, if a new drug proves safe and effective in 90 per cent of trial cases but triggers serious side effects in the remainder then it will not make it to market. However, if it can be shown that all of those with an adverse reaction share the same genetic profile then the drug could be safely approved for the rest of the population. Today drugs have to be developed and tested for use in potentially any human being. One of the really great promises of pharmacogenetics is that this very significant drug development hurdle will be removed.

Pharmacogenetics may well be the medical development that persuades the majority of people to have their individual genome sequenced and stored in their medical record. This would, after all, allow every one of their prescriptions to be matched to their genetic profile. This said, the widespread, routine sequencing of individual genomes is probably at least a decade away. Before that time, a critical pharmacogenetic technology is therefore likely to be the 'gene chip'.

A gene chip is a medical sensor about the size of a matchbox. Each chip features a tiny glass grid or 'DNA microarray'. Every square on this grid then contains a particular DNA snippet. In the lab, a sample of patient cells is squirted on to the microarray. This causes some of the squares on the grid to illuminate, so revealing the 'expression' (or level of activation) of particular genes. By looking at the gene chip under a microscope, doctors (or their computers) can then examine the genetic profile of their patient.

At present, while gene chips are available from commercial suppliers such as Affymetrix and Roche, they are very much a research tool. However, fairly soon they could become the diagnostic workhorse of pharmacogenetics. Indeed, in maybe no more than five or ten years, cancer patients may routinely have cells from their tumour analysed using a gene chip. The readout from this chip would then determine their treatment.

Today, some first generation pharmacogenetic products are just starting to enter the market. For example, a company called AssureRx has developed a genetic test called GeneSightRx. This analyses a patient's genetic makeup to indicate the likely effectiveness of certain psychiatric drugs. All that a doctor has to do is to send a cheek swab to the AssureRx lab. The result is then accessed online, so enabling the best treatment to be prescribed.

Gene Therapy

While pharmacogenetics will significantly improve patient treatments, it is still a diagnostic rather than a directly therapeutic tool. The genetic medicine revolution will therefore not be complete until gene therapy enters routine clinical practice.

Gene therapy aims to correct the gene defects that are responsible for a specific medical condition. Already researchers are investigating a range of techniques that will make this possible. The most common is the insertion of an additional healthy gene into a patient's genome to take on the function of a missing or inactive gene. Alternatively, a healthy gene may be swapped with a defective gene. Yet another approach employs 'selective reverse mutation' to return a defective gene to its previously healthy state. Finally, techniques are also being developed that could in future allow the expression of certain genes to be turned 'on' or 'off'.

Several mechanisms may be used to insert additional or replacement genes into a patient's DNA. Most commonly, gene transfer agents called 'vectors' are used to deliver therapeutic genes to target patient cells. Usually these vectors are viruses that have been genetically modified to carry human DNA. Alternative gene-therapy delivery mechanisms include the direct injection of therapeutic DNA into target cells or the creation of artificial liposomes. The latter are fatty substances that adhere to the surface of cells. By coating genes with liposomes they can therefore be administered to patients and encouraged to enter their cells.

While gene therapy is not a current medical practice, an increasing number of trials are taking place. One of these commenced in Great Ormond Street Hospital in London in 2001. Here, doctors used gene therapy to treat an

18-month old baby called Rhys Evans who suffered from a condition called X-linked severe combined immunodeficiency (X-SCID). This rare, debilitating disease is caused by a single mutated gene and condemns its sufferers to live in sterile conditions as any form of infection can kill them. For this reason, before his treatment Rhys was known as the 'bubble baby' as he was permanently protected in a sealed plastic environment.

In the pioneering treatment, Rhys had a healthy version of his mutant gene added to his genome. The treatment worked and a decade later he is still doing well. Since that time a handful of other children have also received the same gene therapy. However, some have developed leukaemia as a result. Human trials of gene therapies subsequently remain controversial in some eyes. In fact, in the United States they were even banned for a few months in 2003. This followed the death of a young man who was receiving gene therapy for ornithine transcarbamylase deficiency (OTCD), as well as the reports of leukaemia in the Great Ormond Street trials.

Learning how to rewrite a human being's genetic code is inevitably a precarious business. Nevertheless, many people with otherwise untreatable and life-shortening illnesses remain willing to participate in research trials. These include some of those who suffer from cystic fibrosis. This degenerative illness affects the lungs, gut, pancreas and other organs, and is the most common inherited genetic disorder in Caucasians.

People with cystic fibrosis do not possess a working version of a gene called the cystic fibrosis transmembrane conductance regulator (CFTR). This means that they cannot properly regulate their sweat, digestive juices and mucus, and are unlikely to live beyond their mid-30s. However, the UK Cystic Fibrosis Gene Therapy Consortium has recently begun human trials to try to treat cystic fibrosis using gene therapy. To date, patients have used inhalers to introduce liposome gene carriers into their lungs. While some progress is being made, patients have also suffered unanticipated side effects. A genetic cure for cystic fibrosis is therefore unlikely to be delivered this decade, although it does remain a possibility further into the future.

Other bleeding-edge gene therapy projects are also raising hopes for future cures. For example, in 2008 the Moorfields Eye Hospital NIHR Biomedical Research Centre in the United Kingdom reported the results of a clinical trial that used gene therapy to treat inherited blindness. The experiments involved young patients with an eye disease called Leber's congenital amaurosis (LCA). This is caused by an abnormality in the gene RPE65. Researchers inserted healthy copies of this gene into the retinas of three volunteer patients. All three then experienced vision improvements and no side effects. In principle, this work lays the foundation to use gene therapy in the treatment of a range of eye disorders.

Yet more progress has been demonstrated in animal trials. For example, researchers at the University of Texas have used gene therapy to reduce the number and size of lung cancer tumours in mice. At the University of Washington, an injection of cells has also been used to cure some monkeys of their colour-blindness. Meanwhile, researchers working at the London School of Pharmacy have cured cancers in mice by targeting them with nanoparticle genetic therapy treatments. As explained by Dr Andreas Schätzlein, the hope is to use such highly targeted gene therapies to treat human cancer patients in clinical trials 'within a couple of years'.

Future Genetic Enhancement

Later this century it is quite possible than genetic therapy will be used to cure cancer, heart disease, Alzheimer's, asthma, diabetes and a wide range of other diseases. But well before this happens, a great many ethical questions will need to be addressed. Few if any people are likely to argue against the use of gene therapy to cure recognized medical conditions. However, once we have the ability to reliably and accurately reprogram the human genome the whole question of what is 'normal' and what is a 'disability' is going to become far more contentious.

A significant area of debate will concern the application of 'somatic' versus 'germline' gene therapy. The results of somatic gene therapy only affect the patient who is treated. In contrast, germline gene therapies endow the patient with genetic traits that they will pass on to future generations if they reproduce. While today the decision to undergo a medical treatment is a purely personal one, in the future this will not always be the case.

The ethical issues surrounding germline gene therapies will be magnified when it becomes possible to undertake treatments that are not widely accepted as a medical necessity. If in the future a cystic fibrosis patient undergoes a germline therapy that cures her of the disease and prevents it occurring in her descendants then this is unlikely to be controversial. However, let us suppose that a cosmetic germline gene therapy becomes available for altering a person's hair colour. On the one hand, an individual patient may argue for their right to undergo this treatment to save them the time and money they choose to expend constantly dyeing their hair. On the other hand, opponents may argue that one person should not have the right to alter the human gene pool in a manner that will inflict some others in the future with hair that is blue, green or pink.

Future gene therapies are likely to allow people to develop a great many physical attributes that are unavailable via natural means. At the time of writing, no athlete has been detected 'gene-doping' at a major sports event. However, injecting a person with a virus that contains a performance-enhancing gene will become a possibility.

Already an experimental, synthetic virus called Repoxygen has been created that inserts a gene to increase the production of red blood cells. This has been successfully tested in mice and is intended as a future treatment for anaemia. However, as an increased red blood cell count increases the level of oxygen that can be carried to the muscles, the use of Repoxygen in an otherwise healthy person could increase their potential athletic performance. Before the 2006 Winter Olympics there was apparently a report of one coach trying to get hold of Repoxygen.

In the not-too-distant future, gene therapy injections that permanently boost a person's production of human growth hormone are also a possibility. Constant, conventional doping would therefore become a thing of the past, with future gene-doping reprogramming some athlete's bodies to 'naturally' produce more growth hormones and to carry more oxygen in the blood. The ramifications here could clearly be very significant – and not just in athletics if gene-doping occurs at a germline level.

Yet another frightening possibility may be the use of transgenics in future human genetic therapy. As outlined in Chapter 8, transgenics is where genetic material is moved between species. The introduction of human genetic material into animals is now routine as it allows them to be 'humanized' for use in medical research. However, there is potentially no reason why the technique cannot be used the other way around. In the future, some human beings may therefore choose to take on selected animal characteristics.

Cheetahs can run at 70 miles an hour and are the fastest animal on the planet. So why not isolate the relevant cheetah genes and introduce them into humans to enable them to run faster? Or why not mash a few choice genes from some other animals to give future humans better night vision, glowing fingernails or even wings? These suggestions may sound preposterous. But there has to remain the possibility that at least one mad scientist will choose to experiment.

Also, imagine the implications of creating a gene therapy virus that would allow the human digestive system to extract more protein from certain foods. Would future governments be justified in spreading such a virus among a starving population? Back in Chapter 8 we considered the potential of the GM nutraceutical Golden Rice to prevent blindness by providing children with more vitamin A. Would there really be a convenient, ethical line between genetically altering a population's food to improve its health, and genetically altering a population to extract more goodness from its existing food supply? To this really big question I cannot provide an answer. Yet it is the sort of dilemma that future developments in genetic medicine will raise.

* * *

Creating Designer Babies

The use of genetic therapies to cure disease, let alone to alter or enhance human beings, lies may years into the future. In contrast, genetic selection is already starting to occur. As noted earlier in this chapter, couples who conceive using IVF already have the option to screen their embryos for certain medical conditions. However, alongside the opportunity to try to ensure a healthy child, the screening of embryos for desired characteristics is also already taking place.

For example, an organization called the Fertility Institutes in the United States allows couples to use IVF not only to screen for over 400 hereditary diseases, but to choose the sex of their child. As only embryos of the desired sex are implanted, the service provides child sex selection with a 100 per cent guarantee. Avoiding IVF, a company called GenSelect now sells an at-home nutraceutical kit that couples can use to choose the sex of their child with a claimed 96 per cent success rate. The new term used by some to justify this practice is 'family balancing'.

The introduction of technologies that allow parents to choose the sex of their child ought to be recognized as a watershed in human evolution. Already some fertility clinics have the technical ability to select a baby's hair and eye colour. Due to predicted religious opposition, this service has not yet been offered to their customers. But that day will come. Increasingly, prospective parents are therefore going to be making conscious but unregulated changes to the human gene pool.

In the United Kingdom, already 2 per cent of children are born as a result of IVF. Regardless of the ethics, this has to signal that the human race has started to take medical control of its own biological inheritance. Imagine if every couple suddenly opted to have a girl. Removing nature's randomness from the process of creating the next generation could have far-reaching consequences.

The human race used to be regulated by the survival of the fittest. If we still are, then being the 'fittest' is already a measure not just of a person's ability to attract a mate with the most survival-centric characteristics, but of the technological resources a person can bring to bear in the conception process. A great many of the things outlined over the past few pages may have seemed fantastical and even wrong. However, with one in 50 newborns in some nations already owing their existence to the manipulation of life in the laboratory, nothing that has been mentioned here ought to be dismissed out of hand.

Game-changing genetic testing, genetic therapy and genetic selection technologies will be with us in a fraction of an evolutionary blink. Their application could then rapidly alter our species. There is also already ample evidence to suggest that any and all developments in genetic medicine will be rapidly embraced.

22

BIOPRINTING

Often when I give a lecture on future studies I say something about 3D printing. As outlined in Chapter 6, this is a generic term for a range of technologies that create real, solid objects from digital data by building them up one layer at a time. When I inform an audience that some companies are already manufacturing plastic and metal components using 3D printing there is often a murmur of amazement. However, when I next reveal that living tissue has also been 3D printed, at least one person usually lets out a very noticeable gasp.

The 3D printing of biological materials currently goes by a variety of names. These include 'tissue printing', 'organ printing', 'additive cellular assembly' and 'bioprinting'. At present the latter is the most common term and therefore the one that we will use here. This said, as with any bleeding-edge science, the involved terminology may very rapidly change.

Whatever it ends up being called, bioprinting is without doubt a field of research with incredible medical potential. Even future advancements in genetic medicine are unlikely to prove of assistance to people who have their bodies damaged in accidents or who suffer major organ failure.

Today, such patients may recover following a long period of healing or perhaps an organ transplant. But in the future, the option will exist to use a bioprinter to help repair damaged tissue or to create a replacement synthetic organ. OK, so by now you may have let out a very noticeable gasp yourself.

From Photoprinter to Bioprinter

In essence, bioprinting is just an advanced form of the inkjet printing process that millions of people use each day to create hardcopies of their documents or photos. As you are probably aware, conventional inkjet printers electrostatically spray droplets of ink on to paper in order to produce text or an image. It just happens to be the case that the droplets of ink that are squirted out are about the same size as human cells. Replace the cartridges of ink in your desktop printer with cartridges of a liquid cell culture, and you could in theory start printing out thin layers of living tissue.

The above is exactly what bioprinting pioneer Professor Makoto Nakamura initially tried to achieve around a decade ago. In his work as a paediatrician in Japan, Professor Nakamura was painfully aware of the number of children desperate for an organ transplant. With too few organs available, he had to watch many of these children die. For years the professor hoped for medical advancements and conducted research into artificial hearts and other mechanical organs. Then, in 2002, he realized that an inkjet printer could potentially print out human cells, and so began his own bioprinting experiments using a standard Seiko Epson printer.

Unfortunately, Professor Nakamura's first inkjet printer just clogged up. So like many with a hardware problem, he rang customer service. When the Professor first explained that he was trying to use the printer to output human cells he received no help at all. However, eventually one Epson official did show some interest and provided him with technical support. A year later, this enabled Professor Nakamura to become one of the first researchers to output cells that survived an inkjet printing process. He achieved this by encasing the cells in sodium alginate to stop them drying out, and by jetting them into a calcium-chloride solution.

In 2008, a team lead by Professor Nakamura at the Kanagawa Academy of Science and Technology in Tokyo completed a project to build an experimental bioprinter. This has already been used to build a millimetre-wide tube – similar to a human blood vessel – using two different types of cells. The printer can currently produce about 15 mm of biotubing every minute. Professor Nakamura's hope is that in a couple of decades he will be able to produce entire replacement human organs.

While Professor Nakamura's work is amazing, he is not the only bioprinting pioneer. Perhaps most notably, in March 2008 a research group lead by Professor Gabor Forgacs from the University of Missouri managed to bioprint functional blood vessels and cardiac tissue using cells obtained from a chicken. The group's work relied on a prototype bioprinter custom-made by Orlando-based microelectronics manufacturer nScrypt. This device had three print heads, the first two of which were loaded with cardiac and endothelial cells. The third then dispensed a collagen scaffold – now known as a 'bio-paper' – to support the cells during printing.

Unlike Professor Nakamura's bioprinter, the one in-vented by Professor Forgacs and his team did not output one cell at a time. Rather, it dispensed spheroid blobs of 'bio-ink' that each contained tens of thousands of cells. This resulted in a faster process than a cell-at-a-time printer and was gentler on the cells. Moreover, it also encouraged the spheroids of bio-ink to fuse together. As Forgacs explained in 2008, it is not necessary to print all of the details of an organ with a bioprinter, as 'if you initiate the process, Nature will do it for you'.

To prove the point, the cells output by Forgacs' bioprinter amalgamated into living tissue 70 hours after they had been printed out. After 90 hours, the cardiac tissue even started beating like a regular heart muscle.

The First Commercial Bioprinter

Forgacs' bioprinting success stunned the medical world. It also led to the foundation of a company called Organovo to further develop the technology. This commercial organization set to work improving on the design of Forgacs' first experimental bioprinter and the result was the Novo-Gen MMX. Hailed as the world's first commercial bioprinter, this $200,000 piece of hardware is manufactured by an Australian company called Invetech and marketed by Organovo. The first NovoGen MMX was delivered to Organovo's lab in January 2009.

Organovo describes its NovoGen MMX bioprinter as a 'must-have cell and biomaterial sculpting tool'. Like its predecessor, it also has multiple, needle-like print heads. The first of these outputs successive thin layers of a water-based bio-paper made from collagen, gelatine or other hydrogels. These layers then hold in suspension the bio-ink spheroids that are printed or 'injected' into them by a second print head. As with the previous nScript printer, some hours after printing these bio-ink spheroids fuse together into living tissue. The bio-paper then either dissolves or is carefully removed by hand once the cells have fully fused. Figure 22.1 provides an illustration of Organovo's bioprinting process.

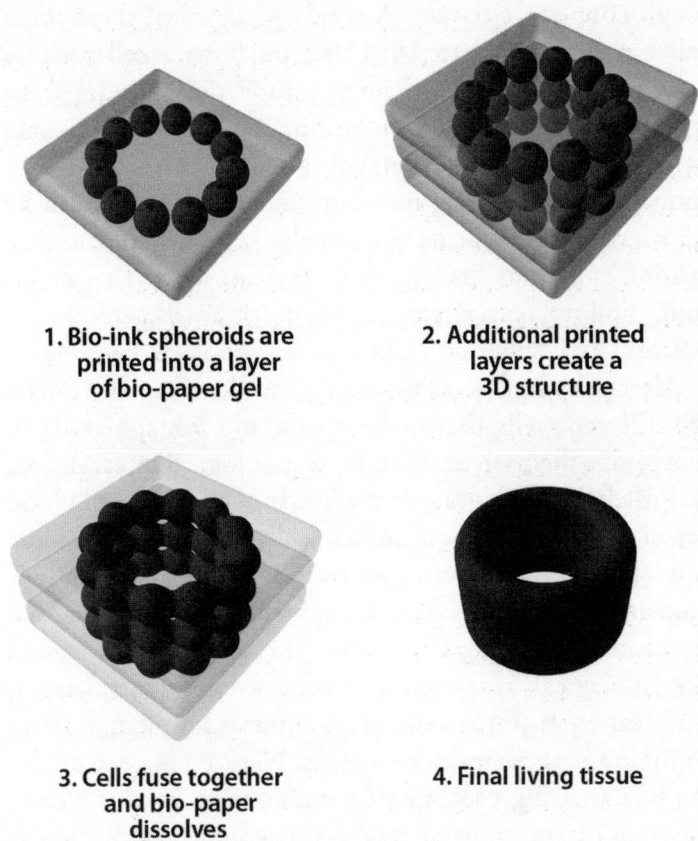

1. Bio-ink spheroids are printed into a layer of bio-paper gel

2. Additional printed layers create a 3D structure

3. Cells fuse together and bio-paper dissolves

4. Final living tissue

Figure 22.1: The Organovo bioprinting process

The bio-ink spheroids output by the NovoGen MMX reportedly contain anywhere between 10,000 and 80,000 cells. To create them, Organovo starts by growing cultures of several different cell types. For example, if the aim is to bioprint blood vessels, three different types of cell are used. These are primary endothelial cells (which form the lining of blood vessels), smooth muscle cells (which allow blood vessels to expand and contract) and fibroblasts (which form tough connective tissue). A solid aggregate of these three cell types is mixed together and put into a cell-packing device that compresses them in a tube and extrudes them like a kind of extremely thin bio-ink sausage. An 'aggregate cutter' next chops the sausage into bits, with the pieces spontaneously forming into bio-ink spheroids that can be transferred into a printing cartridge. From here the tiny bio-ink spheroids finally enter the print head. This precision, hollow needle can move in three dimensions to position each spheroid to an accuracy of a few microns.

After printing has occurred, nature takes over and causes the different cells that make up the bio-ink spheroids to reorganize themselves. With no technological intervention, endothelial cells migrate to the inside of a bioprinted blood vessel, while the smooth muscle cells move to the middle and the fibroblasts to the outside. In more complex bioprinted materials, intricate capillaries and other internal structures also naturally form. The process may sound almost magical. However, as Professor Forgacs explains, it is no different to the cells in an embryo knowing how to configure into complicated organs. Nature has been evolving this amazing capability for millions of years. Once in the right places, appropriate cell types somehow just know what to do.

In December 2010, Organovo announced that it had used a NovoGen MMX to create the first blood vessels to be bioprinted using cells cultured from a single person. It is therefore perhaps not surprising that *Time Magazine* listed the NovoGen MMX as one of its Best Inventions of 2010.

Toward Organs-on-Demand
Organovo has already started to implant bioprinted materials into animals, with some rats having successfully received bioprinted nerve grafts. Human trials are also

anticipated as early as 2015. However, Organovo expects that its bioprinters will initially be used to produce simple human tissue structures for toxicology tests. These will enable medical researchers to tests drugs in the lab on bioprinted models of the liver and other organs. The need to rely on animal tests alone will therefore be reduced.

Once human trials are complete, Organovo hopes that its bioprinters will be used to produce blood vessel grafts for use in heart-bypass surgery. In time, the company's intention is then to apply its technology to supply a much wider range of tissue-on-demand and even organs-on-demand. To this end, researchers are now working on tiny mechanical devices that can artificially exercise and hence strengthen bioprinted muscle tissue before it is implanted into a patient.

While both livers and hearts may one day be bioprinted, Organovo anticipates that its first artificial human organ will be a kidney. In functional terms, kidneys are one of the more straightforward parts of the body. The first bioprinted kidney may in fact not even need to look just like its natural counterpart or duplicate all of its features. Rather, all that future bioprinted kidneys will have to be capable of doing is cleaning waste products from the blood. The creation of such a bioprinted organ is now also not that many generations removed from Organovo's existing bioprinting capabilities.

Another bioprinting research team with the long-term goal of producing human organs-on-demand is the Advanced Tissue Fabrication Center at the Medical University of South Carolina. Here, lead researcher Dr Vladimir Mironov and his colleagues have developed a device called the envisionTEC Bioplotter. Like Organovo's NovoGen MMX, this features a bioprint head that can output bio-ink 'tissue spheroids' and supportive scaffold materials including fibrin and collagen hydrogels. However, in addition, the envisonTEC Bioplotter can also print a wider range of biomaterials. These include biodegradable polymers and ceramics that may be used to support and help form artificial organs. Alternatively, these materials may one day be used as bioprinting substitutes for bone.

Meanwhile, a team lead by Jeremy Mao at the Tissue Engineering and Regenerative Medicine Lab at Columbia University is scoping the application of bioprinting in dental and bone repairs. Already it is becoming routine for some dentists to take a 3D scan of their patient's mouth and for their lab to use this to help produce a prosthetic using a 3D printer. Jeremy Mao and his colleagues are therefore looking to achieve far more than this.

In one of its experiments the team bioprinted a mesh-like 3D scaffold in the shape of an incisor. This was then implanted into the jaw bone of a rat. The scaffold featured tiny, interconnecting microchannels that contained 'stem cell-recruiting substances'. Just nine weeks after implantation, these triggered the growth of fresh periodontal ligaments and newly formed alveolar bone. In time, this research may enable people to be fitted with living, bioprinted teeth or else scaffolds that will cause the body to grow new teeth all by itself.

In a related project, Mao's team is researching techniques that will allow people to 'naturally' regrow new joints around bioprinted scaffolds. Already 3D scans have been taken of the hip joints of several mature rabbits and used to bioprint 3D scaffold meshes upon which cartilage and bone can be regenerated. These scaffolds have then been infused with growth factors and implanted into the rabbits in place of their own hip bones. As the team has reported in *The Lancet*, over a four-month period the rabbits have all grown new and fully functional joints. Some of them have even begun to walk and otherwise place weight on their new joints only three or four weeks after surgery.

In Situ Bioprinting

All of the bioprinting research detailed in the previous section will one day allow the creation in the laboratory of replacement human tissue, regenerative scaffolds and synthetic organs. The surgical grafting and implantation of bioprinted body parts on to and into a patient is therefore destined to become a routine medical practice. One very important consequence should be that organ donor waiting lists will become a thing of the past. The rejection of transplanted organs and other tissue should also cease to be a problem as bioprinted materials will almost always be created from a culture of a patient's own cells. It therefore seems pretty certain that lab-based bioprinting will trigger a medical revolution. This said, already some researchers have begun experiments to take the technology to the next level.

Rather than creating replacement parts outside of the body, the ultimate future bioprinter will be capable of repairing the human body in situ. This means that it will bioprint new tissue directly on to a wound or inside a patient exactly where it is needed. Rather than having bioprinted materials grafted on to them or implanted by a surgeon, future patients will therefore be able to have their bodies repaired one cell or bio-ink spheroid at a time.

One of the pioneers of in situ bioprinting is Anthony Atala of the Wake Forest Institute for Regenerative Medicine in North Carolina. For several years Atala's team has been culturing human cells and placing or 'seeding' them on to pre-built scaffolds in order to produce synthetic organs. For example, the Wake Forest Institute has created artificial skin and bladders by building up layers of cells over appropriately shaped moulds. Back in 2006, seven bladders created in this manner were successfully implanted into human patients and are still working. However, growing tissue on pre-formed scaffolds is a very slow process, with each bladder taking about six weeks to create. Atala's team is therefore now experimenting with a bioprinter that will allow artificial tissue to be built far more quickly and in some instances in situ.

Most notably, Atala's team has been assessing the feasibility of treating burn victims with in situ bioprinting. In these experiments they have used a 3D scanner to produce 3D maps of test injuries inflicted on a number of mice. These maps have then been used to guide bioprint heads that have sprayed skin cells, a coagulant and collagen on to the wounds. The experimental system is already fairly sophisticated and able to determine what needs to be deposited on which part of the wound and at what thickness.

The results from Atala's latest work are very promising, with the wounds on the mice treated with the bioprinter healing in just two or three weeks compared to about five to six weeks in a control group where the wounds were left to heal naturally. There are also some indications that bioskin printing will prove less painful than giving a patient a skin graft. Funding for the skin-printing project is coming in part from the US military, which is keen to develop the technology to help heal wounds on the battlefield. At present the work is still in a pre-clinical phase with Atala progressing his research using pigs. However, trials of in situ bioprinting with human burn victims could be as little as five years away.

The potential to use bioprinters to repair our bodies in situ is pretty mind-blowing. Today most surgery creates a wound through which instruments and usually fingers then enter the patient to perform an internal stitch, staple or graft repair. Following an operation, the patient therefore needs to heal both internally and externally at the wound site.

While today there is no viable alternative to the above approach, in perhaps no more than a few decades it may be possible for robotic surgical arms tipped with bioprint heads to enter the body, repair damage at the cellular level, and then also repair their point of entry on their way out. Patients would still need to rest and recuperate for a few days as bioprinted materials fully fused into mature living tissue. However, most patients potentially could recover from very major surgery in less than a week.

Writing in the January–February 2011 edition of *The Futurist*, bioprinting pioneer Vladimir Mironov imagines how future in situ bioprinting may work in practice. As he muses, a football star may injure his knee with severe cartilage damage mid-season. In an immediate operation, four endoscopic devices would then enter his knee. One would be a camera, another a laser device, a third a tissue plasma evaporator and the fourth a bioprint head capable of outputting both a hydrocell scaffold and cells cultured from a small sample of the patient's own tissue.

Controlled by a robot but watched over by a doctor, the tissue plasma evaporator would remove all damaged tissue. Next, layers of hydrocell would be printed in its place and injected with stem cells that would be polymerized by the laser. The surgical tools would then be removed, with the wound sprayed and sealed with layers of a self-assembling bio-ink. Within 20 minutes the entire operation would be complete, and by next day the footballer would be back on the field with a fully functional knee and no pain. While this scenario is currently science fiction, it is nevertheless where today's first steps in bioprinting could lead us in the future.

Cosmetic Biofutures?

A great many technological innovations that are created for one purpose end up being used for another. For example, modern plastic surgery techniques were developed to help rebuild the bodies and lives of burn victims and others who suffered horrific accidents. However, as we all know, plastic surgery is now performed far more commonly for cosmetic reasons than out of medical necessity. As and when in situ bioprinting evolves into a routine and refined practice, its cosmetic application is similarly likely to skyrocket.

A few decades hence it may become possible to use a bioprinter to radically, rapidly and fairly safely transform the human body. Want bigger muscles without the exercise? Then why not visit your local bioprinting clinic and have them printed into your body that afternoon? Or fancy going skiing but worried about breaking your legs? Then why not have your bones replaced with new ones that feature carbon nanotube enforcements? These top-of-head scenarios may sound both fantastical and scary. Yet they may well be just the tip of a cosmetic bioprinting iceberg.

In time, specialist bioprinters may be created to enable the rapid, in situ removal and replacement of the human face. Such face printers could allow people to obtain a 3D scan of what they want to look like and have it applied as the ultimate form of makeup. Celebrities could sell scans of their faces over the Internet so that you really could decide to look exactly like your favourite star. Or perhaps some people may have their face scanned at the age of 20 and reapplied every ten years to achieve an apparent status of perpetual youth. Other more creative individuals may even choose to design their own faces and change them on a regular basis.

A bioprinted face replacement may sound like a truly horrific procedure that no fool would ever volunteer to undergo. It is therefore well worth remembering that millions of people every year already risk the dangers of surgery purely to try to improve their looks. Vanity has become an enormous business and is probably unlikely to shrink. Once the potential exists to have face-replacement surgery, at least a few crazed individuals are therefore likely to sign up. Of course, once they have successfully undergone the treatment, we may well not know who they are.

* * *

A Frankenstein Machine?

Some already worry that bioprinters will become 'Frankenstein machines' that will allow mad professors to design and create unnatural creatures in their underground lairs. In the absence of sufficient regulation, such fears may also not be entirely unfounded. However, it is probably more reasonable to suggest that bioprinters will be embraced as one of the more 'natural' technologies to be wielded by tomorrow's doctors and surgical robots. Bioprinted organs and tissue will after all normally be created from a culture of a patient's own cells. Most future bioprinters could therefore be considered little more than prosthetic aids to the natural human process of healing and self-repair.

Bioprinters are a very new technology whose far-reaching future applications we still have plenty of time to contemplate. A decade or more hence, everyday bioprinting is also not going to arrive in magical isolation. For a start, bioprinting is likely to blossom just as widespread genetic testing and pharmacogenetics come to the fore, and as the first human gene therapies start to become available. As we shall see in the next chapter, bioprinters will also enter our everyday medical armoury in tandem with a whole host of new, cybernetic prostheses.

The ways in which both individuals and our race may choose to repair and enhance the human form over the coming decades are going to be quite multitudinous. Today, many technology debates are dominated by the available means for accessing and interlinking online resources. But by 2030, we may well be far more obsessed with the available means for repairing and redesigning ourselves.

23

CYBERNETIC ENHANCEMENT

While writing this book I have been diagnosed with a small, double hernia. Whether or not there is any correlation between authoring a book on so many topics and developing this medical condition I will never know! However, I do not have to be a futurist to predict that sometime fairly soon I will undergo surgery. This will involve stapling a couple of polypropylene meshes into my abdomen to keep my intestines at bay. In time, new tissue will hopefully grow around and through these meshes. Unless I am one of the very few patients whose body rejects the plastic, these entirely synthetic supports will then remain part of my anatomy for the rest of my life.

Worldwide, several hundred thousand people a year have some plastic mesh added to their body in a hernia operation. Millions more have artificial lenses fitted in cataract operations, bones mended with metal pins, artificial hip replacements, or plastic valves installed in their hearts. Some individuals also receive greatly more sophisticated technological additions including cochlear implants and pacemakers. At the other end of the scale, millions of people are fitted with dental fillings, crowns or artificial teeth. In aggregate, each year a very large number of people start to inhabit a body that is not entirely organic.

Any creature that becomes an amalgamation of both natural and artificial parts is technically known as a cyborg. Adding artificial technology to any animal therefore not only enhances it capabilities, but changes its very nature. Granted, filling a tooth or stapling in a hernia mesh may not change a person a great deal (although it can cause them to set off some metal detectors). However, future cybernetic enhancements are increasingly going to blur the divide between human and machine. In the broadest sense, this chapter is therefore about the gradual cybernetic evolution of our race.

When the term cyborg is first mentioned, people often imagine some kind of future super-soldier with a human brain mashed into a fearsome robotic body. After all, such frightening visions of cyborgs have been presented by popular science fiction for decades. Not least the Borg in *Star Trek* or the cybermen in *Doctor Who* may spring to mind. However, as the opening of this chapter has hopefully signalled, the repair and augmentation of the human body with artificial parts is already a 'natural' medical practice. The vast majority of future cyborgs will therefore be family members and other fellow citizens rather than scary monsters.

By the second half of this century most people will probably be spending at least some of their time alive in a body with fairly sophisticated cybernetic enhancements. As technology advances and attitudes change, some individuals may even start to actively seek the artificial 'upgrading' of their flesh-based birthing-form. In turn, this may create a divide between enhanced 'post-humans' and everybody else. In parallel with advancements in genetic medicine and bioprinting, cybernetic enhancement is therefore something that wider society will be not be able to ignore.

Prosthetic Futures

In the long term it is probable that just about every part of the human body will be able to be replaced with an artificial alternative. The only likely exception is the biological hardware of the brain. In time, many replacement human body parts are likely to be bioprinted from a culture of a patient's own cells and may even be built in situ. This said, bioprinting has yet to leave the research lab. In contrast, artificial body parts built from plastic, metal and other inorganic components are already a rapidly advancing reality.

Cybernetic enhancements may be divided into those that have an information-processing capacity and those that do not. Until very recently, practically all prostheses fell into the latter category. In the future, artificial hip joints, teeth, heart valves, hernia meshes and so forth are also likely to remain 'dumb'. This is also perfectly reasonable given that all such devices have just one simple, physical function. 3D printing – of both the biological and non-biological variety – will in the relatively near future enable far better dumb prostheses to be tailored for each individual patient. For example, future replacement hip joints will probably be 3D printed to match to an MRI scan of a patient's natural bones. However, until in situ bioprinting becomes the norm, this is probably as far as dumb prostheses will progress.

In contrast, cybernetic enhancements with an information-processing capability look set for rapid advancement. For example, in the future an increasing number of artificial limbs are likely to be smart devices that will be under their wearer's control.

There are in essence two ways for a human being to control an artificial hand, arm or leg. The first is to use body motions – such as a shrug of the shoulders – to pull on cables that mechanically move a prosthetic. While far better than nothing, such body-powered technology is not very sophisticated as it does not rely on information processing. However, more advanced prosthetics do exactly this by using muscle signals to control an electric limb or hand.

A pioneer of muscle-controlled prosthetics is Touch Bionics in Scotland. Here an award-winning product has been developed called the i-LIMB Hand. This is the first prosthetic device with five individually powered digits, and is controlled by 'myoelectrics'. This is a technology that picks up muscle signals from electrodes placed on the surface of the wearer's skin and uses them to activate servo motors. Manufactured from high-strength yet lightweight plastics, the i-LIMB even looks like a real human hand.

Designers of myoelectric prostheses inevitably face the challenge of trying to control many movements from relatively few remaining muscles. To address this, the Center for Bionic Medicine at the Rehabilitation Institute of Chicago is developing a technique called 'targeted muscle reinnervation' (TMR). In TMR, nerves from amputated limbs are transferred – or in effect rewired – to another part of the body. For example, surgeons may re-route nerves from the shoulder of an amputated arm to the ulnar, musculocutaneous, median and radial nerves on the left or right of a patient's chest. In time, the corresponding chest muscles contract when the patient tries to move their amputated limb. Electrodes attached to these chest muscles can then enable the patient to control a prosthetic arm just by thinking about it.

One of the first people to be fitted with a TMR prosthetic was former US marine Claudia Mitchell who lost an arm in a motorcycle accident and was given a TMR-controlled artificial limb in 2007. Claudia can now perform tasks four times faster than when she had a conventional prosthetic. With the nerve endings from her amputated limb re-routed to her chest, she has also experienced 'sensory reinnervation'. This means that touch sensations on her left chest register as if coming from her amputated limb. In the future the hope is to use touch sensors in Claudia's artificial hand to transmit signals back to her re-routed nerves. This could allow Claudia and other patients to obtain accurate touch and temperature feedback from a cybernetic prosthesis.

Another organization working on advanced controllable prosthetics is the Alfred E. Mann Foundation for Biomedical Engineering in the United States. Here bionic neuron or 'BION' technology is being developed. In contrast to myoelectric muscle sensors, BIONs are microchips that can be injected into muscles to pick up signals from the brain. These electrical impulses are then used to control artificial limbs. To date experiments have taken place with both legs and hands controlled by BION implants.

Bionic Ears and Eyes
Re-routing nerves and hard-wiring artificial limbs to the body is an extremely complex and expensive field of research. For this reason the press have sometimes dubbed Claudia Mitchell the '$3.5 million dollar woman'. It is therefore fortunate that interfacing some other forms of cybernetic prosthesis is now far cheaper and even routine.

The electronic device most commonly connected to the human body is a cochlear implant. These are used to restore a sense of hearing to deaf patients who are unable to benefit from a traditional hearing aid. During a surgical procedure an array of several electrodes is implanted into the patient's cochlear to deliver electrical pulses to their auditory nerve. A receiver-stimulator package to which the electrodes are connected is also implanted beneath the patient's skin. People with cochlear implants then wear a small device that interfaces with their implanted technology and enables them to learn to hear again. The first commercial cochlear implants went on the market in the mid-1980s. Since that time approaching 200,000 people worldwide have had them fitted.

While cochlear implants are an established technology, many research teams have been struggling for decades to create a viable bionic eye. However, their labours are now starting to bear fruit. Not least a company called Second Sight in California has created two retinal implants called the Argus 16 and the Argus II. These have already allowed patients blinded from outer retinal degenerations such as Retinitis pigmentosa to regain some degree of vision. The complete system consists of a belt-worn power pack, a tiny camera and transmitter that are mounted in a pair of spectacles, an implanted receiver that is fastened to the inner wall of the eye, and the retinal implant itself.

Second Sight's retinal implants are surgically secured to the patient's retina using a microtack about the width of a human hair. After an implant has been successfully fitted, images from the patient's camera are transmitted to the receiver implanted in their eyeball. A tiny cable then carries these signals to the retinal implant where they cause an electrode array to emit electrical pulses that induce responses in the retina. These are then communicated naturally down the optic nerve. In time, patients can learn to interpret the visual patterns so produced into meaningful images.

The first generation Argus 16 implant had just a 16 electrode array. In comparison to the human eye's 100 million or more photoreceptors this is a tiny number. Nevertheless, the Argus 16 did serve as a useful proof-of-concept. The second generation Argus II then increased the electrode count to 60. Using this system it is just about possible for patients to make out letters. So successful were initial trials of the Argus II that in early 2011 it went on sale as the world's first commercial retinal implant. The price tag at the time was around $100,000.

Second Sight is now working with six national labs, four universities and a commercial partner on a third generation implant with 240 electrodes. A fourth generation 1,024 electrode implant is also planned. With this number of electrodes a workable level of black-and-white vision could be made available. Given that in the United States alone there are 100,000 people with Retinitis pigmentosa – and a further ten million with degenerative retinal diseases – the potential benefits of the technology are obvious. It is also by no means impossible that sometime next decade retinal implants with tens or hundreds of thousands of electrodes could be as widely available as cochlear implants are today.

Connecting to the Brain

Both cochlear and retinal implants use the human nervous system to send signals to the brain. In the other direction, current myoelectric sensors and BION implants effectively take signals from the brain and use them to control an artificial part of the body. In aggregate, these technologies therefore point toward the direct linkage of the human brain with computers and other artificial technologies. By 2030, people with fifth or sixth generation retinal implants may well watch television or use a computer by directly or wirelessly linking up its visual output to their embedded implant. In fact, there are already MP3 music players that interface directly with a cochlear implant in this manner.

If a reliable and safe brain-computer interface (BCI) can be developed it is likely to give rise to a great many new products and services. For a start, enhancing the internal human brain with additional memory and computational capacity may become a possibility. All of the knowledge stored on the Internet could also be on tap to anybody with a suitable BCI implant. With a GPS device additionally embedded, people could also potentially always know where they were.

BCIs may one day even allow the direct transfer of thoughts to and from a computer. Memories could subsequently be stored, uploaded and altered. Virtual and augmented reality could also feel entirely real across all five senses, with nobody mucking around with 3D TVs any more. As and when multiple people can interface their minds with a machine, so people may even be able to directly share their thoughts and think collectively using implanted 'telepathy chips'.

None of the above scenarios are remotely likely anytime soon. Students hoping to plug a memory card into the back of their neck in place of several weeks of revision are therefore going to be disappointed. However, what the previous paragraph ought to highlight is why the subject of directly linking a person to a computer system is now receiving so much attention.

Early experiments with BCIs date back to the Second World War. While progress since that time has largely been sporadic and uneven, in the last decade some promising advancements have been made. Most notably, the BrainGate Neural Interface System has been created. This consists of a 4×4 mm array of 100 electrodes that is placed in contact with the brain, together with a wireless cranial unit that is embedded under the skin but on the surface of the skull. At present, a trolley-load of computers is then needed to decode and interpret brainwave signals from the implant.

The BrainGate Neural Interface System was created in 2002

by a company called Cyberkinetics that was spun off from Brown University in the United States. Since that time the research has blossomed, with BrainGate now being developed by a collaborative research team. This includes researchers from many universities and medical institutions, with financial backing coming from the US military, the US National Science Foundation and many other bodies. The goal of the BrainGate team is to reconnect the brains and limbs of the disabled, so restoring communication, mobility and independence. To this end, in 2008 a group led by Andrew Schwartz at the University of Pittsburgh embedded the BrainGate system into the motor cortex of a monkey. This primate then learnt to feed itself by controlling a robotic arm with its mind.

Embedding electronic sensors into the brain may offer spectacular future medical possibilities. Yet unfortunately there are still significant practical challenges to overcome. Not least scarring often occurs when an array of sensors is surgically embedded. This prevents the nervous system sending signals, so rendering the sensor array useless. Widespread, surgically implanted BCI developments will therefore probably have to wait until synthetic biology or nanotechnology allow new types of organic sensors to be fashioned that will be much better tolerated by the body. Alternatively, developments in genetic medicine may one day allow a human brain to grow its own biological BCI connector.

EEG Brain-Computer Interfaces
While making direct, electronic connections to the brain is problematic, it is possible to bypass the involved difficulties by using external sensors to read brainwave patterns. Taking this approach, many researchers have used electroencephalography (EEG) sensor arrays to create BCIs

that have allowed human test subjects to control robots and other machines. Using this technique, in June 2010 a team of undergraduates at Northeastern University in the US managed to steer a robot over the Internet via thought alone. The basic technology really is starting to become child's play.

In time, EEG control devices are likely to be used to control artificial prostheses. Foreshadowing this, a research group at the École Polytechnique Fédérale de Lausanne in Switzerland has already built a thought-controlled wheelchair. The occupant of the chair wears a skull-cap sensor array, with their brain activity read by the sensors and processed by an artificial intelligence system called 'shared control'. As explained by laboratory assistant Michele Tavella, who has piloted the chair, 'when I want to turn left, I imagine moving my left hand. [It is all] very natural and very quick. I can send a command in about a second'.

Amazingly, it took Tavella only a couple of hours to learn to use the thought-controlled wheelchair. It is therefore not unreasonable to predict that EEG-based BCIs will become a common means of controlling not just wheelchairs and body prosthetics, but a whole host of other devices. In fact, the first personal EEG brain interfaces are already on the market.

For example, a company called Emotiv now sells a neural interface headset called the emotive EPOC. Priced at $299, this can be used to control PC applications including the arcade games *Emotipong*, *Cerebral Constructor* and *Jedi Mind Trainer*. For those wishing to experiment further, a developer headset and software toolkit are also available.

Another pioneer hoping to make EEG brain interfaces a mass-market phenomenon is NeuroSky. This company has developed a technology called ThinkGear for sensing and filtering brainwave patterns. As it explains:

Our mission is to create a paradigm shift in medical biosensors and make them accessible for a broad market outside the hospital. Small. Fast. Mobile. Simple. For games. For athletes. For patients. For real people. This leap requires an understanding of the fundamental neuroscience and the engineering behind the magic.

While much of NeuroSky's work is intended to support industrial and academic clients, the company has already produced a $99 EEG BCI headset for the consumer market. This has been branded as both the MindWave and the XWave. Under the former name the headset can already be used to control a custom video player. Sold as the XWave, the device provides an EEG 'mind interface for an iPhone'. Compatible apps include a brainwave visualizer, an attention and meditation trainer, and a game called *Tug of Mind*. You can learn about more XWave iPhone apps at plxwave.com.

Given that first generation hardware is already on sale, it is quite possible that EEG brain interfaces will be as common as touchscreens and mice by the end of the decade. Not that many years hence we may therefore be composing our tweets and e-mails and controlling Power-Point-style presentations just by thinking about them. The question may then be raised of whether it would be more convenient to have the required EEG sensors wirelessly embedded just below the skin rather than worn on a headset. It is probably a pretty safe bet that at least some people a decade from now will go for the hassle-free embed option.

In Search of Enhancement

Artificial limbs controlled via TMR, BIONs or embedded brain interfaces are almost certainly destined to improve some people's quality of life. So too will future cochlear and retinal implants and even BCIs. These points noted, at present it is extremely unlikely that most people would choose to exchange a natural body part for an artificial alternative. Yet fairly soon this may no longer be the case. Just as cosmetic surgery has evolved from being a medical necessity for a very few into a mass consumer industry, so by 2030 some individuals may be consciously choosing to have their bodies cybernetically enhanced.

Already there are a few people who have chosen a bionic body part over a real one. For example, in 2010, a patient at the Medical University of Vienna became the first person to elect to have his hand amputated in favour of a TMR-controlled robotic replacement. This particular individual had lost all function in his real hand following an accident at work. He therefore had good reason to exchange non-functional flesh and bone for at least partly functional plastic and metal. Nevertheless, his decision may be recorded in history as an evolutionary milestone.

Other people have also voluntarily opted to have electronic implants added to their healthy bodies. Perhaps most famously, world-renowned cybernetics researcher Professor Kevin Warwick from the University of Reading has on two occasions chosen to enhance himself. In an initial experiment dubbed 'Cyborg 1.0', the professor had a silicon chip transponder surgically implanted in his forearm. This then allowed him to operate doors, lights and heaters within his university department.

In a more ambitious venture called 'Cyborg 2.0', Professor Warwick underwent a fairly extensive operation to implant a 100-electrode array into the median nerve fibres in his left arm. This neural interface allowed him to control an electric wheelchair and an artificial hand. The implant was also bio-directional, so permitting Kevin to feel sensations when signals were fed to his electrode array. This bi-directional functionality was demonstrated further when a second array was implanted into the arm of the professor's wife. These were then linked together, so allowing the pioneering academic and his spouse to experience how the other felt pain.

Today Professor Warwick has become a cult figure who is inspiring others to cross the cyborg frontier. Indeed, one of my own undergraduate students once asked me for his contact details so that he could request his own implanted chip. While this particular young man got nowhere on that occasion, others are unlikely to be disappointed in the future. As already noted, direct brain implants hold the promise of all sorts of future possibilities for the able-bodied as well as the disabled. A consumer brain implant industry is therefore one day going to exist and for pretty good reason.

Today a great many people spend a large proportion of their time using a computer for work and leisure. While most modern screens and interfaces are pretty functional, their prolonged use is by no means optimal and almost certainly leads to eye complaints and other health problems. Direct brain interfaces that could allow some computer-based interactions to take place without the use of our biological eyes and hands could therefore be beneficial for many people's long-term health. In time, doctors may even positively encourage some of their patients to get a computer interface port surgically added to their body.

People wishing to undertake certain jobs may in the future also be required to undergo specific cybernetic enhancements. For example, soldiers may require retinal, optic nerve or brain implants to provide them with tactical AR readouts and night vision. They could also be supplied with faster, stronger limbs like those given to Steve Austin in the 1970s TV series *The Six Million Dollar Man*. Surgeons themselves may be similarly enhanced with neural ports that would enable them to directly interface with robotic surgical instruments including in situ bioprinters. Language translation brain implants could also be a necessity for diplomats, politicians and global business executives. Many a manager may also choose to have an augmentative brain implant that would boost their mental capacity and hence their competitive advantage.

Perhaps the most likely workers to require cybernetic enhancement will be deep-space astronauts. As discussed in Chapter 15, human beings are not terribly well suited to space travel beyond the confines of the Earth's orbit. Hybrid human beings with many of their body parts replaced with cybernetic alternatives will therefore be more able to comfortably withstand journeys to Mars and beyond. They could also have a greatly diminished requirement for oxygen, food and water in favour of raw electrical power, as well as the ability to hibernate for months or years at a time on a long trip.

* * *

The Post-Human Cyborg?

A cyborg may be defined as any being that is a product of both nature and artificial technology. In this context, the entirety of human civilization is now a cyborg entity. Nearly all of us who live in a developed nation have become dependent on a wide range of artificial systems and infrastructures to keep us alive. Not least an adequate supply of water, food and power is a survival prerequisite way beyond most people's individual control. Many aspects of our lives are additionally dependent on the Internet cloud. Directly enhancing our bodies as well as our lives with artificial technology may therefore be argued to be a 'natural' continuation of an ongoing evolutionary process.

For decades films and TV shows have portrayed cyborgs as humans mashed with copious quantities of shiny metal and plastic, not to mention a great many flashing LEDs. However, we already know that the reality will be very different. By the time next-generation cyborgs are created, the line between the biological and the technological will well and truly have disappeared. Indeed, perhaps the greatest driver of our future cybernetic enhancement will be our pending industrial transition to organic manufacturing and medical technologies that will seamlessly interface with our bodies. No post-human cyborg will look like the plastic-and-wires Borg in *Star Trek*. Unless, of course, this is a form that some of our descendants choose to inhabit.

In tandem with developments in genetic medicine, bioprinting, synthetic biology, computing and nanotechnology, cybernetic enhancement is just one of those revolutionary technologies that are destined to alter the human race. Exactly what will happen as this cocktail of developments starts to drive human evolution is currently unclear. This said, one thing that is pretty much guaranteed is that individual lifespans will be able to be increased. The next chapter therefore delves into the Holy Grail of life extension.

24

LIFE EXTENSION

For many years the average human lifespan has been increasing. Back in 1900 most people lived for around 35 years, with infant mortality rates incredibly high. By the end of the 20th century, average global lifespan had then almost doubled to about 67. Today, the World Bank reports that life expectancy at birth is 83 in Japan, 80 in the United Kingdom, 78 in the United States, 73 in China and 64 in India. The country with the lowest life expectancy is currently Zimbabwe where people are expected to live on average for just 44 years.

In the developed world, average lifespans will almost certainly continue to increase for the foreseeable future. Not least this will be due to those medical developments outlined in the previous three chapters. Provided that good mental health can be maintained, most individuals are also likely to welcome continued life extension. However, as we push our average time alive well beyond three score years and ten, a balance will increasingly need to be struck between quantity and quality of life. It is also inevitable that retirement ages and attitudes toward the old will have to change in the face of a rapidly ageing population.

This chapter looks at the subject of life extension on two different levels. Largely it reviews life extension possibilities for the individual. More broadly, it then examines the implications of extended individual lifespans for wider civilization. For any one person, finding and exploiting all possible ways to live longer may be a sensible and completely understandable activity. Yet for our entire species, the mass pursuit of life extension could prove a dangerous game.

The Cards on the Table

Life extension has been a common phenomenon for a very long time. Some people may still bemoan the implications of all of those scientific 'advances' of the 20th century. However, even though in the last 100 years we have learnt to kill as never before, we have also become far better at taking care of ourselves.

Across the last couple of centuries, improved sanitation infrastructures have allowed modern cities to free themselves of those waterborne diseases that quite literally plagued millions not that many generations ago. Motorized transportation and domestic appliances have also taken much of the hard labour out of routine living, so reducing the wear and tear on our bodies. Vaccines have in addition all but eliminated many life-threatening diseases in many countries. Antibiotics, advanced diagnostic methods and improved surgical techniques have also played their part in driving the average human lifespan to its current high.

Looking ahead, we may well be on the verge of another life extension revolution. For a start, improved sanitation and the wider implementation of existing healthcare techniques are likely to extend the average lifespan in many developing nations. Improvements in diet and lifestyle could also prove life extension wild cards at both the individual and population level. However, for those who can afford them, genetic medicine, bioprinting, cybernetic enhancement and nanotech healthcare will be by far the most startling life extension tools.

While many technological forces may be in motion, their interactions and interdependencies effectively place just five cards in the hand of any contestant playing the life extension game. As shown in Figure 24.1, the available options come down to dietary anti-ageing, lifestyle optimization, curing and preventing disease, biological reprogramming, and organ repair and replacement. The first two of these are already an option for most people, while the final three rely on fundamental scientific advances. The following sections will now explore each of the available options in turn.

Dietary Anti-Ageing

People who eat better tend to live longer, healthier lives. In the face of this fact, some Western nations may admittedly be experiencing an obesity epidemic. However, there are now also an increasing number of people who are actively pursuing dietary anti-ageing. This involves making changes to their diet and taking nutritional and other supplements.

Most people are aware that they can optimize their health and life expectancy by eating as well as possible. Not least the governments of many nations encourage their citizens to eat at least five portions of fruit and vegetables a day. People who do this will then on average live a year or two longer than those who do not.

In addition to eating healthier foods, there is now some evidence that the consumption of certain specific supplements may increase both lifespan and the quality of life enjoyed in old age. For this reason, the Life Extension Foundation has reported that anti-ageing and regenerative medicines have become the fastest growing medical speciality around the globe.

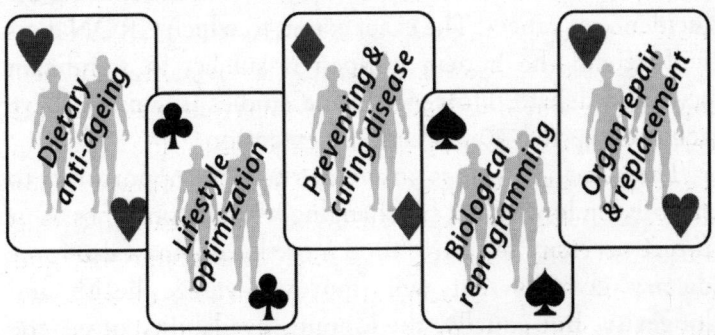

Figure 24.1: The life extension deck of cards

Popular anti-ageing supplements currently include resveratrol, the steroid hormone pregnenolone, the amino-acid derivative carnitine, antioxidant vitamins, and calcium supplements. In animal experiments, some of these have delivered significant anti-ageing results.

For example, in October 2010 a group of Italian academics demonstrated that a cocktail of amino-acids improved the life expectancy of mice by about 12 per cent. In September 2010, Dr Vladimir Skulachev – a long-time anti-ageing researcher and head of the Bioenergetics Department at Moscow State University – even claimed to have developed an anti-oxidant pill that will significantly increase the human lifespan. According to the good doctor just a few more years of testing are necessary before he will definitely know for sure.

Beyond eating well and taking supplements, a scientifically supported method for extending healthy life is to adopt a calorie restriction and optimal nutrition (CRON) diet. This involves reducing your intake of calories to a level 20 to 40 per cent lower than typical, while still consuming necessary levels of vitamins and nutrients. Research studies have already shown that CRON diets lessen the degeneration of stem cells, as well as reducing the incidence of cancer. The exact extent to which CRON diets will extend the human lifespan is subject to significant scientific debate. However, some studies in animals have achieved up to a 40 per cent life extension.

The human race does on average have the opportunity to start living longer just by changing what it consumes. Our future necessity to source food more locally may also force dietary changes that will improve average health and longevity. But equally, the looming availability of genetic therapies, bioprinters, cybernetic prostheses and other healthcare innovations may lead more people to believe that it does not matter what they eat as future doctors will always be able to cure their ills. At the population level, dietary life extension therefore remains a significant wild card.

Lifestyle and Lifespan

Like any other machine, how fast the human body will wear out has to depend to a reasonable extent on how well it is treated and maintained. Or as the fightageing.org website so neatly puts it, one of the best ways to defeat ageing is to stop damaging your own health. Obvious measures here include reducing alcohol consumption, stopping smoking and taking enough exercise. All of these are things that everybody knows about but not everybody does. A mass change in the behaviour of the population could therefore have a significant impact on global life expectancy.

Several studies have shown that taking regular exercise adds several years to a person's life. For example, it has been reported that highly active 65 year olds will live on average 5.7 years longer than those who are inactive. In 2009, a study published in *The Lancet* also indicated that being obese reduces life expectancy by between two and four years, while being very obese shortens lifespan by between eight and ten years. Some studies have even linked being very obese to a 20-year reduction in lifespan. While average global lifespans are increasing, a certain proportion of the population are therefore currently likely to live shorter lives than their parents.

Throughout most of human history, life expectancy was most strongly correlated with *access to resources* (such as a good diet, sanitation and healthcare) rather than the *individual choice* to make use of those resources available. It is therefore bizarre that, in the face of rising global affluence, some of the population are now making lifestyle decisions that will significantly reduce their life expectancy. We sadly live in a world in which public money has to be spent on reinforcing ambulances to ferry the very obese to hospital.

Disease Cure and Prevention

Across the 20th century, improvements in traditional healthcare that helped to cure and prevent disease were paramount in achieving lifespan improvements. As the 21st century advances, this is also probable to remain the case as medical practice enters a new age. Genetic testing and genetic therapies hold particular promise for the detection and cure of many currently fatal diseases, with pharmacogenetics set to allow cancer treatments to be individually targeted and more successful within a few decades. In the longer term, genetic therapies for curing an increasing number of cancers are also likely to be created. Several studies have now also demonstrated that antioxidants (such as N-acetyl-L-cysteine) can prove very effective in eliminating toxins, boosting our immune systems and fighting cancer. Just as antibiotics were the medical breakthrough of the first half of the 20th century, so cures for cancer could well go down in history as the healthcare watershed of the first half of the 21st.

Genetic therapies are also likely to deliver significant results in treating other currently fatal conditions including heart disease. For example, it may well become possible to treat victims of heart attacks with an injection of regenerative stem cells that will repair their cardiac tissue. Stem cells may potentially also prove invaluable in the development of successful treatments for conditions ranging from Parkinson's disease to Alzheimer's.

Advances in disease cure and prevention will also not just be limited to the administration of new drugs and tailored genetic therapies. As discussed in Chapter 7, nanotechnology is also likely to play a significant role. In the coming decades very basic nanobots are going to be injected into patients either to detect a specific medical condition or to enable targeted drug delivery at the cellular level. However, further into the future nanobots may be developed to supplement our natural immune systems. Functioning a bit like supplementary, cybernetic antibodies, these tiny machines could constantly roam our bloodstreams to seek out infections and mutated cells. They would then destroy them on the spot before any traditional disease could manifest itself.

While the human immune system does an amazing job of continual disease control and self-repair, its ability to fight certain pathogens is limited. Medical technology is therefore always likely to be required to maintain let alone increase currently achieved levels of life expectancy. In this pursuit, most future genetic therapies will only prove useful once a patient starts to show some symptoms of a disease. The promise of augmentative nanotechnology immune systems is therefore to enable the constant intervention of medical technology inside our bodies before any conventional approach can even start to detect that anything is wrong. Our ultimate cybernetic enhancement may therefore turn out to be a self-sustaining, self-replicating artificial immune system administered via a simple injection.

Reprogramming our Biology

Nanotech immune systems lie a very long way into the future. There are, however, several other ways that cutting-edge technologies may be used to enable life extension. For example, genetic therapies may be developed to slow or even 'cure' the ageing process by reprogramming our genetic code.

Given that all adults have grown from an embryo and usually live healthily for many decades, it is quite obvious that the human body is capable of creating and naturally rejuvenating all of its constituent parts. The genetic 'problem' we therefore face is to persuade our biology not to cease its natural regenerative processes. Or as Dr Julian Whitaker of the Whitaker Wellness Institute explains:

> When we are in our mother's womb, thousands of genes orchestrate our growth in that environment. After birth, these genes are naturally turned off and other genes are activated to give us the appropriate genetic direction for growth and development. Then, around age 25, our genes start shutting down. This loss of genetic power continues, as gradual as the ageing process, until we die.

If we could reset our 'regeneration clocks' to turn our regenerative genes back on (or to stop them shutting down in the first place) then in theory we could control and even prevent the 'natural' ageing cycle. While this may sound impossible, genetic anti-ageing research has been underway for years. For example, back in 1993 a researcher called Cynthia Kenyon discovered that the *daf-2* gene in a roundworm controlled its longevity. By making just one change to this gene – out of the creature's genome of 19,000 genes – she then managed to double the worm's lifespan as well as improving its general health. Slowing the ageing process of a living thing via genetic modification is therefore already more than science fiction.

Several research studies have suggested that ageing in mammals can be slowed or even reversed by reactivating an enzyme called telomerase that protects the tips of the chromosomes in their DNA. For example, research published in November 2010 by Ronald DePinho of the Harvard Medical School reported on some mice that had been engineered to lack telomerase. Initially these rodents rapidly aged and became decrepit. However, DePinho's team had re-engineered their mice with inactivated telomerase that could be reactivated with a chemical injection halfway through the experiment. When they flicked this genetic control to return the mice to normal telomerase levels, their rapid ageing was dramatically reversed. For a start, the mice regained their fertility. Their spleens, livers and intestines also all recuperated from their previously degenerated state. Mice with restored telomerase were even observed to undergo some brain regeneration. As DePinho commented, this suggests that there can be a 'point of return for age-associated disorders'. Or, in other words, the 'natural' ageing process may have a genetically controllable reverse gear.

Studies like DePinho's have been lauded by many as demonstrating the potential of telomerase enhancement as a human anti-ageing therapy. However, other scientists have raised serious concerns because telomerase often mutates in human cancers and can help tumours to grow faster. Telomerase's supporters counter-argue that a higher concentration of the enzyme in the body ought to reduce DNA damage, so preventing healthy cells from becoming cancerous in the first place. We do not yet know which side is right. However, it is easy to predict that we will hear a lot more about telomerase and its potential anti-ageing application over the next few years.

Taking an alternative approach, recent research part-funded by the Life Extension Foundation has suggested that genes from stem cells could be used to slow or prevent the ageing of other cells. In experiments conducted by Michael West of BioTime Inc., the 'developmental ageing' of adult human cells in a laboratory dish was reversed by introducing some stem cell genes. While this work is in its very early stages, once again it signals that in future our natural ageing cycle could be at least partly controlled via genetic therapies.

Rather than seeking an overall genetic 'cure' for the ageing process, some scientists are trying to locate specific genes that may turn certain regenerative processes back on. For example, in 2009 scientists at the University of Rochester found the gene that prevents tooth regeneration beyond childhood. In the future a genetic therapy may therefore be developed to reactivate this gene, so allowing people to grow a new set of teeth in later life. Some other creatures – such as sharks and crocodiles – already regrow lost or damaged teeth and even limbs. Providing humans with a similar genetically controlled opportunity to regrow lost or damaged body parts is therefore not that outlandish a proposition.

Organ Repair and Replacement
The regrowth of a lost or damaged body part could probably not occur quickly enough to allow a person to

recover from an accident or another medical emergency. The fifth and final card in the life extension deck is therefore organ repair and replacement. The two key future technologies that will enable this are bioprinting and cybernetic enhancement. As detailed in Chapter 22, bioprinting may within decades enable existing organs to be repaired in situ at the cellular level, as well as allowing new organs to be printed in a lab from a culture of a patient's own cells. In tandem, cybernetic enhancement is going to allow more and more effective inorganic body part replacements. In time, as 3D printing becomes a mainstream method for the customized production of inorganic things, bioprinting and 'artificial' cybernetic enhancement may even technologically converge.

While bioprinting and cybernetic enhancement are going to offer significant possibilities for extending life, alternative and more traditional means of organ repair and replacement will also remain part of the medical mix. For a start, conventional surgery will still be with us for decades as a means of organ repair. Donated organ transplants are also likely to continue for the foreseeable future.

At present, the only source of replacement human organs is another human being. In some instances an organ such as a kidney may be obtained from a living family member or other live donor. In all other instances, organs are donated after death and matched as closely as possible to the physiology of the patient. Even so, the rejection of donated organs remains a significant medical problem. Most patients requiring a human organ donation also have to wait for a long period of time and many die waiting.

Bioprinted organs are clearly one long-term solution. Once this technology reaches common application, organ donor waiting lists ought to become a thing of the past and organ rejection should also greatly diminish. However, before widespread organ printing arrives it is possible that those requiring an organ transplant will receive a transgenic organ. For example, a pig may be 'humanized' by introducing genetic material from the patient into its DNA. The pig's heart, liver, lungs, kidneys or other organs would then potentially become good transplantation candidates with a relatively low risk of rejection.

One advantage of future transgenically humanized animal organs over bioprinted alternatives could be their immediate availability. For example, it may become possible to purchase a health insurance policy that includes the humanization of a pig with the insuree's genetic material. This animal would then be reared and cared for on a farm near a private hospital. Its organs would therefore always be on 'standby' in living, pristine readiness should the policyholder require an urgent organ transplant. Not everybody may like the idea of walking around with pig organs inside them, but already biomeshes and other implants made from pig skin are used in some abdominal repair surgery. Just one example is a material called Permacol that is manufactured from pig skin by a company called Covidien.

Within a couple of decades, transplant surgery is likely to be using organs from human donors, bioprinters, transgenic animals and cybernetic body part manufacturers as finances, ethics and patient needs dictate. As a consequence, death as a result of a major organ failure is likely to be less common than it is today. Of course, this by no means implies that replacement organs will be available to everyone and in every country. Of all the aforementioned technologies, only bioprinting is likely to be scalable for mass use at reasonable cost.

The opportunity for more routine organ replacement may also start to raise some interesting questions. Not least, it may become difficult for some people to state how old they are. At present we still take age as a strong indicator of fitness. However, by the middle of this century there could well be many people whose brain is over 100, but who have hearts, lungs, livers and kidneys that are only in their 20s or 30s. Such individuals may also have cybernetic limbs built from nanocomposite materials and synthetic bio-muscles that can outperform those of any 18 year old. In the plug-and-play (or print-and-play) organ-mashing world of tomorrow, people who would today be retired may still be digging the roads.

Life Extension Implications

As and when the five cards of life extension start to be played, so human beings will have begun to play at God. In turn this is likely to trigger a number of important debates. For some the key issues will be purely ethical. However, far more pragmatically, all of us will be practically impacted if a great many people start to use technology to prevent them from 'dying on time'.

Even if the application of future genetic therapies, genetic engineering and cybernetic enhancement are ignored, a significant ageing of the global population now seems inevitable. Respected anti-ageing physician Ron Klatz has already predicted that more than half of the baby-boom generation will live healthy lives beyond 100. The Centre for Ageing in London also forecasts that there will be about 700 million people aged 65+ in the world by 2020. In the United States alone, the number of centenarians already stands at 80,000 and is expected to exceed a million by 2050. It is also anticipated that at least 30 per cent of centenarians will in the future have no significant deterioration in their thinking ability.

In most developed nations the majority of people currently expect to retire sometime before they are 70.

However, even with moderate ongoing life extension this will no longer be economically sustainable. In the next two decades, most developed nations are likely to pass the point where at least 20 per cent of their population will be over 65. In the United Kingdom, by 2025 around 5 per cent of the population is now expected to be over 85. As a consequence, a retirement age well beyond 70 will probably have to be introduced. This said, in the future retirement will probably become a more gradual transition – with more people perhaps working part time between the ages of 65 and 75. Thinking back to the last section, retirement ages may even start to be calculated based on the average age of an individual's body parts. Linked to this, people who have received life extension therapies may also be expected to work longer, and especially so if their treatment has been paid for by the State.

Life extension and an ageing population will also have an inevitable impact on the dynamics of family structures. Today, it is uncommon for more than four or maybe five generations to be alive at the same time. Yet later this century children could routinely be meeting their great-great-great-great-great-grandparents. Alternatively, if genetic anti-ageing therapies allow women to remain fertile for longer, it may become common for couples to start families in their 50s or beyond. Others may choose to conceive their embryos in their 20s during their genetic prime, but only grow them to term several decades down the line.

As medical technologies advance, there is sadly the danger that we will sustain a greater and greater proportion of the population in poorer and poorer mental health. Nobody wants to be old and senile – let alone old and senile for a great many decades. Even if an army of future robot carers could look after a mass senile population, such a scenario hardly represents a Utopian dream. The Hippocratic oath that doctors make to always maintain life – as well as the decisions that individuals make to repair and sustain their bodies – will therefore need to be reviewed unless stem cell and other therapies provide effective cures for Alzheimer's and related conditions. It is very unlikely indeed that we will ever bioprint somebody a new brain.

*   *   *

The Greatest Future Challenge?

In the face of those issues already identified in Part I of this book, an expanding and ageing population will present human civilization with yet another tremendous challenge. Can our planet possibly sustain nine billion who live to 100 or more? Let alone nine billion 140 year olds? Using current models of resource allocation, resource utilization and energy production, the answer has to be that it cannot. But with the innovations outlined elsewhere in this book? Well, perhaps.

Increasingly, being old will need to be viewed as a privilege that has to be planned and paid for. For this reason, some people may start to consider very old age a potential hassle that is not worth the pre-commitment. Across the world, euthanasia is already on the rise as people start to place quality of life before quantity. In a similar fashion, decades hence some individuals may opt for sub-optimal medical treatments in order that their bodies will not live on for too long. Of course, many others will not be lucky enough to have the choice of deciding roughly how long they want to live.

Today, those with the shortest life expectancy live in poverty in the poorest countries. Regardless of the techno-logical possibilities outlined over the last few chapters, it is likely that in the future the main determinant of lifespan will remain a person's wealth. Already, many people in developed nations can sit on the Internet and concoct credible plans for maximizing their lifespan. At present such plans are likely to include little more than dietary and lifestyle adjustments and the consumption of a few anti-ageing supplements. But increasingly, as we have seen, a wider and wider variety of life-extension options will become available.

Sustaining itself is what the code of life does best. While some people may consider many of the potential practices outlined in this chapter to be unethical, it would therefore be staggering if most of them do not become a reality sooner rather than later. By evolving into a hive species, humanity has already artificially increased the average person's life expectancy several decades beyond what is 'natural'. This process is also destined to continue. Indeed, with the life extension cards soon to be in play, some of today's children may be the first to have 200 candles on a birthday cake.

25

TRANSHUMANISM

Most of our early ancestors must have had it pretty tough. For a start they had to hunt and forage for food while avoiding creatures that wanted to eat them. The climate was also not always entirely stable, with glaciers on more than one occasion driving early humans from their lands. To an external observer, the chances of the human race surviving – let alone evolving to greatness – may therefore have seemed rather slim.

As is patently obvious, our ancestors did survive and thrive. This they achieved by evolving to become more intelligent and by inventing increasingly sophisticated tools. Just like our early ancestors, today the human race faces the prospect of some significant survival challenges. We therefore once again need to up our game by developing superior levels of intelligence and crafting next generation technologies.

Perhaps the biggest question before us today is the manner in which we are going to evolve. For millions of years our evolution has been an unconscious process beyond individual control. Granted, some great thinkers and inventors have played a far greater role than the majority in catalysing human progress. However, never before has anybody been able to take a conscious decision that could fundamentally influence our future physical or mental form.

As many of the chapters of this book have signalled, the opportunity will soon arise for the evolution of all life on Earth to be determined by humanity. Whatever happens, both the human species and the planet will evolve. The question is simply the extent to which we ought to use our knowledge and near-future capabilities to turn evolution into a conscious process.

The Transhumanist Philosophy

The previous 24 chapters have each been about a single future challenge or a new technology. In contrast, this last chapter concerns a particular philosophy that the human race may choose to adopt in order to most successfully survive. This philosophy is known as 'transhumanism' and represents the view that we should take a proactive role in upgrading the human species.

The word 'transhumanism' was first coined by biologist Julian Huxley in 1927. Writing in his book *Religion without Revelation*, Huxley noted that 'the human species can, if it wishes, transcend itself'. He then added that 'we need a name for this new belief. Perhaps *transhumanism* will service: man remaining man, but transcending himself by realizing new possibilities'.

In 1990 a philosopher called Max More wrote an essay entitled 'Transhumanism: Toward a Futurist Philosophy' that is regarded by many as the foundation of modern transhumanistic thought. Within, More defined transhumanism as 'a class of philosophies of life that seek the continuation and acceleration of the evolution of intelligent life beyond its currently human form and human limitations by means of science and technology'.

Today, a 6,000-member non-profit organization known as Humanity+ provides a focal point for transhumanist activity. Formerly known as the World Transhumanist Association (WTA), Humanity+ believes that the 'human species in its current form does not represent the end of our development but rather a comparatively early phase'. It therefore advocates the 'ethical use of technology to expand capacities' in pursuit of 'better minds, better bodies and better lives'.

Humanity+ maintains a detailed 'Transhumanist Declaration'. This was first drawn up by an international group of contributors in 1998 and notes that humanity now stands on the brink of being able to overcome 'cognitive shortcomings, involuntary suffering, and our confinement to planet Earth'. The Declaration goes on to state that policy-makers need to exercise 'inclusive moral vision' in weighing the risks and benefits of new technologies. It also advocates the well-being of all sentient life – including humans, non-human animals, artificial intellects and modified life forms – and strongly favours 'personal choice' in the adoption of enhancement technologies such as those detailed in the previous four chapters. You can read the full Transhumanist Declaration at humanityplus.org.

A Rising Debate

Today, few people actually call themselves transhumanists. In the future this will probably also remain the case. This said, most people 20 years ago were not a member of the Green Party and the vast majority are not affiliated with the environmental movement today. Nevertheless, green policies and activities have become mainstream in the past two decades and now colour most economic activity and political debate. In a similar manner, at least some notions of transhumanism are likely strongly to permeate human civilization as the technological potential of those developments outlined in the rest of this book continues to accrue.

While transhumanists may advocate the maximum ethical exploitation of all new technologies, a great many people currently believe that we ought not to 'meddle with nature' or 'play at God'. As scientists continue to put new opportunities on the table, a battle of ideologies is therefore almost certain to ensue. We are, however, unlikely to witness a clash of total extremes, as most 'anti-transhumanists' (or bio-conservatives) already accept the use of a great many technologies. The growing transhumanism debate will therefore question where the lines are to be drawn and what level of proactive evolution we ought to embrace.

No ethical argument is ever easy to settle. But in the past arriving at laws and moral codes to confine certain areas of scientific development was far easier than it is becoming today. Already the Internet is allowing knowledge to transcend all national, political and cultural boundaries. Activities that may be banned in one territory can therefore easily continue in another. Even more significantly, the demarcations that used to exist between different areas of technological development are now starting to disappear.

The New Industrial Convergence
In 1980 Nicholas Negroponte, the Director of the Media Lab at the Massachusetts Institute of Technology, suggested that developments in digital technology were about to blur the lines between the traditional industrial sectors of computing, telecommunications and the media. Specifically, Negroponte predicted that by 2000 the 'computing', 'communications' and 'content' industries would have very significant overlaps. This insightful prediction also proved to be correct.

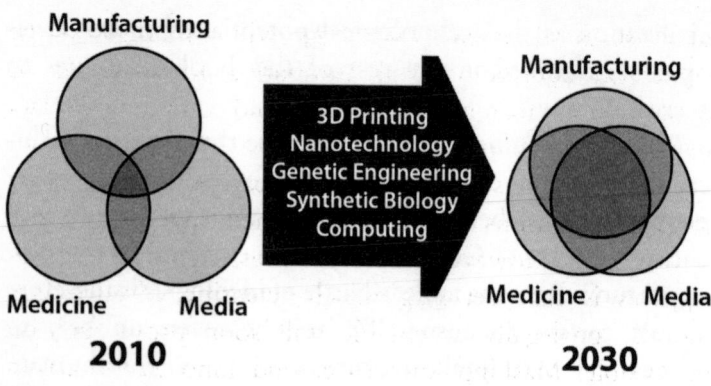

Figure 25.1: The New Industrial Convergence

While between 1980 and 2000 we were witness to the First Industrial Convergence, today we are just entering a far more radical second phase. As illustrated in Figure 25.1, whereas three decades ago it was computing, communications and content that were losing their distinction, over the next 20 years it is manufacturing, medicine and the media that are set to converge. This is going to happen because many of the developments already detailed in this book are causing engineers, doctors and computer scientists to develop common techniques and technologies.

As we have seen in previous chapters, 3D printing is set to revolutionize manufacturing methods and medical practice, with both future products and body parts to be created one thin layer at a time. Nanotechnology will additionally deliver not just new materials and manufacturing methods, but also quantum computers and atomic-precision medical manipulation. Genetic engineering and its upstart brother synthetic biology will further intermix manufacturing, medicine and the media as we learn to use the same technologies to reprogram our food, grow products on the vine, heal our bodies and build DNA microprocessors. All of these developments and more will also rely on the continued development of computing to allow us to digitally store, manipulate, visualize and communicate data in new ways.

The New Industrial Convergence carries with it a great many implications that could on their own consume a whole book. However, one of its most significant consequences is that deciding which scientific advances are morally or legally acceptable will soon prove nigh-on impossible. Mashing knowledge and innovations across industrial sectors is already rapidly becoming the norm. Legacy legal systems based on discretely black-boxed industrial sectors and age-old moral divides will therefore soon be outdated.

For example, at present most countries tightly regulate genetic engineering. Yet synthetic biology and bioprinting receive far less regulation, with nanotechnology research and manufacturing subject to hardly any. Advances in computing – including those in artificial intelligence – are then entirely free of any ethically driven regulatory constraints.

In the days when there was a clear line between medical, manufacturing and computing advancements, the above state of affairs really did not matter. But as we have seen, soon computer scientists may be creating new forms of intelligent life, while others will be building new biological entities by printing them out or mashing them together with BioBricks purchased over the web. In this Brave New World, our current regulatory shambles ought therefore to be a cause of great concern even for those who have bought into transhumanity hook, line and sinker. We need to stop regulating industries and start regulating broader principles and fast.

God and the New Religion

So far this book has avoided the topic of religion. However, the debate that will surround the application and regulation of many future technologies is almost certain to be heavily influenced by our wider systems of belief. Genetic engineering, synthetic biology, nanotechnology, artificial intelligence, bioprinting and cybernetics all raise fundamental questions about the meaning of life itself. They therefore all have religious connotations.

Since ancient times religion has been a bedrock of civilization. Across history, people with the deepest religious beliefs have also frequently been in conflict with those who have promoted new ideas or scientific advancements. Nicolaus Copernicus (with his theory that the Earth rotated around the Sun) and Charles Darwin (with his theory of evolution) were just two of those whose theories brought them into significant conflict with the Church. Many modern technologies and medical practices have also been opposed by at least some religious leaders at one time or another. Or, as biochemist J. B. S. Haldane wrote in 1924, 'there is no great invention, from fire to flying, that has not been hailed as an insult to some god'.

Religions provide their followers with a sense of meaning and security in an otherwise uncertain and often difficult world. It is therefore hardly surprising that new ideas and technologies that challenge the status quo may be viewed by religions with some level of suspicion. Some transhumanists – such as Max More – subsequently view religion and transhumanism as alternative philosophies that cannot coexist. As More argues, transhumanism is an evolutionary transition beyond humanism, and the latter by definition rejects deities, faith and worship.

Fortunately, most transhumanists do not take such a literal view. Given the uncertainty and ethical conundrums that transhuman practices are soon likely to raise, they may even give rise to a religious renaissance. Even if this does not occur, God will find a place in transhuman evolution. Increasingly, science is going to be posing some very difficult questions that only those with strong convictions may be able to answer.

As practitioners of manufacturing, medicine and the media all learn to digitally manipulate matter on the nanoscale, there is the possibility that some people will start to view human beings as no more than sophisticated machines. The development of powerful and even sentient artificial intelligences may additionally be used to support a purely 'nihilist' or 'reductionist' view of life. However, even if we learn to understand and program every gene and perhaps every atom in our bodies, it need not necessarily imply that we will cease to believe in the metaphysical qualities of our minds, nor states of existence beyond scientific explanation.

Future sentient artificial intelligences may even be worshipped as beings of divine creation rather than proof of the non-existence of God. Religions that evolve to embrace life that extends beyond the biological could also become the ethical lynchpins of a dawning Transhuman Age. It is, after all, pretty certain that people with bioprinted body parts will soon be seeking solace and certainty in churches, temples, synagogues and mosques.

Across history, religion and science have typically only come into major conflict when their followers have presented opposing views of the nature of physical creation. Recognizing this, many religions are already letting scientists and doctors get on with the explanation and manipulation of the physical world in a manner that has not castrated their ability to care for the soul. Almost certainly those who dispute Darwin will in future battle anybody who seeks to use technology to play at God. However, it is also probable that some creationists will in future be seeing the world through cybernetic eyes.

Rather than being philosophical opposites, transhumanity and most religions may well prove highly complementary. As was mentioned back in Chapter 1, in the face of many inevitable future challenges some people are starting to believe that 'we are all doomed'. To see beyond this growing viewpoint requires just one important thing. And that one thing happens to be faith. Whether such faith is in a God, in technological advancement or in both really does not matter. On the brink of so many global challenges, the world needs billions of people who believe in a positive tomorrow.

Toward Immortality?

Most religions give people hope in part by promising some form of external afterlife or reincarnation. In contrast if not necessarily in opposition, those who believe in transhumanism put a faith in technology to prevent their life from coming to a premature end. Life extension mechanisms including biological reprogramming, cybernetics and synthetic organ replacement have been discussed in previous chapters. However, some transhumanists believe that even more radical mechanisms may potentially be employed to keep people alive. On the edge of science and fantasy, these options include cryonics and uploading.

Cryonics uses very low temperatures to preserve the human body for potential 'reanimation'. Today, two companies – the Cryonics Institute and the Alcor Life Extension Foundation – offer people the service of entering cryonic suspension in liquid nitrogen when they die. The idea is that their body will be preserved until a point in time when medical technology will be able to cure the condition that killed them and also repair any damage caused by the freezing process.

People who opt for cryonic suspension are most probably placing their faith in the development of advanced future nanorobots that could be injected to mend their bodies and restore their brains. At present the Cryonics Institute will freeze a person on death and keep them indefinitely suspended for a one-off fee of $28,000. Alternatively, insurance policies to pay for the process start at $30 a month. In June 2011 103 people (and 76 pets) were resting in the company's cryostasis storage facility.

While cryonic suspension seeks to preserve the body on death, the transhuman notion of uploading is intended to electronically preserve only the mind. As Christine Peterson, the chairman of the Personal Life Extension Conference, put it in 2010, 'our brains are grey pudding and we aren't backed up properly'. To overcome this impediment, in the future neural interfaces could potentially be developed to allow the human mind and memories to be uploaded into a computer. If such a process could preserve consciousness then this may allow somebody to live forever by downloading their mind into a succession of robotic or bioprinted bodies. Alternatively, uploaded individuals might simply roam and muse externally in the virtual reality of the Internet. Whether such an entirely digital afterlife would be heaven or hell has to depend on your point of view.

Our Digital Legacy

Uploading a person's mind to a computer is at present pure science fiction. However, other means of progressing to some form of digital afterlife are starting to become available. There are, after all, two ways to achieve digital immortality. One is to find a means of remaining electronically sentient for the rest of eternity (or at least until the end of human civilization). The other is to find a way of having one's existence digitally etched into future human experience. It all depends on whether those seeking digital immortality view consciousness as a critical requirement. If not, and all that is required is the ability to influence and interact with those to come, then several options are now on the table.

For example, LifeNaut.com is a web-based research project that 'allows anyone to create a free back-up of their mind and genetic code'. While the ultimate goal of the project 'is to explore the transfer of human consciousness to computers/robots and beyond', already visitors can create a 'MindFile' or a DNA 'BioFile'. The former is a digital database of personal reflections captured in video, images, documents and audio. This is then used to drive an interactive avatar with which others may interact, and which will respond based on your own individual attitudes, values, mannerisms and beliefs. This could allow somebody to continue to interact with you after your death.

Already some people have achieved a level of digital immortality. For example, the popular online game *World of Warcraft* features an avatar called Caylee Dak that was created by a player named Dak Krause. While Dak died of leukaemia in 2007, other players are still interacting with his Caylee digital representation, which may now live forever online.

In a sense the Internet is starting to make a great many of us digitally immortal whether we want it to or not. In the developed world, over 90 per cent of children now spawn Internet content before they are two years old. Many of us will also consciously upload gigabytes of data and opinion before we die, while also leaving a vast digital trail of our everyday activities and interactions. Reflecting this, Yanko Design has created a solar-powered digital gravestone called the E-Tomb. Intended to mark a grave in the traditional manner, this device also wirelessly connects those who visit it with content from the deceased's web spaces including their blogs, tweets and Facebook wall.

Leaving a digital footprint or avatar to interact with others after your death is a concept far removed from uploading your consciousness into a computer. However, the fact that the former is already a possibility may perhaps signal a direction of travel. Immortality is about how we make our mark – about how we make our lives matter – and about how we may, in some small way, make a positive contribution to the future.

* * *

Playing with Pandora

According to Greek mythology, the first woman – Pandora – was given a beautiful box by Zeus, the King of the Gods. The only condition was that the box was never to be opened. Unfortunately, as Zeus had anticipated, Pandora's curiosity was so powerful that she opened the box, so releasing death, disease and many other evils.

Today, our own Pandora's box of transhuman possibilities is brimming with a great many temptations. As our sciences and knowledge digitally converge at the nanoscale, so the potential will soon exist to control and augment the complexities of our own biology, to create new forms of intelligent life, and so to become Gods ourselves. We may, however, still have time to question whether we really ought to do this.

For anybody with strong transhumanist leanings, the ethical dilemmas on the horizon may be relatively easy to address. However, for the rest of the population a great deal of philosophical uncertainly lies ahead. As discussed at the start of Chapter 21, future studies deals with two fundamental questions. The first is 'how will we live in the future?' while the second is 'what will we become?' The former question inevitably and perhaps rightly tends to garner the majority of popular attention. How we will feed and fuel civilization beyond the Age of Plenty is, after all, a fundamental concern. Yet equally we ought not to forget that how we choose to live in the future could have a fundamental impact on the very nature of ourselves.

The human race is almost certainly evolving to play at least some conscious role in its own biological destiny. As far as we know, no other species has ever progressed to achieve such an evolutionary milestone. Our early ancestors learnt to create fire long before they knew everything that they could do with it. And so it remains with technological innovation to this day.

Epilogue
SINGULARITY OR DECLINE?

We will all spend the rest of our lives in the future. It is therefore only natural to wonder what the future may be like. Decades hence, will our economies be stagnating due to depleted natural resources? Or will genetic engineering, nanotechnology, 3D printing and solar power have enabled us to overcome our grand challenges and create a new Golden Age?

This book has addressed many of the specifics that lie behind the above important questions. This said, anybody who has read the last 25 chapters ought to have developed just a hint of futuristic schizophrenia. On the one hand, it has been outlined how – within a couple of decades at most – our petroleum-fuelled economy will come to an end, our diet will have to change, and our current obsession with moving so many people and things around the planet will need to be curtailed. On the other hand we have also learnt about many significant technological breakthroughs that may help us to survive and thrive. Following centuries of relative butchery, a new age of medicine is about to dawn. New manufacturing methods could also trigger a 21st-century Industrial Revolution. After eons of growing up alone, the human race may also soon be sharing its first planet with new forms of intelligent, synthetic life.

Chapter 17 outlined the concept of the Singularity. This is the idea that we are accelerating toward a point of extreme technological accomplishment. If this is true then we may soon witness an explosion of many cutting-edge scientific developments. Today, genetic engineering, nanotechnology, 3D printing, artificial intelligence and many other disciplines are all primed to enter the mainstream and become mass-market phenomena. Very significantly, all of these disciplines are also converging. An innovation made or problem solved in one area will therefore rapidly lead to progress on a great many related frontiers. Make a breakthrough in artificial intelligence, genetic manipulation or nanoscale manufacturing, and virtually all other current barriers to progress are likely to fall away. If this sounds nonsense, then consider just how many areas of science and technology have rapidly advanced in the wake of low-cost computer processing power.

Beyond the Cabaret
In 1995 I wrote a book called *Cyber Business* that predicted the future of the Internet and mobile communications. For several years thereafter I gave talks on how online developments were about to alter our business and personal lives. At the time, my suggestions that people would soon buy things using a computer, access information on a wireless pocket device and socialize in 'personal virtual networks' were frequently dismissed. For this reason, most of my talks were after-dinner speeches or delivered as a bit of light-hearted relief during a company away-day or similar corporate event.

Then, in the late 1990s, Dot Com mania took hold. As a result, my wacky little talks about the Internet rapidly evolved from after-dinner entertainment into keynote addresses that opened events. Or, in other words, once what I was talking about started to enter the mainstream I ceased to be booked as the cabaret.

Last week I gave my first presentation based on the content of this book. Hardly to my surprise, it was an after-dinner address. Today, every single topic between these covers – from Peak Oil to 3D printing, synthetic biology to space travel – remains cabaret material. People are interested to hear about these things, certainly. But nevertheless, the 25 topics we have looked at are still considered to have little direct, mainstream significance.

As mentioned in the Prologue, too many people continue to act as if the future will be just like the present. Most probably this is because they see no reason for the world to change or are fairly content with their current lives. The majority of people are probably also unaware of many of the things mentioned herein, or else dismiss them as gimmicks or science fiction. The most fundamental challenge for future gazers and future shapers is therefore to jolt everybody else out of their largely inactive complacency.

The Time for Action is Now

Everybody now needs to understand that human civilization is either rushing headlong into the Singularity or accelerating toward collective decline. Not least due to the ongoing depletion of our natural resource base, the world of tomorrow cannot be a clone of today. Like it or not, we are now rapidly approaching a distinct fork in the road, with either future direction to involve changed and challenging times ahead.

In addition to knowing that there are two quite distinct futures on offer, we can be fairly certain that the chances of us heading toward Singularity or decline will depend on actions taken by us all over the next 20 years. This is also the case for four reasons. For a start, Peak Oil, climate change, Peak Water, food shortages and broader resource scarcity have yet to really kick in and affect human civilization to a large extent. In other words, the Age of Plenty has not ended just yet, which leaves us with a last little bit of breathing space in which to collectively act.

Secondly, and despite the ongoing fallout from the global financial crisis of 2008, the economies of most nations are still functioning effectively, with most governments and large organizations worldwide able to command the resources, conformity and respect required to engage in long-term strategic action. This means that the mechanisms we require to shape a positive future are still very much intact and waiting to be used effectively.

The third reason that makes the next two decades so critical is that over this period most people – at least in developed nations – are likely to remain in a position where they could, if they really wanted to, make changes in their lifestyles for the benefit of those to come.

And lastly, as we have seen across this book, an incredible range of scientific tools and possibilities on the near horizon will be able to lead us toward Singularity rather than decline if we do not fight against them and can sustain ourselves long enough to allow these developments to reach fruition.

What the above mean in aggregate is that we are still able to fix the world. Our biggest challenge is therefore persuading enough people right now that we are better working toward a positive future rather than squandering the remaining years of plenty in pursuit of selfish individual pleasure. The best way to do this is almost certainly to always present solutions in addition to information on the challenges that lie ahead. Just telling people about Peak Oil, Peak Water, looming food shortages and resource depletion either gets their backs up or simply spreads doom and gloom. But detail these challenges and explain how electric cars, solar power, nuclear fusion, nanotechnology and genetic engineering will all help to solve the issues they raise, and people are far more likely to be catalysed into positive action. Most people will make self-sacrifices for a better tomorrow, but only if tempted with a little hope.

Today, many if not most people accept at least the premise of climate change. Granted, the extent to which we should alter our lives in response may still cause considerable arguments. Some people believe that we ought to make radical cuts in our greenhouse gas emissions right now, while others prefer to plan for the consequences or hope for long-term, geoengineering solutions. Either way, what really matters is that climate change is now being discussed along with a range of possible solutions.

If we could begin the widespread discussion of possible solutions to our other pending global challenges then future-shaping progress could really start to be made. Granted, a few individuals do cry 'electric cars', 'vertical farms', 'synthetic biology' and 'space travel' when others mention Peak Oil, Peak Water, future food shortages and broader resource depletion. Yet sadly at present their lone voices are usually drowned out by the bellowing tones of the doom-mongers. That, or they disappear into the background babble of the mass of people who still do not accept or even realize that tomorrow will not be a gentle continuation of today.

This book has presented 25 things that I hope have made you aware not just of how radically the world is set to change, but more importantly of how humanity can take control and create a very positive future. Armed with this information you are now in a position to help others to focus on positive future solutions. It is time for humanity to get its collective head out of the sand, and that is going to require the conviction and leadership of a great many people of whom you can be one.

The last 50 years or so have been a period of relative stability, particularly for those in the West. But the Sun is now setting on this particular Golden Age. In addition to the 25 things outlined in this book, China is set to become the dominant global superpower if only it can maintain its water supplies. A global, viral pandemic is also long overdue and could arrive before medical advancements are able to prevent it from killing tens of millions. Terrorism and religious fundamentalism are also on the rise. If nothing else, we live in interesting and precarious times that will demand our constant re-education.

*   *   *

Tomorrow's World

Future gazing can on occasions be bittersweet. Recognizing the possibilities of tomorrow may sometimes fill us with hope for better things to come. However, it can also be difficult to accept that new medical treatments and adequate mechanisms to feed and fuel the world will arrive too late to help so many people today.

Future gazing is indeed not as abstract an activity as it may at first appear. Contemplating the power of future quantum computers or our conquest of space may prove an interesting diversion from our daily routines. Yet learning about future technologies that will not arrive in time to save loved ones or ourselves can strike far closer to home. We therefore need to remember that while we may be worse off than some of those to come, most of us are still far more blessed than our ancestors.

In July 1957 British Prime Minister Harold Macmillan claimed that people had 'never had it so good'. While at the time he was probably right, in the following half century the level of prosperity in most developed nations only continued to rise. For many decades most populations have had access to all of the water, food, energy and raw materials that they could reasonably demand. Healthcare has also improved tremendously, while the world has been at relative peace.

Look forward a decade or two and our halcyon days may in some respects be coming to an end. No longer will so many people be able to take water, food, energy and raw materials for granted. Things are not going to run out entirely. However, shortages and price rises will soon require most of us to develop consumption patterns that are somewhat more considered and thrifty than today. The basic challenge for billions in the decades ahead will be to demand things less but value things more.

Despite many pending resource constraints, in the future many aspects of our lives are likely to go on improving. Singularity or no Singularity, healthcare advancements are pretty certain to further increase our quality and quantity of life. Changes in our patterns of consumption are also likely to go hand-in-hand with more local living and the greening of our cities. For those who wish to live to excess, the next few decades may well prove a disappointment. However, for the rest of us, the greener, healthier, more local and less resource-intensive future now on offer may well turn out to be an improvement on today.

FURTHER READING

In addition to the below, a hyper-linked list of references is available from www.explainingthefuture.com/25things.

Prologue: Future Gazing as Future Shaping

Christopher Barnatt, *Challenging Reality: In Search of the Future Organization* (Chichester: John Wiley & Sons, 1997)

Thomas Lombardo, *The Evolution of Future Consciousness* (Bloomington, IN: Author House, 2006)

Chapter 1: Peak Oil

Antony Froggatt and Glada Lahn, *Sustainable Energy Security: Strategic Risks and Opportunities for Business* (London: Lloyds 360 Risk Insight White Paper, 2010)

Life. After the Oil Crash – www.LifeAfterTheOilCrash.net

The Oil Drum – www.TheOilDrum.com

OPEC – www.opec.org

Paul Roberts, *The End of Oil: The Decline of the Petroleum Economy and the Rise of a New Energy Order* (London: Bloomsbury, 2004)

Steve Sorrell, Jamie Speirs, Roger Bentley, Adam Brandt and Richard Miller, *Global Oil Depletion: An Assessment of the Evidence for a Near-term Peak in Global Oil Production* (London: UK Energy Research Centre, 2009)

Chapter 2: Climate Change

Daniel Howden, 'Deforestation: The Hidden Cause of Global Warming', *Independent* (14 May 2007)

Intergovernmental Panel on Climate Change – www.ipcc.ch

Kenneth I. Roy, *Solar Sails – An Answer to Global Warming?* (Oak Ridge, TN: Ultimax Group White Paper no. 2001–3, presented at the Space Technology & Applications International Forum, 2001)

Nicholas Stern, *The Economics of Climate Change: The Stern Review* (London: HMSO Publications, 2006)

Jessica Wilson and Stephen Law, *A Brief Guide to Global Warming* (London: Robinson, 2007)

Chapter 3: Peak Water

Lester R. Brown, 'Aquifer Depletion', *Encyclopedia of Earth* (23 January 2010)

Circle of Blue – www.circleofblue.org

Dipak Kumar Dash, 'Delhi Water Table Falling by 2m/Yr', *Times of India* (22 March 2010)

Peter, H. Gleick, Heather Cooley, Michael Cohen, Mari Morikawa, Jason Morrison and Meena Palaniappan, *The World's Water 2008–2009: The Biennial Report on Freshwater Resources* (Oakland, CA: Island Press, 2008)

Geoffrey Lean, 'Water Scarcity 'Now Bigger Threat than Financial Crisis', *Independent* (15 March 2009)

Pacific Institute: The World's Water – www.worldwater.org

United Nations: Water for Life – www.un.org/waterforlifedecade

Chapter 4: Food Shortages

Lester R. Brown, 'How to Feed 8 Billion People', *The Futurist* (January–February 2010)

Census of Marine Life – www.coml.org

Jeremy Hance, 'Rich Countries Buy Up Agricultural Land in Poor Countries, Mongabay.com (26 May 2009)

Jim Lane, 'China's Increase in Meat Consumption Using 3 Times More Grain than US Ethanol Industry', *Biofuels Digest* (25 April 2008)

Dale Allen Pfeiffer, 'Eating Fossil Fuels', FromTheWilderness.com (2004)

World Economic Forum – www.weforum.org

Chapter 5: Resource Depletion

Keith Bradsher, 'Earth-Friendly Elements, Mined Destructively', *New York Times* (25 December 2009)

David Cohen, 'Earth's Natural Wealth: An Audit', *New Scientist* (23 May 2007)

James Lovelock, *The Revenge of Gaia: Why the Earth is Fighting Back and How We Can Still Save Humanity* (London: Penguin, 2006)

Cahal Milmo, 'Concern as China clamps down on rare earth exports', *Independent* (2 January 2010)

Samuel K. Moore, 'Supply Risk, Scarcity, and Cellphones', *IEEE Spectrum* (March 2008)

United Nations Environment Programme, *Uncoupling Natural Resource Use and Environmental Impacts from Economic Growth* (Washington, DC: United Nations, May 2011)

Chapter 6: 3D Printing

Lin Edwards, 'Introducing Cornucopia, the Food Printer', *PhysOrg.com* (23 July 2010)

Fab@Home – www.fabathome.org

'The Printed World', *The Economist* (10 February 2011)

RepRap – www.reprap.org

Ariel Schwartz, 'The Urbee Hybrid: the First 3-D Printed Car', *Fast Company* (29 October 2010)

SolidScape – www.solid-scape.com

Stratasys – www.stratasys.com

3D Systems – www.3dsystems.com

Ashlee Vance, '3-D Printing Spurs a Manufacturing Revolution', *New York Times* (13 September 2010)

Z Corporation – www.zcorp.com

Chapter 7: Nanotechnology

Eric K. Drexler, *Engines of Creation 2.0* (York, PA: WOWIO, 2007)

Robert Lee Hotz, 'They Walk. They Work. New DNA Robots Strut Their Tiny Stuff', *Wall Street Journal* (12 May 2010)

Kirk L. Kroeker, 'Medical Nanobots', *Communications of the ACM* (September 2009)

Corie Lok, 'Small Wonders', *Nature* (2 September 2010)

National Nanotechnology Initiative – www.nano.gov

Project on Emerging Nanotechnologies – www.nanotechproject.org

Mark Stephen, 'Nanotechnology: The Next Small Thing', *Canadian Plastics* (September–October 2009)

Chapter 8: Genetic Modification

AquaBounty Technologies – www.aquabounty.com

Andy Coughlan, 'Engineered Maize Toxicity Claims Roundly Rebuffed', *New Scientist* (22 January 2010)

Encyclopaedia Britannica, *The Britannica Guide to Genetics* (London: Robinson, 2009)

GloFish – www.glofish.com

Golden Rice Project – www.goldenrice.org

Louise Gray, 'Giant Salmon Will Be First GM Animal Available for Eating', *Sunday Telegraph* (27 June 2010)

Richard Monastersky, 'Firefly Gene Sets Tobacco Plants Aglow', *Science News* (15 November 1986)

Ozgene – www.ozgene.com

Paul J. H. Schoemaker and Joyce A. Schoemaker, *Chips, Clones and Living Beyond 100: How Far Will the Biosciences Take Us?* (Upper Saddle River, NJ: FT Press Science, 2010)

Koh You-Sang, 'Expanding Applications and Uses of Biotechnology', *SERI Quarterly* (April 2010)

Chapter 9: Synthetic Biology
BioBricks Foundation – www.biobricks.org

Biotech Industry Organization Synthetic Biology Resource Centre – www.bio.org/ind/syntheticbiology

Nancy Gibbs, 'The Risks and Rewards of Synthetic Biology', *Time* (28 June 2010)

Thomas Knight, 'Engineering Novel Life', *Molecular Systems Biology* (13 September 2005)

Roberta Knok, 'DNA's Master Craftsmen', *Nature* (4 November 2010)

New England BioLabs – www.neb.com

Open Wetware – www.openwetware.org

Parts Registry – www.partsregistry.org

Rachel Swaby, 'Scientists Create First Self-Replicating Synthetic Life', *Wired* (20 May 2010)

Synthetic Biology – SyntheticBiology.org

Nicholas Wade, 'Genetic Engineers Who Don't Just Tinker', *New York Times* (8 July 2007)

Chapter 10: Vertical Farming
Biotecture – www.biotecture.uk.com

Dickson Despommier, *The Vertical Farm: Feeding the World in the 21st Century* (New York, NY: Thomas Dune, 2010)

Hydro-Stacker – www.hydrostacker.com

LED Grow Lamps – www.ledgrowlamps.co.uk

Sunlight Direct – www.sunlight-direct.com

Valcent Products – www.valcent.net

Vertical Farm – www.verticalfarm.com

Windowfarms – www.windowfarms.org

Chapter 11: Electric Vehicles

Aeroscraft – www.aeroscraft.com

Betterplace – www.betterplace.com

Ryan Chin, 'Sustainable Urban Mobility in 2020', *The Futurist* (July–August 2010)

Duffy Boats – www.duffyboats.com

General Motors Chevrolet Volt – www.chevrolet.com/volt

MINI E – www.mini.co.uk/MINI_E

Renault ZE Range – www.renault-ze.com

Solar Impluse – www.solarimpulse.com

Tesla Motors – www.teslamotors.com

Urbee – www.urbee.net

Chapter 12: Wind, Wave and Kinetic Power

Alternative Energy News – www.alternative-energy-news.info

Christopher Flavin, *Low Carbon Energy: A Roadmap* (Washington, DC: Worldwatch Institute, 2008)

Green Ocean Energy – www.greenoceanenergy.com

Ocean Power Technologies – www.oceanpowertechnologies.com

Pavegen Systems – www.pavegensystems.com

Pelamis Wave Power – www.pelamiswave.com

Quiet Revolution – www.quietrevolution.com

Renewable Energy Focus – www.renewableenergyfocus.com

Renewable UK – www.bwea.com

Wind Energy The Facts – www.wind-energy-the-facts.org

Chapter 13: Solar Energy

Covalent Solar – www.covalentsolar.com

John C. Mankins, 'A Technical Overview of the "SunTower" Solar Power Satellite Concept', *Acta Astronautica* (vol. 50, no. 6, 2002)

Sunlight Direct – www.sunlight-direct.com

Solar Energy at Home – www.solar-energy-at-home.com

Solar Facts – www.solar-facts.com
3GSolar – www.3GSolar.com

Chapter 14: Nuclear Fusion
Christopher Barnatt, 'Helium-3 Power',
    ExplainingTheFuture.com (2011)
European Nuclear Society – www.euronuclear.org
International Thermonuclear Experimental Reactor –
    www.iter.org
Egon Larsen, *Atomic Energy: The Layman's Guide to the
    Nuclear Age* (London: Pan Books, 1958)
World Nuclear Association, *Nuclear Fusion Power*,
    www.world-nuclear.org/info/inf66.html (May 2010)

Chapter 15: Space Travel
Ansari X-Prize – http://space.xprize.org/ansari-x-prize
Arienespace – www.arianespace.com
NASA – www.nasa.gov
Orbital Sciences Corporation – www.orbital.com
Space X – www.spacex.com
Space Elevator Conference – www.spaceelevatorconference.org
Space Elevator Reference – www.spaceelevator.com

Chapter 16: Cloud Computing
Amazon Web Services – www.aws.amazon.com
Christopher Barnatt, *A Brief Guide to Cloud Computing*
    (London: Robinson, 2010)
Nicholas Carr, *The Big Switch* (New York, NY: W. W. Norton,
    2008)
Google Docs – http://docs.google.com
Internet World Stats – www.internetworldstats.com
Mark McDonald and Dave Aron, *Reimagining IT: The Gartner
    2011 CIO Survey* (Stamford, CT: Gartner, 2011)
OnLive – www.onlive.com

Chapter 17: Artificial Intelligence

Association for the Advancement of Artificial Intelligence – www.aaai.org

Blue Brain Project – http://bluebrain.epfl.ch

Thomas Chesney, *Searching for Patterns* (Nottingham: Nottingham University Press, 2009)

Kevin Kelly, *What Technology Wants* (New York, NY: Penguin, 2010)

Natasha Lomas, 'Artificial Intelligence: 55 Years of Research Later – and Where is AI now?', Silicon.com (8 February 2010)

Patrick Tucker, 'The AI Chasers', *The Futurist* (March–April 2008)

Singularity Institute – www.singinst.org

Chapter 18: Augmented Reality

Thomas Husson with Mark Mulligan and Annie E. Corbett, *Mobile Augmented Reality: Beyond the Hype, A Glimpse into the Mobile Future* (Cambridge, MA: Forrester Research, 17 December 2010)

Junaio – www.junaio.com

Kirk L. Kroecker, 'Mainstreaming Augmented Reality', *Communications of the ACM* (July 2010)

Layar – www.layar.com

Wikitude World Browser – www.wikitude.org

Chapter 19: Quantum Computing

Clive Cookson, 'Computers Set for Quantum Leap', *Financial Times* (16 September 2010)

D-Wave Systems – www.dwavesys.com

FuturICT Project – www.futurict.ethz.ch/FuturICT

Paul Marks, 'Google Demonstrates Quantum Computer Image Search', *New Scientist* (11 December 2009)

J.R. Minkel, 'First "Commercial" Quantum Computer Solves Sudoku Puzzles', *Scientific American* (13 February 2007)

Patrick Tucker, 'What Quantum Computing Means for National Security', *Futurist* (July–August 2010)

Chapter 20: Robots
ASIMO – www.asimo.honda.com

BigDog – www.bostondynamics.com/robot_bigdog.html

Sharon Gaudin, 'MIT builds swimming, oil-eating robots', *ComputerWorld* (26 August 2010)

Erico Guizzo, 'World Robot Population Reaches 8.6 Million', *IEEE Spectrum* (14 April 2010)

Erik Hayden, 'Robot Blob Pillow Will Cure Loneliness', *Atlantic Wire* (24 November 2010)

Paul Kellett, 'Robotic Warehousing: A New Market Opportunity for Robot Manufacturers and Integrators?', *Robotics Online* (7 February 2011)

John Markoff, 'War Machines: Recruiting Robots for Combat', *New York Times* (27 November 2010)

Robonaut 2 – robonaut.jsc.nasa.gov

Robotics Industry Association – www.robotics.org

Aaron Saenz, 'Japan's Robot Picks Only the Ripest Strawberries', *Singularity Hub* (4 December 2010)

TOPIO – www.topio.tosy.com

Chapter 21: Genetic Medicine ✓
Geoffrey Carr, 'Biology 2.0', *The Economist* (17 June 2010)

Encyclopaedia Britannica, *The Britannica Guide to Genetics* (London: Robinson, 2009)

International Cancer Genome Consortium – www.icgc.org

Paul J. H. Schoemaker and Joyce A. Schoemaker, *Chips, Clones and Living Beyond 100: How Far Will the Biosciences Take Us?* (Upper Saddle River, NJ: FT Press Science, 2010)

Ker Than, 'Human Genome at Ten: 5 Breakthroughs, 5 Predictions', *National Geographic News* (31 March 2010)

US Department of Energy's genomic websites –
www.genomics.energy.gov

Chapter 22: Bioprinting

Emma Marris, 'How to Print a Blood Vessel', *Nature* (20 March 2008)

Vladimir Mironov, 'The Future of Medicine: Are Custom-Printed Organs on the Horizon?' *Futurist* (January–February 2011)

Stuart Nathan, 'Building Body Parts with 3D Printing', *Engineer* (24 May 2010)

Organovo – www.organovo.com

Aaron Saenz, 'New Skin Printer Could Print You Some New Skin', Singularityhub.com (4 November 2010)

Chapter 23: Cybernetic Enhancement

Adam Bluestein, 'The Future of the Human Body', *Inc.* (1 October 2009)

Jennifer Bogo, 'Next Gen Digital Sight Could Cure Blindness', *Popular Mechanics* (29 September 2010)

BrainGate – www.cyberkineticsinc.com

Nic Fleming, 'Woman with Bionic Arm Regains Sense of Touch', *Daily Telegraph* (2 February 2007)

Ben Goertzel, 'Brain-Computer Interfacing: From Prosthetic Limbs to Telepathy Chips', *H + Magazine* (13 July 2009)

NeuroSky – www.neurosky.com

Touch Bionics – www.touchbionics.com

Patrick Tucker, 'Prospects for Brain-Computer Interfacing', *The Futurist* (September–October 2010)

Kevin Warwick, *I, Cyborg* (Urbana, IL: University of Illinois Press, 2002)

Chapter 24: Life Extension

Ewen Callaway, 'Telomerase Reverses Ageing Process', *Nature* (28 November 2010)

Calorie Restriction Society – www.calorierestriction.org

Robin P. Ertl, Jichun Chen, Clinton M. Astle, Theodore M. Duffy and David E. Harrison, 'Effects of Dietary Restriction on Hematopoietic Stem-Cell Aging are Genetically Regulated', *Blood* (September 2008)

Gregory M. Fahy and Saul Kent, 'Immortal Stem Cells for Anti-Aging Therapies', *Life Extension Magazine* (June 2010)

Fight Aging.org – www.fightaging.org

Florian Kohlbacher and Cornelius Herstatt (eds), *The Silver Market Phenomenon: Marketing and Innovation in the Aging Society* (Berlin: Springer, 2008)

Life Extension Foundation – www.lef.org

Aaron Saenz, 'Amino Acids Extend Mice Life 12% – Could it Work on Humans?', SingularityHub.com (15 October 2010)

Chapter 25: Transhumanism

William Sims Bainbridge, 'Avatars and Virtual Immortality', *The Futurist* (March–April 2011)

Nick Bostrum, 'A History of Transhumanist Thought', *Journal of Evolution and Technology* (vol. 14, no. 1, April 2005)

Cryonics Institute – www.cryonics.org

Extropy Institute – www.extropy.org

J. B. S. Haldane, *Daedalus; or, Science and the Future* (London: K. Paul, Trench, Truber & Co, 1924)

Humanity+ – www.humanityplus.org

LifeNaut – www.LifeNaut.com

Max More, *Transhumanism: Towards a Futurist Philosophy*, www.maxmore.com/transhum.htm (1990)

Epilogue: Singularity or Decline?

Christopher Barnatt, *Cyber Business: Mindsets for a Wired Age* (Chichester: John Wiley & Sons, 1995)

INDEX